THIRD EDITION

MW00612151

Teaching Resources A

UNIT 1: WORLD MYTHS AND FOLKTALES
UNIT 2: THE AFRICAN LITERARY TRADITION
UNIT 3: THE ANCIENT MIDDLE EAST
UNIT 4: GREEK AND ROMAN LITERATURES
UNIT 5: INDIAN LITERATURE
UNIT 6: CHINESE AND JAPANESE LITERATURES
UNIT 7: PERSIAN AND ARABIC LITERATURES

HOLT, RINEHART AND WINSTON

A Harcourt Classroom Education Company

Austin • New York • Orlando • Atlanta • San Francisco • Boston • Dallas • Toronto • London

STAFF CREDITS

Director: Mescal Evler
Manager of Editorial Operations: Bill Wahlgren
Project Editor: Patricia McCambridge
Component Editors: Scott Hall, Tracy DeMont
Editorial Staff: *Managing Editor*, Marie H. Price; *Editorial Operations Coordinator*, Lori De La Garza; *Copyediting Manager*, Michael Neibergall; *Senior Copyeditor*, Mary Malone; *Copyeditors*, Joel Bourgeois, Elizabeth Dickson, Gabrielle Field, Suzi A. Hunn, Jane Kominek, Millicent Ondras, Theresa Reding, Désirée Reid, Kathleen Scheiner; *Project Administration*, Heather Cheyne, Mark Holland, Marcus Johnson, Jill O'Neal, Joyce Rector, Janet Riley, Kelly Tankersley; *Word Processors*, Ruth Hooker, Margaret Sanchez, Gail Coupland, Laura Kadjar
Permissions: Carrie Jones
Design: *Art Director, Book Design*, Richard Metzger; *Design Manager, Book & Media Design*, Cristina Bowerman
Prepress Production: Beth Prevelige, Simira Davis, Joan M. Lindsay
Media Production: *Production Manager*, Kim A. Scott; *Production Coordinator*, Belinda Barbosa; *Production Supervisor*, Nancy Hargis
Manufacturing Coordinator: Michael Roche

Photo credit (front cover): Peking lion, Super Stock

Printed in the United States of America

ISBN 0-03-056523-5

1 2 3 4 5 6 862 03 02 01 00

The blackline masters in this *Teaching Resources* booklet for *World Literature* have been organized by unit, corresponding to the first seven units in the student textbook. Within the unit divisions, blackline masters are organized by selection. In addition, this booklet contains a variety of worksheets designed to help students understand the organization of the textbook in general. The following blackline masters are included in this booklet:

- Previewing the Anthology Worksheets
- Unit Introduction Tests
- Vocabulary Activity Worksheets
- Vocabulary Tests
- Review and Response Worksheets
- Language Skills Worksheets
- Selection Tests
- Word Analogies/Extending Vocabulary
- Unit Review Tests/Applying Skills I
- Critical Thinking and Writing Worksheets/Applying Skills II

Due to the variety of tests and worksheets, time limitations may prohibit the use of every item provided for a given selection or unit. Therefore, you may wish to select only those blackline masters appropriate to the needs of a particular group of students.

Following are descriptions of the tests and worksheets, arranged in the order in which they generally appear in this booklet.

PREVIEWING THE ANTHOLOGY WORKSHEETS

This *Teaching Resources* booklet begins with a special series of lessons on Previewing the Anthology. These lessons help students understand the basic structure of the anthology: the Table of Contents, the Unit, the Selection, and the Back Matter. Completion of these worksheets will enable students to get the most out of the text and its special features, such as the Reader's Guide page and the reference materials that comprise the back matter.

SELECTION WORKSHEETS

Vocabulary Activity Worksheets

Worksheets designed to help students develop vocabulary skills are provided for many of the selections in *World Literature.* Each worksheet teaches five to ten key words from a selection (or, occasionally, from a group of selections)—words that are important to an understanding of the selection and to the development of a working vocabulary. In addition to a definition, each item on the worksheet features special information about the word or its usage and a sample sentence that places the word in context. Blank lines following each item allow for immediate application of new knowledge in an original sentence. These worksheets may be used to preteach vocabulary words and skills, or they can be used to ensure students' mastery of words and skills after teaching the selection. The words taught on the worksheet, which also appear in the student textbook's Glossary, are underscored and defined in the Annotated Teacher's Edition and tested on an accompanying Vocabulary Test.

Vocabulary Tests

Objective vocabulary tests scorable to 100 points are provided for selections for which there is a Vocabulary Activity Worksheet. Students are tested on the five to ten words from the selection that were covered on the worksheet. The tests may be used to check mastery of vocabulary words from the selection; they may also be used for in-class review and discussion of word meanings.

Review and Response Worksheets

These worksheets are provided for every selection in the student text. The worksheets will enable students to review important features of each selection—the characters and events of a short story, the central imagery in a poem, and so on. A Reader's Response box on every worksheet elicits the students' personal reactions to the selection and helps them to articulate the reasons for their reactions. After successfully completing a Review and Response Worksheet, the students will be better prepared to discuss the selection in class and approach the study questions that follow each selection with greater confidence. The worksheet will also be helpful to students as they review for tests. In addition, completion of the Review and Response Worksheets for a unit will help students to succeed on the Unit Review Test.

Language Skills Worksheets

These worksheets are based on selections in the textbook. They have been designed to integrate the teaching of literature with language study. Each worksheet helps the students apply some aspect of language study to their writing. Each Language Skills lesson teaches a traditional aspect of grammar, usage, or mechanics. Three exercises for practicing the new language skill accompany each lesson: the first exercise requires students to identify correct and incorrect examples of the language element being taught; the second provides practice in writing; and the third provides practice in revising and proofreading, with an emphasis on the language element that is focused upon in the worksheet lesson.

Selection Tests

Objective tests on basic reading comprehension are provided for every prose selection and for some groups of poetry selections. Each test contains five to ten items and is scorable to 100 points.

UNIT TESTS AND WORKSHEETS

Unit Introduction Tests

At the beginning of each unit, an objective, multiple-choice test on basic reading comprehension is provided for every unit introduction. Each test is scorable to 100 points. Unit 9 contains introductions to two different time periods; therefore, two separate Unit Introduction Tests are provided at the beginning of the unit.

Word Analogies/Extending Vocabulary

At the end of each unit, a ten-item word analogy exercise is provided. Because each analogy item is based on a vocabulary word taken from one of the selections in the unit, a Word Analogies exercise should not be administered until students have completed a unit and worked through the Vocabulary Activity Worksheets and Vocabulary Tests for each selection in the unit. Each word analogy item is based on one of the following relationships: synonym-to-synonym, synonym-to-antonym, person-to-characteristic, greater degree-to-lesser degree, cause-and-effect, class-to-species, action-to-object, person-to-task, object-to-characteristic, condition-to-characteristic, part-to-whole, and tool-to-purpose.

Unit Review Tests/Applying Skills I

Each unit ends with a cumulative Unit Review that allows students to apply skills learned in the unit. The test is divided into three parts: reading comprehension, identification of characters or events, and essay questions. The questions on this 100-point test are drawn from the selections covered in the unit.

Critical Thinking and Writing Worksheets/Applying Skills II

These worksheets allow students to apply their newly acquired skills to a literary selection not included in the student textbook. Students are asked to read these brief literary passages and respond to both objective questions and essay questions that demand literal and interpretive understanding of the material.

Answer Keys

Comprehensive Answer Keys providing answers and possible responses to all unit worksheets and tests appear at the end of every unit.

Previewing the Anthology

Unit 1: World Myths and Folktales

Unit 2: The African Literary Tradition

Unit 3: The Ancient Middle East

Unit 4: Greek and Roman Literatures

Unit 5: Indian Literature

Unit 6: Chinese and Japanese Literatures

Unit 7: Persian and Arabic Literatures

NAME ____________________ CLASS ____________________ DATE __________ SCORE __________

PREVIEWING THE TABLE OF CONTENTS

(Textbook pages v–xiii)

The **Table of Contents**, at the front of your anthology, is a listing of each selection and special feature in the text. It is arranged in the order of the page number on which each item begins. The following information can help you to use the Table of Contents.

1. The anthology is divided into eleven units. Each unit represents the literature of one or more world cultures and/or time periods. In the Table of Contents, the number and title of each unit appear in **colored** type.

2. Most of the units have one major introduction, the title of which appears just below the heading **Time Line**. Units 3, 4, 6, and 9, however, each include the literature of two major cultures or time periods and have two major introductions. Each unit also includes briefer, two- to four-page introductions that present major works or kinds of works. The word ***Introduction*** appears before each of these shorter introductions.

3. Titles of selections whose authors are not definitively known appear in **boldface** type. For other selections, the author's name usually appears in **boldface.** Titles of these selections appear under the author's name. The names of the three full-length dramas in the anthology also appear in **boldface** type.

4. Three special features appear at the end of every unit. Labels for these features appear in **orange** type. The specific topic for each feature follows in regular type. In each unit, other special features focus on particular authors or selections. These special features appear in **blue** type. Titles of these features are indented beneath the author, selection, or period to which they apply.

Understanding the Table of Contents

Use the Table of Contents in your anthology to answer the following questions. Write your answers on the blanks provided.

1. On which page does the first unit begin? ____________________

2. Unit 4 includes the literatures of two major cultures. What are they? ____________________

   ____

3. What is the title of the selection that begins on page 29? ____________________

4. How many individual selections appear in Unit 1? ____________________

(continued)

5. On which page near the end of the anthology does the Glossary begin? ______________

6. On what page does the Renaissance Literature introduction to Unit 9 begin? ______________

7. What is the title of Unit 10? ______________________________

8. What is the title of the last special feature that appears at the end of every unit? __________

____

9. What is the topic of the **Behind the Scenes** feature in Unit 1? ______________

10. How many poems by Pablo Neruda appear in Unit 11? ______________

Applying Skills

Use the Table of Contents in your anthology to fill in the blank for each item below.

1. In Unit 8, an important element of literature in Dante's *Inferno* is

   ____________________.

2. A Russian writer in Unit 11 who won the Nobel Prize is ____________________.

3. Based on the content of the **Language and Culture** feature for Unit 10, you can assume

   that the ____________________ began to appear around the nineteenth century.

4. The selections on pages 635–636 are from the sacred Muslim text called the

   ____________________.

5. In the Unit 6 special feature **Language and Culture**, you learn that

   ____________________ is a form of Japanese poetry.

NAME ________________ CLASS ________________ DATE ________ SCORE ________

Previewing the Anthology

PREVIEWING THE UNIT

Each **Unit Opener** in the anthology features a map as well as a box that provides the time, place, and literary significance of that unit's literature. The Unit Opener also includes a **go.hrw.com** logo and a keyword or keywords that will take the user to Internet links that serve as resources supporting the unit selections. Next is a **Time Line** that shows important events of the unit's time period and culture. (Unit 1 does not have a Time Line.) The **Unit Introduction** that follows discusses the historical and literary events of the place and time. At the end of each unit, the two-page feature **Language and Culture** focuses on an important literary or historical aspect of the culture represented in the unit. **Language Skills** features offer instruction and practice in an important grammar, usage, or mechanics skill as it applies to writing. **Critical Thinking and Writing** features give instruction in a critical thinking skill, such as analyzing characterization, and practice in applying that skill in a writing assignment.

Understanding the Unit

In the left-hand column below are items of information that can be found within a unit. In the right-hand column are sources for that information. Match each item with its most likely source. Sources may be chosen more than once. Place the letter of the source in the blank before each item of information.

______ 1. Literature in this unit comes from China and Japan.

______ 2. Understanding subject-verb agreement is important to good writing.

______ 3. An important event in the history of Arabic literature is the founding of the Islamic religion by Mohammed.

______ 4. Both direct and indirect characterization can be used to write a character sketch.

______ 5. In early Japan, professional warriors known as *samurai* helped to defend the estates of wealthy aristocrats.

a. Unit Introduction
b. Critical Thinking and Writing
c. Language Skills
d. Unit Opener

(continued)

Applying Skills

Use your anthology to answer the following questions. Write your answers on the blanks provided.

1. According to the **Unit Opener** pages for Unit 3, what are some literary forms found in the Hebrew Bible? ______________________________

2. In the **Unit Introduction** to Unit 7, one subheading is **Persian Prose**. What masterpiece of Persian prose is mentioned there? ______________________________

3. According to the Unit 10 feature **Language and Culture**, why were Gothic novels an unusual literary form? ______________________________

4. According to the Unit 3 feature **Critical Thinking and Writing**, what kind of writing assignment is presented? ______________________________

5. According to the **Unit Introduction** to Roman literature, which begins on page 372, when did the Roman empire *begin* its decline and fall? ______________________________

6. According to the Unit 4 **Language and Culture** feature, what does the expression *Achilles' heel* mean today? ______________________________

7. According to the **Unit Opener** pages for Unit 1, what is a one-sentence definition of *myth*?

   ____

8. According to the Unit 3 **Time Line**, when did legends about the hero Gilgamesh first begin to appear on cuneiform tablets? ______________________________

9. According to the Unit 6 **Language Skills** feature, what is it that pronouns must agree with?

   ____

10. According to the Unit 8 **Time Line**, when was the papacy set up in Rome? ______________

NAME ______________ CLASS ______________ DATE ________ SCORE ________

PREVIEWING THE SELECTION

Each major selection in your book has a consistent selection structure that begins with an introduction to the selection or a short biography of the author. Immediately preceding the selection or selections is a **Reader's Guide** page or box with these sections: *Background* (general information about the selection), *Writer's* (or *Oral*) *Response* (a prereading writing or speaking suggestion) and *Literary Focus* (a discussion of an important literary concept in the selection). A short purpose-setting **headnote** after the selection's title tells a bit about the selection and indicates things to look for or think about as you read.

After the selection there are several types of questions. **First Thoughts** asks for your initial response to the selection. **Identifying Facts** asks factual questions about the selection. **Interpreting Meanings** consists of critical thinking questions. **Applying Meanings** asks you to apply what you have learned from your reading to a larger question—about your life or society, for example. There may also be a **Creative Writing Response,** which assigns a creative writing activity, and/or a **Critical Writing Response,** which proposes a form of literary analysis. In addition, a **Speaking and Listening** or **Language and Vocabulary** activity follows some selections.

Understanding the Selection

Answer the questions on the blanks provided.

1. Which part of the selection structure would you read to find out where the author was born?

   ____

2. In which part of the selection structure might you find an explanation of the use of **characterization** in the selection?

   ____

3. Which part of the selection structure might ask you to create a news report about the death of a character in the selection?

   ____

4. Which part of the selection structure might instruct you to imagine what a place looks like as you read?

   ____

(continued)

5. Would a question about the theme, or message, in a selection be most likely to be found under **Identifying Facts** or **Interpreting Meanings?**

____

Applying Skills

All the quotations below come from the selection structure of Victor Hugo's poem "Russia 1812," on textbook page 1017. Identify the source of each quotation by placing the letter of the source in the blank before the quotation.

______ 1. "The son of one of Napoleon's officers, Hugo spent his childhood in Madrid, Naples, and Paris."

______ 2. "Did this poem make you sympathize with the French army? What specific words and phrases helped form your response?"

______ 3. "As you read, notice what emotions are stirred in you by the imagery of the poem."

______ 4. "Imagery is descriptive writing that appeals to our senses of sight, hearing, smell, touch, or taste. 'Russia 1812' presents a vivid picture of the retreat from Moscow."

______ 5. "Imagine that you are a reporter for either a French or a Russian newspaper in 1812. Write a news story—with a catchy headline—describing the French retreat from Moscow."

a. headnote
b. Creative Writing Response
c. Critical Writing Response
d. First Thoughts
e. Reader's Guide
f. Identifying Facts
g. author biography

NAME ______________ CLASS ______________ DATE ________ SCORE ________

PREVIEWING THE BACK MATTER

(Textbook pages 1434–1499)

The back matter of your anthology includes the following materials.

Writing About Literature, page 1434. Here you will find information on writing answers to essay questions, on writing and revising an essay, and on documenting sources for a research report.

A Handbook of Literary Terms, page 1440. Here you will find definitions and examples of literary terms used in the text. Page references at the end of definitions tell you where in the text to find additional information about the terms.

Grammar, Usage, and Mechanics: A Reference Guide, page 1455. Here you will find discussions and examples of major concepts in grammar, usage, and mechanics. Page references in the guide refer you to **Language Skills** features that contain further information on a given topic.

Glossary, page 1474. Here you will find the definitions of the more difficult words that appear in the selections.

Index of Skills, page 1489. This index gives page numbers for the five major types of skills covered in the anthology: literary skills, language and vocabulary skills, speaking and listening skills, composition skills, and critical thinking skills.

Index of Authors and Titles, page 1496. This index is an alphabetical listing, with page numbers, of every author, selection, and translator in the anthology.

Understanding the Back Matter

On the blanks provided, list the back matter feature where you would look to find each of the following items.

1. The definition of the term *theme* ______________
2. An exercise in reading a poem aloud ______________
3. Help in using pronouns correctly ______________
4. The definition of the word *disperse* ______________
5. An exercise in writing a character sketch ______________

(continued)

6. The page number of Sophocles' play *Oedipus Rex* ______________
7. The definition of the term *tragedy* ______________
8. Information on organizing an essay ______________
9. Page numbers of sonnets by William Shakespeare ______________
10. Help with correcting problems in subject-verb agreement ______________

Applying Skills

Use the back matter of your anthology to answer the following questions. Write your answers on the blank provided.

1. A short definition of the literary term *paradox* is ______________.
2. A selection by Guy de Maupassant begins on page ______________.
3. One critical thinking skill covered in the anthology is ______________.
4. One widely accepted style for documenting sources in a research paper is ______________ ______________.
5. The first thing to do in preparing an answer to an essay question is to ______________ ______________.

PREVIEWING THE ANTHOLOGY

PREVIEWING THE TABLE OF CONTENTS

(Textbook pages v–xiii)

Understanding the Table of Contents

1. 1
2. Greek and Roman
3. "Theseus"
4. seven
5. 1474
6. 796
7. The Nineteenth Century: Romanticism to Realism
8. Critical Thinking and Writing
9. The Brothers Grimm
10. two

Applying Skills

1. allegory
2. Aleksandr Solzhenitsyn
3. gothic novel
4. Koran
5. senryu

PREVIEWING THE UNIT

Understanding the Unit

1. d 2. c 3. a 4. b 5. a

Applying Skills

1. psalms, historical narratives, proverbs
2. the *Gulistan* of Saadi
3. The emphasis was to arouse terror both in the heroine and in the reader.
4. narrative essay
5. during the late second and third centuries A.D.
6. It refers to a weak, or vulnerable, spot in a plan or a person's character.
7. A *myth* is a story about a beginning.
8. around 2500 B.C.
9. their antecedents
10. A.D. 451

PREVIEWING THE SELECTION

Understanding the Selection

1. author biography
2. Reader's Guide (Literary Focus)
3. Creative Writing Response
4. headnote
5. Interpreting Meanings

Applying Skills

1. g 2. d 3. a 4. e 5. b

PREVIEWING THE BACK MATTER

(Textbook pages 1434–1499)

Understanding the Back Matter

1. A Handbook of Literary Terms
2. Index of Skills
3. Grammar, Usage, and Mechanics: A Reference Guide
4. Glossary
5. Index of Skills
6. Index of Authors and Titles
7. A Handbook of Literary Terms
8. Writing About Literature
9. Index of Authors and Titles
10. Grammar, Usage, and Mechanics: A Reference Guide

Applying Skills

1. an apparent contradiction that is actually true
2. 1034
3. Responses will vary.
4. parenthetical citations
5. read the question carefully and be sure you understand what it is asking

Notes

NAME ______________________ CLASS ______________________ DATE __________ SCORE __________

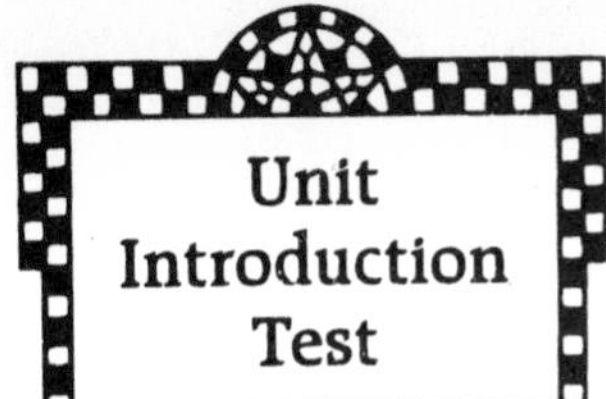

UNIT 1: WORLD MYTHS AND FOLKTALES

(Textbook pages 2–7)

INTRODUCTION/World Myths and Folktales

Directions: In the space provided, write the letter of the best answer to each question. *(10 points each)*

1. Which of the following statements is true about myths and folktales?
   a. They are basically love stories.
   b. The characters in them are always real people.
   c. They are the world's oldest stories.
   d. They never make sense to people of other cultures. 1.______

2. "The Storytelling Stone" explains
   a. the origin of stones
   b. the origin of gossip
   c. how the Seneca Indians learned to carve stone
   d. how storytelling originated among the Seneca Indians 2.______

3. Which of the following statements is true about myths?
   a. They were originally written down.
   b. They are rare and exist in only a few cultures.
   c. They are usually silly and meaningless.
   d. They attempt to explain the human experience. 3.______

4. What was probably the original purpose of myths?
   a. Most likely myths had a religious purpose.
   b. The subject has never been explored.
   c. Myths were designed solely to entertain.
   d. Myths were intended to frighten people. 4.______

5. Myths arose because of a need to
   a. divide people into various ethnic groups
   b. explain human progress
   c. replace prayers and rituals
   d. try to make sense of the universe 5.______

6. Most stories that explain the origins of a belief, a custom, or a natural phenomenon are classified as
   a. tall tales
   b. myths
   c. fables
   d. science fiction 6.______

(continued)

7. A basic difference between myths and folktales is that folktales
   a. are nonreligious
   b. never involve magic
   c. are never told as entertainment
   d. are always written rather than oral

   7. ______

8. Folktales were originally
   a. told by professional storytellers
   b. understood only by the nobility
   c. created by the common people
   d. part of very few world cultures

   8. ______

9. Common examples of folktales include
   a. hymns, odes, and sonnets
   b. drama, science fiction, and detective stories
   c. poems with gods and goddesses as main characters
   d. legends, tall tales, and fables

   9. ______

10. Myths and folktales are alike in that they both
    a. explain important truths about life
    b. have no significance for people today
    c. deal with everyday events in a down-to-earth way
    d. avoid basic questions of life and death

    10. ______

NAME ______________________ CLASS ______________________ DATE __________ SCORE ________

How the World Was Made

retold by Alice Marriott and
Carol K. Rachlin

(Textbook page 11)

REVIEWING THE SELECTION

1. Circle the word that best describes how Maheo feels about the animals that he creates.

   unhappy angry pleased indifferent gloomy

2. The snow goose, the loon, and the mallard all fail to find land. Why does it seem likely that the little coot will fail also?

   ____

   ____

3. What role does Grandmother Turtle play in the creation of the earth?

   ____

   ____

4. How does Maheo create the first man?

   ____

   ____

5. How does Maheo create the first woman?

   ____

   ____

Reader's Response

Several of the animals that play roles in this Cheyenne myth are described in vivid detail. Which animal do you find most appealing? Write a sentence or two giving reasons for your answer.

____

____

____

____

NAME ______________________ CLASS ____________________ DATE ________ SCORE ________

How the World Was Made

retold by Alice Marriott and Carol K. Rachlin

(Textbook page 11)

PUNCTUATING AND CAPITALIZING DIALOGUE

Dialogue consists of characters speaking in their own words. Use quotation marks before and after a speaker's exact words. Do not use quotation marks when a speaker's exact words are not given.

EXAMPLES "There should be water beings," Maheo told his Power. (quotation marks)
The loon asked Maheo to provide a place for the birds to build their nests. (no quotation marks)

Begin each complete sentence of dialogue with a capital letter. When a single sentence of dialogue is interrupted by an expression (or *tag line*) such as *he said* or *she asked*, begin the second part of the quoted sentence with a small (or *lowercase*) letter. In dialogue, a new paragraph usually begins whenever the speaker changes.

EXAMPLES **"L**isten to me, Maheo," said the goose. "This is good water that You have made, on which we live."
"Little brother," said Maheo, **"n**o man can do more than his best."

Follow these rules for using commas, question marks, and exclamation marks in dialogue.

1. Set off the speaker's exact words from the rest of the sentence by commas or by a question mark or an exclamation mark.
2. Always place commas and periods inside closing quotation marks.
3. Place question marks and exclamation marks inside the closing quotation marks if the speaker's exact words are a question or exclamation. Otherwise, place them outside the closing quotation marks.

EXAMPLES "Tell us how we can help You," said all the water peoples.
"Grandmother Turtle," Maheo asked, "do you think you can help me?"

Exercise 1. Identifying Dialogue

The following sentences are from "How the World Was Made." Quotation marks have been deleted from the sentences that contain dialogue. Use clues in the sentences to decide which items contain dialogue, the direct words of a speaker. Place a check mark (√) in the blank before each item that contains dialogue.

______ 1. The snow goose was gone a long time.

(continued)

_____ 2. I do not see You, but I know that You exist, the goose began.

_____ 3. Tell us how we can help You, said all the water peoples.

_____ 4. What have you brought us? Maheo asked her.

_____ 5. How beautiful their wings are in the light, Maheo said to his Power, as the birds wheeled and turned, and became living patterns against the sky.

_____ 6. Out of this salty water, Maheo knew, he could bring all life that ever was to be.

_____ 7. Maheo looked at the Earth Woman and he thought she was very beautiful: the most beautiful thing he had made so far.

_____ 8. He is alone with the Grandmother Earth as I once was alone with the void, said Maheo. It is not good for anyone to be alone.

_____ 9. I am very old and very slow, but I will try, the turtle answered.

_____ 10. In the beginning there was nothing, and Maheo, the All Spirit, lived in the void.

Exercise 2. Punctuating and Capitalizing Dialogue

Punctuate and capitalize the following items. Insert quotation marks, commas, and other marks of punctuation as necessary. Capitalize each direct quotation that is a complete sentence. (It may not be necessary to punctuate or capitalize all the items.) In the one item that contains two paragraphs, mark the paragraph break with the symbol ¶.

EXAMPLE “A basic purpose of mythology is to explain how things came to be,” the teacher explained.

1. The teacher said in the Greek story of the origin of the world, Chaos existed in the beginning.

2. The children of Chaos the teacher added were Night and Erebus, the place of death.

(continued)

3. Ancient Greeks believed that Love was the child of Night and Erebus.

4. The next event was the creation of Light the teacher went on. The companion of Light was Day.

5. What about the creation of people a student asked. In one Greek story the teacher responded it was the Titan Prometheus who created humans as they are today.

Exercise 3. Writing Dialogue

Write an original, short dialogue between two people or animals who are wondering about how something in nature came to be. You may use one of the following items as a topic of discussion or choose one of your own.

thunder	waterfalls	volcanoes	rain
wasps	spiders	rattlesnakes	the moon

Write the dialogue using correct capitalization and punctuation. Indent whenever a new paragraph is needed to show a change of speakers. (Change speakers at least twice.)

NAME ____________________ CLASS ____________________ DATE ________ SCORE ________

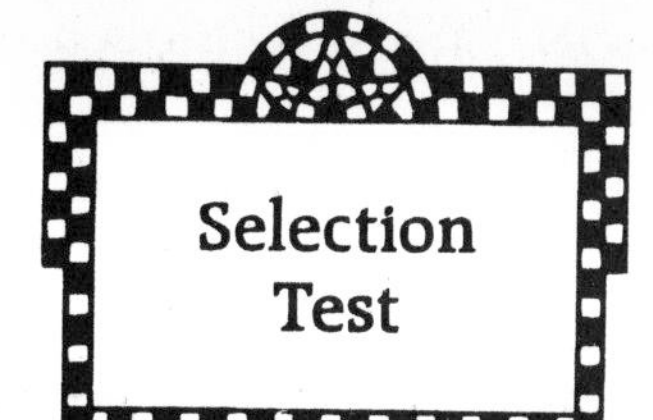

How the World Was Made

retold by Alice Marriott and
Carol K. Rachlin

(Textbook page 11)

READING COMPREHENSION

Directions: In the space provided, write the letter of the best answer to each question. *(10 points each)*

1. Why does Maheo decide to use his great power?
   a. He believes power is good only if it is used to create.
   b. He is afraid that someone else may create the world.
   c. He wants to establish a home for the buffalo.
   d. He has been lonesome for a very long time. 1. ______

2. As a result of the snow goose's advice, Maheo
   a. makes the world's first tree
   b. creates a great white whale
   c. fills the sky with light
   d. gives birds the power of flight 2. ______

3. Maheo asks for help from the birds
   a. even though he does not need their help
   b. because he can make only four things by himself
   c. so that his creations will be beautiful
   d. because the birds have more power than he does 3. ______

4. Maheo's wish for the coot is that it will
   a. always be able to outswim other birds
   b. live forever
   c. be protected by what it brought from the bottom of the lake
   d. be punished for its failure 4. ______

5. Once Maheo has a large mud ball, his problem is
   a. how to make it smaller
   b. when to destroy it
   c. what to rest it on
   d. how to make it perfectly round 5. ______

6. Maheo rewards the turtle by making it
   a. eternally youthful
   b. taste so bad no one will eat it
   c. fast enough to beat a rabbit in a race
   d. at home under water, within the earth, or above ground 6. ______

(continued)

7. Trees and grass become
   a. the hair of Grandmother Earth
   b. a resting place for Maheo
   c. a gift to the snow goose
   d. the only reward for the mussels and snails

   7. ______

8. Maheo creates the first humans
   a. with the help of a coot
   b. from his own rib bones
   c. from the down of a snow goose
   d. from a fish's gill

   8. ______

9. Maheo creates animals
   a. to feed and care for humans
   b. because he has nothing else to do
   c. to show the snow goose who is boss
   d. as a punishment for the turtle

   9. ______

10. After creation, Maheo
    a. becomes angry at the buffalo
    b. withdraws to his home in the sky
    c. continues to watch all his creatures
    d. regrets what he has done

    10. ______

NAME ______________________ CLASS ______________ DATE ________ SCORE ______

THE WOODEN PEOPLE *from the* POPOL VUH

translated by Dennis Tedlock (Textbook page 18)

REVIEWING THE SELECTION

1. Circle the letter of the sentence that tells how the creation god Maker, Modeler created the manikins.
   a. He molded them from resin that fell from the sky.
   b. He made them of mud.
   c. He carved the men from the wood of the coral tree and made women from the pith of reeds.

2. Why does the father-god Heart of Sky become disappointed with the manikins? What does he decide to do about them? ______________________________

   ____

   ____

   ____

3. Circle the letter of the sentence that describes the dogs' complaint about the manikins.
   a. The manikins treat the dogs badly.
   b. The dogs fear the manikins will drown them in the flood.
   c. The dogs fear the manikins will crush them.

4. According to the myth, why do monkeys look something like people? ______________

   ____

   ____

   ____

Reader's Response

The myth of the Wooden People gives a vivid picture of the manikins. Below is a list of adjectives. Circle those adjectives that convey the impression of the manikins that is created in the myth.

ugly	thoughtful	capable	thoughtless	happy
clever	well-liked	wooden	incompetent	ungrateful

NAME ______________________ CLASS ______________________ DATE __________ SCORE ________

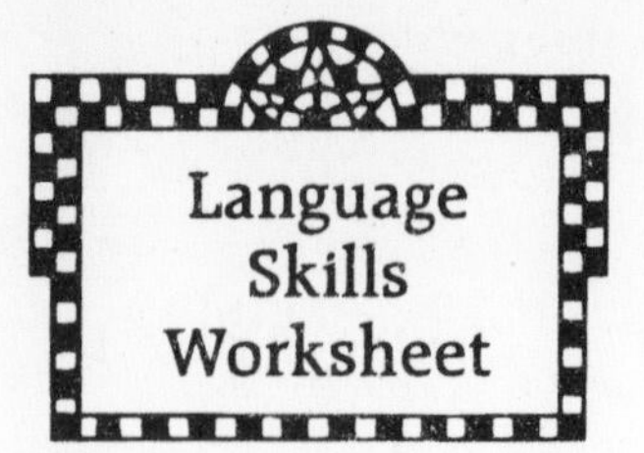

THE WOODEN PEOPLE from the POPOL VUH

translated by Dennis Tedlock (Textbook page 18)

APPOSITIVES AND APPOSITIVE PHRASES

An **appositive** is a noun or pronoun that usually follows another noun or pronoun to identify or explain it.

EXAMPLE The manikins, *woodcarvings*, had nothing in their hearts or minds. (The appositive, *woodcarvings*, identifies or explains the noun *manikins*.)

An appositive often includes modifiers. When it does, it is called an **appositive phrase.**

EXAMPLE Heart of Sky, *the father-god of the Quiché Mayans*, wanted the manikins to remember him. (The appositive with its modifiers identifies or explains *Heart of Sky*.)

Appositives and appositive phrases are usually set off from the rest of the sentence by commas, as shown in the examples above.

Exercise 1. Identifying Appositives and Appositive Phrases

The following sentences are based on the passage from the Popol Vuh. Underline each appositive or appositive phrase once in the following sentences. Underline the noun or pronoun that the appositive identifies or explains twice. (Two of the sentences have no appositives.)

EXAMPLE The Popol Vuh, or Book of Counsel, is sacred to the Quiché Mayans.

1. The wooden people were an experiment, a cutout, for humankind.
2. The Maker, Modeler, the Quiché Mayan god of creation, made major mistakes in designing the wooden people.
3. The manikins had no sweat and no fat.
4. Heart of Sky planned a dire humiliation, a great flood, to get rid of the defective woodcarvings.
5. One of the avengers, Tearing Jaguar, ripped the manikins apart.
6. Even the usually loyal dogs, the best friends of many people today, turned against the wooden people.
7. The manikins tried to hide in caves, a refuge from the ongoing destruction, but the caves slammed shut against them.
8. Nearly everyone on earth was destroyed.
9. The builder and sculptor left behind just one sign, monkeys.
10. The wooden people, mere manikins, disappeared from the earth.

(continued)

Exercise 2. Writing Sentences with Appositives

For each set of sentences below, write a new sentence containing an appositive or appositive phrase. (Use the information in parentheses to create your appositive or appositive phrase.)

EXAMPLE The man's body was shaped from the wood of a coral tree.
(The man's body was a carving.)
The man's body, a carving, was shaped from the wood of a coral tree.

1. The Quiché Mayans had a god of creation. (This god was the Maker, Modeler.)

____

____

2. "The Wooden People" tells the story of a mistake by the god of creation. ("The Wooden People" is a myth.)

____

____

3. The manikins got little sympathy even from their dogs. (The manikins were mere bones and tendons at the end.)

____

____

4. Their everyday utensils complained of sooty faces. (These utensils were tortilla griddles and cooking pots.)

____

____

5. These human beings would have to be replaced by a better design. (The human beings were worthless woodcarvings.)

____

____

(continued)

Exercise 3. Revising a Paragraph

Revise the paragraph that appears below by inserting appositives or appositive phrases that you create from the following sentences. Add each of these appositives at an appropriate place in the paragraph. Include the necessary punctuation. Use a caret (^) to show where you insert each appositive. The first one is done for you as an example.

- The Popol Vuh is the Quiché Mayan book of creation.
- The manikins are woodcarvings.
- The father god is Heart of Sky.
- The disaster is to be a flood.
- The two jaguars are Crunching Jaguar and Tearing Jaguar.
- The dogs were their faithful companions in the past.
- The poor woodcarvings are now friendless outcasts.
- The one animal in the forest today that is left as a reminder of the manikins is the monkey.

, the Quiché Mayan book of creation,

The Popol Vuh ^ tells the story of how the Maker, Modeler creates a race of manikins who are disappointing to the gods. The Mayan father god decides to eliminate the wooden people in a great disaster. The wooden people are crushed, pounded down to bones and tendons by water and animals, including two jaguars. Even their dogs attack the wooden people, snarling that they will kill the poor woodcarvings. Only one animal in the forest today has any features to remind people of the destroyed manikins.

NAME ______________________ CLASS ____________________ DATE ________ SCORE ________

THE WOODEN PEOPLE *from the* POPOL VUH

translated by Dennis Tedlock (Textbook page 18)

READING COMPREHENSION

Directions: In the space provided, write the letter of the best answer to each question. *(10 points each)*

1. The story of "The Wooden People" is mainly about
   a. a great rain of resin from the sky
   b. the successful creation of a humble yet talented group of people
   c. the creation and destruction of an unsatisfactory group of people
   d. an attempt by humans to defeat and replace their creator 1. ______

2. The manikins lack
   a. something in their hearts and minds
   b. sons and daughters
   c. faces
   d. the ability to walk 2. ______

3. The creator is unhappy with the wooden people because they
   a. worship false gods
   b. eat forbidden foods
   c. have no memory of their creator
   d. spend too much time playing games 3. ______

4. Heart of Sky is
   a. a race of wooden people
   b. the great father-god of the Quiché Mayans
   c. a terrible flood
   d. a demon 4. ______

5. The god Maker, Modeler
   a. creates the wooden people
   b. is also known as Sudden Bloodletter
   c. is happy with the wooden people
   d. eats the flesh of the wooden people 5. ______

6. Even dogs and turkeys turn on the wooden people because the animals
   a. want to please Heart of Sky
   b. believe the wooden people have treated them badly
   c. find the coral wood good to eat
   d. hope to rule in place of the wooden people 6. ______

(continued)

7. The tortilla griddles and cooking pots say they are unhappy about
   a. soap and water
   b. pain and soot
   c. being beaten by the wooden people
   d. not receiving anything from the wooden people 7. ______

8. This myth explains the origin of
   a. rain
   b. monkeys
   c. tortillas
   d. snow 8. ______

9. One typical mythic element in "The Wooden People" is that
   a. animals and inanimate objects speak
   b. people are mere woodcarvings
   c. animals obey humans
   d. humans are sensitive and caring 9. ______

10. "The Wooden People" is an example of a myth intended to
   a. predict the future
   b. portray a lost golden age
   c. honor a master woodcarver
   d. explain origins 10. ______

NAME ______________ CLASS ______________ DATE ________ SCORE ________

COYOTE AND THE ORIGIN OF DEATH

retold by Richard Erdoes and Alfonso Ortiz

(Textbook page 23)

REVIEWING THE SELECTION

1. Why do people first begin to die? ______________________________

____

2. According to the medicine men, where will the spirits of dead people be restored to life?

____

3. How does the Coyote make death eternal? ______________________________

____

4. Why do people refuse to give Coyote anything to eat? ______________________________

____

Reader's Response

This myth suggests that the spirit of the dead is like a wind or a whirlwind. Does this comparison make sense to you? Write two or three sentences explaining your answer.

____

____

____

____

____

____

____

____

____

NAME ________________ CLASS ________________ DATE ________ SCORE ______

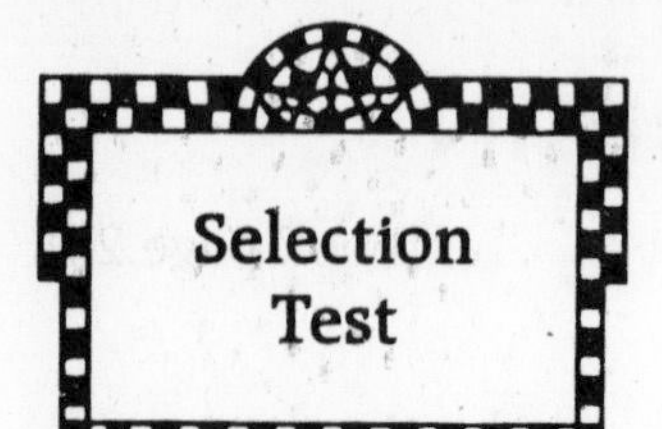

COYOTE AND THE ORIGIN OF DEATH

retold by Richard Erdoes and Alfonso Ortiz

(Textbook page 23)

READING COMPREHENSION

Directions: In the space provided, write the letter of the best answer to each question. *(20 points each)*

1. In "Coyote and the Origin of Death," permanent death enters the world because
   a. the people disobey their gods
   b. one chief takes a foolish gamble
   c. a trickster closes a door
   d. the medicine men decide to punish the first person who dies
   1.______

2. The character Coyote
   a. sets out to do evil
   b. is himself tricked into causing eternal death
   c. possesses no positive traits
   d. is a clever trickster
   2.______

3. The reason the council considers the idea of death is that the earth
   a. is becoming overcrowded
   b. suffers from ecological damage
   c. has a number of people who cannot get along together
   d. is overrun with greed
   3.______

4. The majority of voters at the council support
   a. permanent death
   b. temporary death
   c. no death
   d. permanent death for some and temporary death for others
   4.______

5. "Coyote and the Origin of Death" explains not only the origin of death but also
   a. the origin of the earth and its inhabitants
   b. the bad traits of the coyote
   c. the destruction and rebirth of the Caddo culture
   d. the popularity of the coyote
   5.______

NAME ______________________ CLASS ______________ DATE ________ SCORE ______

THESEUS

retold by Robert Graves

(Textbook page 29)

REVIEWING THE SELECTION

1. What task does his mother give Theseus? ______________________________

____

2. What signal does Theseus plan to use if he kills the Minotaur? ______________

____

3. Who falls in love with Theseus? ______________________________

4. How does Theseus escape from the Labyrinth? ______________________________

____

5. Why does Aegeus jump into the sea? ______________________________

____

Reader's Response

Complete this sentence: In my opinion, the most interesting character in "Theseus" is

______________ because ______________________________

____

____

____

____

____

____

NAME ______________________ CLASS ______________ DATE ________ SCORE ______

THESEUS

retold by Robert Graves (Textbook page 29)

ADJECTIVES: DEGREES OF COMPARISON

An **adjective** is a word used to modify a noun or pronoun. It answers one of these questions: *Which kind? Which one? How many?*

EXAMPLES The sword has a *golden* snake on its blade. (The adjective *golden* modifies the noun *snake.* It answers the question *Which kind?* or *Which one?*)

The sword he chose is the *magic* one. (The adjective *magic* modifies the pronoun *one.* It answers the question *Which kind?* or *Which one?*)

Many cultures have myths about quests. (The adjective *many* modifies the noun *cultures.* It answers the question *How many?*)

To show comparisons, you must change the forms of most adjectives. There are three **degrees of comparison: positive, comparative,** and **superlative.** The correct form to use for regular comparison often depends on the number of syllables in the word. If you are not certain about how to form the comparative forms of an adjective, use your dictionary. Here are some general rules to follow.

One syllable: Add *-er* for comparative, *-est* for superlative.

Two syllables: Add *-er, -est;* in some cases, add *more* for comparative, *most* for superlative.

Three or more syllables: Add *more, most.*

EXAMPLES	Positive	Comparative	Superlative
	slow	slower	slowest
	jealous	more jealous	most jealous
	reasonable	more reasonable	most reasonable

A few adjectives have **irregular** comparative forms:

good, better, best *bad, worse, worst*

Exercise 1. Identifying Forms of Adjectives

Underline the adjective in each of these sentences about the story of Theseus. In the space before each sentence, write *P* if the form is positive, *C* if it is comparative, or *S* if it is superlative.

______ 1. Aegeus feared that his oldest nephew might kill Aethra.

______ 2. He thought she would be safer if she stayed in Corinth.

______ 3. If travelers were the right size for the bed, Procrustes smothered them.

(continued)

_____ 4. If travelers were shorter than the bed, he lengthened them with the rack.

_____ 5. The angry Athenians sent Theseus to be eaten by Minotaur.

_____ 6. Medea was the most powerful witch in Athens.

_____ 7. When Theseus deserted her, Ariadne decided on a more glorious marriage—to Dionysus, the god of wine and revelry.

_____ 8. Aegeus awaited the return of Theseus with great anxiety.

_____ 9. Theseus declared himself "the bravest king alive."

_____ 10. The riskiest adventure that Theseus undertook was a descent to Tartarus.

Exercise 2. Writing Sentences with Comparisons

Rewrite each sentence below using the correct form of the adjective in parentheses.

EXAMPLE Some readers feel that Theseus is the (boastful) hero in Greek mythology.
Some readers feel that Theseus is the most boastful hero in Greek mythology.

1. Theseus was (strong) than most fourteen-year-olds.

____

2. Procrustes is one of the (notorious) innkeepers in literature.

____

3. Minos was a (powerful) king than Aegeus.

____

4. Androgeus of Crete was the (brilliant) competitor at the Athletic Games.

____

____

5. Ariadne's wedding gift from Dionysus was a (splendid) jeweled coronet than Theseus could have given her.

____

____

(continued)

Exercise 3. Revising a Paragraph

The paragraph that follows provides additional background for "Theseus." Ten adjectives have been underlined. Two of these are used correctly; the other eight are not. Cross out each form that is incorrect and write the correct positive, comparative, or superlative form above it. The first correction is shown as an example.

most successful

Minos of Crete was one of the ~~successfulest~~ kings in Greek mythology. His wife enjoyed more greater luxury than most people. Minos wanted his queen to live in absolutely the grander palace he could provide. Therefore he hired Daedalus, the most skillful craftsman available, to build a palace at Knossos. But then foolish Minos angered Poseidon by refusing to sacrifice a white bull. The queen, too, was most interested in protecting the bull than in pleasing Poseidon. She hid the bull in a hollower wooden cow and observed it closely. When Poseidon learned of this deception, he imposed an awfuler punishment on the queen than she could have imagined. He arranged for her to give birth to the Minotaur, the horrible monster possible. To protect his kingdom from the monster, Minos called on Daedalus to build an even most elaborate construction than before: the Labyrinth.

NAME ______________________ CLASS ______________________ DATE ________ SCORE ________

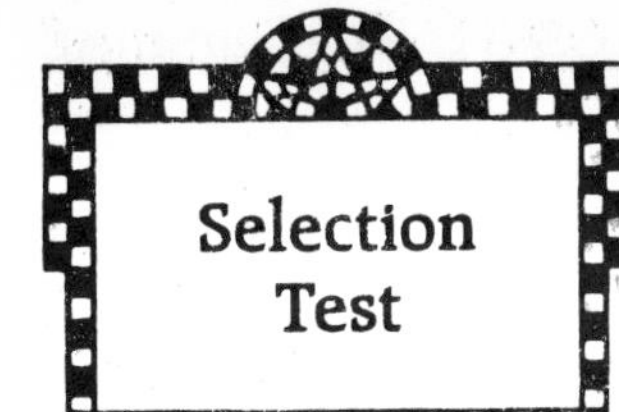

THESEUS

retold by Robert Graves (Textbook page 29)

READING COMPREHENSION

Directions: In the space provided, write the letter of the best answer to each question. *(10 points each)*

1. In the story of Theseus, the gods
   a. do not get involved with the lives of human beings
   b. hate all humans
   c. are always generous and kind
   d. are active in the lives of humans
   1.______

2. Why does Princess Aethra claim that Theseus' father is the god Poseidon?
   a. The real father, Aegeus, does not want a son.
   b. Aegeus fears for his son's safety.
   c. Aethra is secretly in love with Poseidon.
   d. Aethra has abandoned her husband.
   2.______

3. How does Theseus treat both the giant Sinis and the innkeeper Procrustes?
   a. He treats them both with respect.
   b. He requests their help.
   c. He treats them as they have treated others.
   d. He befriends them despite their faults.
   3.______

4. What enables Theseus to kill the Minotaur?
   a. Theseus' superior strength
   b. Theseus' superior eyesight
   c. A magic potion from Theseus' mother
   d. The help of Minos's daughter, Ariadne
   4.______

5. How is Theseus able to escape from the island of Crete?
   a. He follows a magic thread back to Athens.
   b. His ships are faster than Minos's.
   c. Poseidon, his protector, creates a hurricane to stop Minos's ships.
   d. Theseus bores holes in the Cretan ships, causing them to sink.
   5.______

6. What happens to Ariadne, daughter of King Minos?
   a. She returns to Athens with Theseus and rules there as queen.
   b. She refuses to leave Crete.
   c. She marries the god Dionysus.
   d. She is killed by the Minotaur.
   6.______

(continued)

7. When Theseus returns to Athens, he
   a. becomes king after his father dies of grief
   b. is imprisoned
   c. is killed
   d. seizes the throne from his father
   7.______

8. Theseus can best be described as
   a. physically strong, brave, and boastful
   b. clever, courageous, and immortal
   c. humble, thoughtful, and loyal
   d. all-powerful and all-knowing
   8.______

9. What contributes to Theseus' downfall?
   a. He is overly proud of his achievements and abilities.
   b. His courage fails.
   c. He loses his physical powers.
   d. He makes his friend Peirithous angry.
   9.______

10. Which of these statements best sums up the theme of "Theseus"?
   a. Even a great hero can be defeated by a character flaw.
   b. Heroes in Greek mythology can overcome all obstacles.
   c. Pride and boastfulness usually lead to success.
   d. Greek gods have none of the faults of human beings.
   10.______

NAME ______________________ CLASS ______________________ DATE __________ SCORE __________

OSIRIS AND ISIS

retold by Padraic Colum

(Textbook page 35)

DEVELOPING VOCABULARY

Directions: Read carefully the explanation of each word. Then write a sentence of your own using that word. In your sentence, include clues to the word's meaning.

oratory (ôr′ə·tôr′ē, är′-) ***n.*** Public speaking, especially in a traditional manner. ▶ The English word *orator* has exactly the same spelling and meaning as its Latin root. ■ The speaker brought the crowd to its feet with her brilliant oratory. **Page 35**

ORIGINAL SENTENCE ____

____

abyss (ə·bis′) ***n.*** The void or chaos that existed before the world's creation. ▶ This word derives from Greek word parts meaning "without bottom." ■ Egyptian mythology tells how the world was created from the abyss called Nuu. **Page 35**

ORIGINAL SENTENCE ____

____

reckoning (rek′ən·ing) ***n.*** Counting or calculation. ▶ This noun comes from an Old English verb, similar to a German verb, meaning "to count." ■ An abacus is a device for reckoning with movable beads. **Page 35**

ORIGINAL SENTENCE ____

____

abode (ə·bōd′) ***n.*** Home; dwelling place. ▶ The Bible speaks of "shepherds abiding in the field"; *abide* and *abode* are closely related words. ■ The Greek gods were thought to abide in a lofty abode on Mt. Olympus. **Page 35**

ORIGINAL SENTENCE ____

____

diversified (də·vur′sə·fīd′) ***adj.*** Varied. ▶ In Latin, *diversificare* means "to make different." ■ Meadows, woods, and low hills made up a diversified landscape. **Page 36**

ORIGINAL SENTENCE ____

____

(continued)

resplendent (ri·splen′ dənt) ***adj.*** With much splendor; dazzling; shining brilliantly. ▶ The word *splendid,* meaning "shining," is from the same Latin root as *resplendent.* ■ The royal crown was resplendent with precious jewels. **Page 36**

ORIGINAL SENTENCE ______________________________

____

solder (säd′ər) ***v.*** To join with a melted metal compound. ▶ Notice that the *l* is not pronounced in this French-derived word. ■ You will need the proper tool to solder the handle to the metal cup. **Page 36**

ORIGINAL SENTENCE ______________________________

____

divinity (də·vin′ə·tē) ***n.*** Quality of being like God or a god; a god or deity. ▶ This word comes from the same Latin root as *deity.* ■ Being immortal is one of the qualities of divinity. **Page 37**

ORIGINAL SENTENCE ______________________________

____

lamentation (lam′ən·ta′shən) ***n.*** An outward show of grief; wailing or crying. ▶ Words from Latin like this one are often long; most synonyms for *lamentation,* by contrast, are short: *weeping* (Old English); *wailing* (Old Norse); *grieving* (Old French). ■ The lamentation of the wives and children of the lost sailors was sad to hear. **Page 37**

ORIGINAL SENTENCE ______________________________

____

mete (mēt) ***v.*** To distribute or dole out; usually used with *out.* ▶ Be careful not to confuse *mete* with its familiar homonyms *meet* and *meat.* ■ A judge metes out justice according to the law. **Page 38**

ORIGINAL SENTENCE ______________________________

____

NAME ______________________ CLASS ______________ DATE ________ SCORE ______

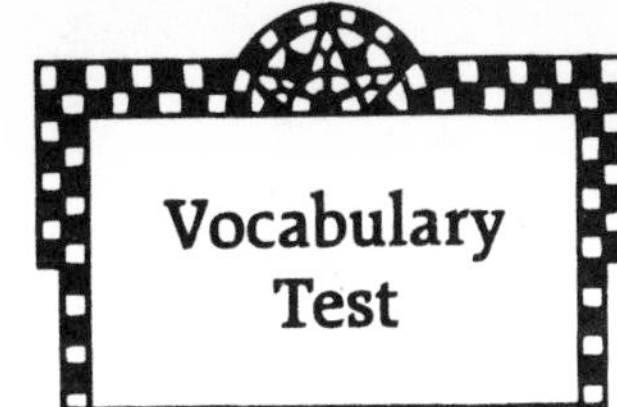

OSIRIS AND ISIS

retold by Padraic Colum

(Textbook page 35)

VOCABULARY TEST

A. Match each word in column I with the correct definition in column II. Place the letter of the definition you choose in the space provided. *(7 points each)*

I	II
______ 1. abode	a. dazzling; shining brilliantly
______ 2. abyss	b. wailing or crying
______ 3. diversified	c. counting or calculation
______ 4. divinity	d. the void or chaos that existed before the creation of the world
______ 5. lamentation	e. to join parts with a melted metal compound
______ 6. mete	f. varied
______ 7. oratory	g. home; dwelling place
______ 8. reckoning	h. the quality of being like God or a god
______ 9. resplendent	i. public speaking
______ 10. solder	j. to distribute or dole out

B. From the words in column I above, choose the word that best completes the sentence. Write the appropriate word in the blank provided. *(6 points each)*

11. By my ______________________, we made a $200 profit from the garage sale.

12. Queen Anne was ______________________ in her jeweled crown and fur-trimmed velvet robes.

13. The Greeks saw Zeus as a god; they also believed in the

    ______________________ of Athena.

14. Our band presented a ______________________ concert, ranging from show tunes to rock.

15. Dr. Martin Luther King, Jr., was famous for his ______________________, especially his great speech at the Lincoln Memorial in 1963.

NAME ______________ CLASS ______________ DATE ________ SCORE ________

OSIRIS AND ISIS

retold by Padraic Colum

(Textbook page 35)

REVIEWING THE SELECTION

Match each name at the left with the phrase or meaning connected with it in the myth. Write the correct letter in the blank provided.

_____ 1. Nephthys

_____ 2. Osiris

_____ 3. Astarte

_____ 4. Re

_____ 5. Horus

_____ 6. Isis

_____ 7. Seth

_____ 8. Queen's child

_____ 9. Thout

_____ 10. Nuu

a. child of Osiris and Isis
b. the formless abyss
c. person who fits into the wooden chest
d. the Wise One
e. queen of the city where the chest is now a tree
f. wife of Seth who turns against him
g. the Violent One
h. Egyptian sun god
i. person who loses immortality because of a misunderstanding
j. wife whose love is undying

Reader's Response

In "Coyote and the Origin of Death," a trickster makes death permanent by closing the door to a grass house. In "Osiris and Isis," death occurs when a wooden chest is sealed shut. Which version of the origin of death do you find more interesting? Write two or three sentences giving your choice and telling why.

____

____

____

____

NAME ______________________ CLASS ______________ DATE ________ SCORE ______

Osiris and Isis

retold by Padraic Colum

(Textbook page 35)

ACTIVE AND PASSIVE VOICE

In most English sentences, the **subject** performs the action. The **object** of the sentence receives the action. (Not all verbs have objects.)

EXAMPLE Osiris (S) makes (V) laws (O). (*Osiris*, the subject, performs the action—*makes*. The object, *laws*, tells what he makes; it receives the action.)

A verb that expresses action performed by the subject is in the **active voice.**

Sometimes, the object—the receiver of the action—becomes the subject. The subject of the active sentence may be expressed in a *by* phrase. (This phrase does not always appear in the sentence.)

EXAMPLE Laws (S) were made (V) *by Osiris.* (The object of the active sentence above has become the subject. The action expressed by the verb is performed *upon* the subject.)

A verb that expresses action performed *upon* the subject is in the **passive voice.**

A verb in the passive voice consists of a form of *be* plus a past participle. When the performer of an action is unknown or unimportant, it is often omitted from a passive sentence.

EXAMPLE Sometimes Osiris (S) is pictured (V) with green skin. (The performer of the action is not included because it is not important in this context.)

Exercise 1. Identifying Active and Passive Voice

In the blank before each sentence, write *A* if the verb is in the active voice; write *P* if the verb is in the passive voice.

_______ 1. The Earth and the Sky were separated by Re.

_______ 2. Osiris showed people how to honor the gods.

_______ 3. Seth made a chest into which only Osiris would fit perfectly.

_______ 4. Seth's attendants nailed the cover on the chest.

_______ 5. Then the cover was soldered with melted lead.

_______ 6. In time, the chest was covered by the bark of a tree.

(continued)

______ 7. Isis searched everywhere for the chest.

______ 8. Isis was told about the tree by a group of children.

______ 9. However, the tree had been cut down.

______ 10. The fragrance from Isis' hand attracted the queen.

Exercise 2. Writing Sentences in Active and Passive Voice

Rewrite each sentence from Exercise 1. If the sentence is in the active voice, rewrite it in the passive. If the sentence is in the passive voice, rewrite it in the active. When no performer of the action appears in a passive-voice sentence, use *Someone* as the subject of your active-voice sentence.

EXAMPLE "Osiris and Isis" has been called a great love story.
Someone has called "Osiris and Isis" a great love story.

1. ______________________________

____

2. ______________________________

____

3. ______________________________

____

4. ______________________________

____

5. ______________________________

____

6. ______________________________

____

7. ______________________________

____

(continued)

8. ____

____

9. ____

____

10. ____

____

Exercise 3. Revising a Paragraph

The passive voice can be useful when the performer of an action is unknown or unimportant. However, too many passive-voice sentences can make your writing weak and awkward. Revise the following paragraph. Eliminate the passive voice in each sentence in which the performer of the action is stated. (*Hint*: Look for prepositional phrases beginning with *by*.) A sample revision is shown.

The queen gave Isis her child to nurse. At night, Isis would put wood strips from the column ~~would be put~~ on the fire ~~by Isis~~. The child would then be placed on the fire by her. The baby was not burned by the flames, however. One night the child was snatched from the fire by the queen. The queen was told by Isis what Isis had been doing. If the child had been left in the fire for just two more nights, it would have gained immortality. Because it was taken from the fire by the queen, it would be given a long life by the gods, but not immortality. When Isis's divinity was revealed by her to the queen, the queen gave her the chest she had sought for so long.

NAME ______________________ CLASS ______________________ DATE __________ SCORE __________

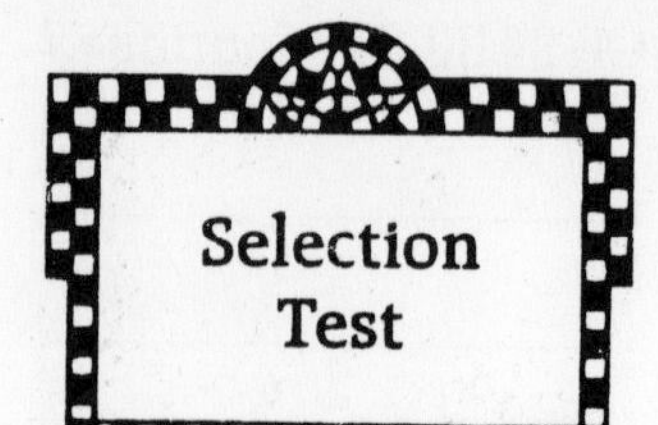

OSIRIS AND ISIS

retold by Padraic Colum

(Textbook page 35)

READING COMPREHENSION

Directions: In the space provided, write the letter of the best answer to each question. *(10 points each)*

1. What happens during Osiris' reign?
   a. war and disease
   b. starvation
   c. peace and prosperity
   d. the worship of false gods

1. ______

2. Osiris brings humans
   a. fire
   b. agriculture, law, and religion
   c. the knowledge that mortals could overthrow the gods
   d. greed and pride

2. ______

3. Why is Seth jealous of Osiris?
   a. Osiris causes green things to grow everywhere.
   b. Osiris has a beautiful wife.
   c. Osiris has many children.
   d. Osiris has a great treasure.

3. ______

4. Seth tricks Osiris by
   a. building a false bottom in a chest
   b. disguising himself
   c. measuring Osiris' shadow
   d. taking Isis away from Osiris

4. ______

5. The one person who fits perfectly into Seth's wooden chest is
   a. Thout
   b. Osiris
   c. Nephthys
   d. Isis

5. ______

6. Seth's attendants throw the sealed chest holding the body of Osiris
   a. into the river
   b. into a thicket of young trees
   c. over a high wall
   d. into a well

6. ______

(continued)

7. Seth's splendid chest eventually becomes
   a. part of a sailing vessel
   b. a monument in a park
   c. worthless scrap
   d. part of a column in a king's house

   7. ______

8. Isis tries to give the queen's child
   a. gold and rubies
   b. the gift of immortality
   c. the fragrant chest
   d. a kingdom to rule

   8. ______

9. According to "Osiris and Isis," death first came into the land when
   a. Seth moved to the desert
   b. the fragrant tree was cut down
   c. Seth tore the body of Osiris into fourteen pieces
   d. Osiris was closed up in the chest

   9. ______

10. What happens when Isis puts the pieces of Osiris' body back together?
    a. Nothing changes.
    b. Peace and fertility return to the land.
    c. Seth dies.
    d. Seth's evil offspring is born.

    10. ______

NAME ______________________ CLASS ______________________ DATE __________ SCORE __________

GREEN WILLOW

retold by Paul Jordan-Smith

(Textbook page 41)

DEVELOPING VOCABULARY

Directions: Read carefully the explanation of each word. Then write a sentence of your own using that word. In your sentence, include clues to the meaning of the word.

amiable (ā′ mē·ə·bəl) ***adj.*** Friendly or good-natured. ▶ This word derives from the Latin word *amicus*, meaning "friend." ▪ Ann was an amiable person, popular with the other employees. **Page 41**

ORIGINAL SENTENCE ____

____

mean (mēn) ***adj.*** 1. Of little value; inferior. 2. Poor in appearance; shabby. ▶ This adjective comes from an Old English word meaning "common." ▪ The mean streets of the slum were depressing. **Page 42**

ORIGINAL SENTENCE ____

____

afford (ə·fôrd′) ***v.*** 1. To be able to pay for. 2. To give. ▶ *Afford* derives from an Old English word meaning "to advance or further." ▪ Listening to music afforded us great pleasure. **Page 42**

ORIGINAL SENTENCE ____

____

condescend (kän′di·send′) ***v.*** To deal politely with a person whom one considers of lesser status. ▶ *Condescend* comes from Latin word parts meaning "to descend with." ▪ The general condescended to dine in the enlisted men's mess hall. **Page 43**

ORIGINAL SENTENCE ____

____

reverie (rev′ ər·ē) ***n.*** Dreamy imagining; daydreaming. ▶ *Reverie* derives from an Old French word that referred to a degree of rejoicing and revelry that bordered on delirium. ▪ The student sat under the trees, enjoying a reverie about the joys her summer trip to Mexico would bring. **Page 44**

ORIGINAL SENTENCE ____

____

NAME ______________________ CLASS ______________________ DATE ________ SCORE ________

GREEN WILLOW

retold by Paul Jordan-Smith

(Textbook page 41)

VOCABULARY TEST

A. Match each word in column I with the correct definition in column II. Place the letter of the definition you choose in the space provided. *(10 points each)*

	I	II
______	1. afford	a. to deal with a person of inferior status
		b. of little value
______	2. amiable	c. to give
		d. friendly
______	3. condescend	e. dreamy imagining
______	4. reverie	
______	5. mean	

B. In the space provided, write the letter of the word or phrase closest in meaning to the word in italics. *(10 points each)*

______ 6. The mayor, happy to see us, welcomed us with an *amiable* smile.
a. formal b. fake c. good–natured

______ 7. Penelope wore the same *mean* cotton dress and shabby sandals as her sister.
a. unkind b. inferior c. boring

______ 8. The windows on the east side *afford* an excellent view of the skyline.
a. furnish b. buy c. block

______ 9. The four-star general would not *condescend* to speak to a mere corporal.
a. lower himself b. pause for a moment c. give the command

______ 10. Lost in her *reverie*, Kai did not realize that the soup was boiling over.
a. conversation b. depression c. daydreaming

NAME ______________ CLASS ______________ DATE ________ SCORE ______

GREEN WILLOW

retold by Paul Jordan-Smith

(Textbook page 41)

REVIEWING THE SELECTION

On line 1 below is an event that happens early in the story "Green Willow." On line 5 is an event that occurs at the end of the story. On lines 2, 3, and 4, list three important events that occur between the events given. List these events in the order in which they take place in the story.

1. The samurai is caught in a heavy snowstorm.
2. ______________________________
3. ______________________________
4. ______________________________
5. The old priest tells the story of Green Willow.

Reader's Response

The samurai in this myth pays a high price for his brief period of happiness. Do you think that the price he pays is too high? Write two or three sentences explaining your answer.

____

____

____

____

____

____

____

____

____

NAME ______________ CLASS ______________ DATE ________ SCORE ________

GREEN WILLOW

retold by Paul Jordan-Smith (Textbook page 41)

READING COMPREHENSION

Directions: In the space provided, write the letter of the best answer to each question. *(10 points each)*

1. At the opening of the tale, Tomotada is a
   a. samurai
   b. daimyo
   c. farmer
   d. priest 1. ______

2. The Lord of Noto sends Tomotada on a quest
   a. to Echizen to find a wife
   b. to the Lord of Kyoto
   c. to a small village to settle a disagreement
   d. to a mountain district to find Noto's lost child 2. ______

3. Tomotada becomes anxious on his quest because
   a. it is snowing and his horse is tired
   b. he feels he is unworthy of the Lord of Noto's trust
   c. his health is bad
   d. he fears that he cannot succeed 3. ______

4. As a samurai, Tomotada
   a. is pledged never to marry
   b. may not accept hospitality from others
   c. must not accept rewards of money
   d. is not allowed to marry without the consent of his lord 4. ______

5. When Tomotada asks to marry Green Willow,
   a. she runs away to a nearby village
   b. her parents oppose the marriage
   c. her father tells Tomotada to accept his daughter as a gift
   d. the Lord of Kyoto refuses to give Tomotada permission to marry 5. ______

6. Tomotada must decide whether to
   a. remain with the Lord of Noto or leave him and join the Lord of Kyoto
   b. stay with his new wife or complete his assigned task
   c. return to his daimyo or become a priest
   d. become a beggar or live with his aging parents 6. ______

(continued)

7. Tomotada and Green Willow live happily together until
   a. he decides to return to the palace of the Lord of Noto
   b. he learns that she has fallen in love with a farmer
   c. she suddenly tells him she will die
   d. she decides to return to her parents' house

7. ______

8. Green Willow finally confesses that she
   a. has been unfaithful
   b. has never loved Tomotada
   c. is the spirit of a tree
   d. cannot have children

8. ______

9. A monk on his way to Echizen stops beside a stream and sees
   a. the stumps of three willow trees
   b. a magnificent modern shrine
   c. two elderly samurai
   d. a stone statue of Green Willow

9. ______

10. The old priest at the end of the story is
   a. a wandering poet
   b. Green Willow
   c. the Lord of Noto
   d. Tomotada

10. ______

NAME ______________________ CLASS ______________ DATE ________ SCORE ______

THE WHITE SNAKE

Jakob and Wilhelm Grimm
translated by Jack Zipes

(Textbook page 47)

REVIEWING THE SELECTION

1. What remarkable thing happens when the servant tastes the white snake? ______________

____

2. How do each of the following animals repay the servant for helping them?

   a. the three fish ______________________________

   ____

   b. the ants ______________________________

   ____

   c. the three ravens ______________________________

   ____

3. What finally convinces the princess to accept the servant as her husband? ______________

____

____

Reader's Response

Do you think the princess's demands for her future husband are fair and reasonable? If your answer is yes, check Yes—and give two reasons for believing so. If your answer is no, check No—and give two reasons for believing so.

Yes ________ No ________

1. ____

____

2. ____

____

NAME ________________ CLASS ________________ DATE ________ SCORE ______

THE WHITE SNAKE

Jakob and Wilhelm Grimm
translated by Jack Zipes

(Textbook page 47)

PREPOSITIONS AND PREPOSITIONAL PHRASES

A **preposition** is a word that shows the relationship of a noun or a pronoun to some other word in the sentence.

EXAMPLES *After* lunch the servant brought the king another dish.
One day the servant tasted a piece *of* the white snake. (*After* and *of* are prepositions.)

Frequently Used Prepositions

about	among	behind	of	since
across	around	during	off	through
after	at	into	over	to
against	before	like	past	toward

A preposition that consists of more than one word is a **compound preposition.**

aside from	because of	in front of	next to
as well as	in addition to	in spite of	on account of

A preposition always introduces a prepositional phrase. A **prepositional phrase** is a group of words beginning with a preposition and usually ending with a noun or pronoun. The noun or pronoun that ends the prepositional phrase is the **object of the preposition.**

EXAMPLE The servant went *into the courtyard.* (The prepositional phrase is *into the courtyard.* The preposition is *into.* The object of the preposition is *courtyard.*)

Be careful not to confuse prepositions with look-alike adverbs. Adverbs lack objects.

EXAMPLE The servant walked *past* some ducks. (preposition)
The servant walked *past.* (adverb)

The word *to* can also be tricky. When followed by a noun or pronoun, it is a preposition. When followed by a verb, however, it is usually an infinitive that can be used as a noun, adjective, or adverb.

EXAMPLES He gave the ring *to* her. (preposition)
The servant wanted *to travel.* (infinitive used as adverb)

(continued)

Exercise 1. Identifying Prepositional Phrases

Underline each prepositional phrase in the following sentences about "The White Snake." There are two prepositional phrases in each sentence. (Remember that prepositions may consist of more than one word.)

EXAMPLE "The White Snake" is a German folktale collected <u>by the Brothers Grimm</u> <u>in the early nineteenth century</u>.

1. The servant begins his journey with high hopes for adventure.
2. He soon sees three fish trapped among the reeds in a pond.
3. The servant feels sorry for them and frees them from their trap.
4. Later he stops to listen to an ant king complaining about people's horses.
5. The servant turns onto a different path, and, because of this, the ant king thanks him.
6. In a big city the servant hears that the king's daughter is looking for a husband.
7. The king tells the servant to retrieve a ring from the depths of the sea.
8. In spite of his first success, the servant faces a series of other difficult tasks.
9. He succeeds, partly on account of the animals' help, partly through his own efforts.
10. The princess's attitude changes from scorn to love when she receives the golden apple.

Exercise 2. Writing with Prepositional Phrases

Combine the sentences in each of the following items. Make each into a single sentence containing one or more prepositional phrases. Use the information in parentheses to form the prepositional phrases.

EXAMPLE There are many common elements. (Fairy tales have these common elements. The Brothers Grimm wrote the fairy tales.)

<u>There are many common elements in the fairy tales of the Brothers Grimm. (or . . .</u>

<u>written by the Brothers Grimm.</u>)

1. The heroes of fairy tales are often people. (The people lack social status. But they have good hearts.)

____

____

(continued)

2. Fairy-tale heroes often show kindness. (People receive this kindness. The people are in distress.)

____

____

3. Their kindness is frequently repaid. (Magic repays the kindness. Or a last-minute rescue repays it.) Use two different prepositions.

____

____

4. The servant discovers the needs. (This is "The White Snake" servant. Various animals have needs.)

____

____

Exercise 3. Revising a Paragraph

Revise the following paragraph about "The White Snake" by inserting an appropriate prepositional phrase that has the object shown in parentheses. The carets (^) indicate where to insert the prepositions. The first sentence is done for you as an example.

The mother and father ravens are standing (^ *next to the* nest) and trying to push the baby ravens (^ *out of the* nest). The unfortunate young ravens are lying (^ground) and crying (^plight). The servant dismounts (^horse) and proceeds to kill the horse (^sword). He leaves the horse's carcass (^young ravens) and continues his journey (^foot). (^journey), he arrives (^big city) where there is a great deal (^noise) and a huge crowd (^streets). Here he learns that the king's daughter is looking (^husband). She insists on finding a man who is entirely (^fear). The servant is so dazzled (^beauty) that he goes (^king) and declares himself a suitor. The king and princess make success difficult (^him), but he eventually triumphs (^obstacles).

NAME ______________________________ CLASS ______________________ DATE __________ SCORE ________

THE WHITE SNAKE

Jakob and Wilhelm Grimm
translated by Jack Zipes

(Textbook page 47)

READING COMPREHENSION

Directions: In the space provided, write the letter of the best answer to each question. *(10 points each)*

1. After the servant takes a bite of the white snake, he is able to
   a. read the king's mind
   b. turn into the animal of his choice
   c. understand the language of animals
   d. speak French as well as German

   1. ______

2. The servant is suspected of
   a. stealing the king's crown
   b. taking the queen's ring
   c. stealing valuable papers
   d. poisoning the snake

   2. ______

3. The missing object is found in
   a. an anthill
   b. the throne room
   c. the queen's suite
   d. a duck

   3. ______

4. When the king offers him a reward, the servant chooses to
   a. become a member of the king's court
   b. be given a horse and travel money
   c. marry the king's daughter
   d. accept nothing

   4. ______

5. On his travels, the servant saves
   a. a duck, three fish, and some ants
   b. the king's daughter
   c. three fish, some ants, and some ravens
   d. his horse

   5. ______

6. The princess's suitors are required to
   a. perform a difficult task
   b. court her with gifts of rare perfumes
   c. be of a certain age and height
   d. serenade her with original love songs

   6. ______

(continued)

7. When the servant returns the ring from the sea,
   a. the king agrees to let him marry the princess
   b. the king declares it is the wrong ring
   c. the princess orders the servant beheaded
   d. the princess rejects the servant because of his humble birth — 7. ______

8. The sacks are refilled with millet seeds by
   a. three ravens
   b. the princess
   c. an army of ants
   d. the servant — 8. ______

9. The servant obtains the golden apple from the tree of life by
   a. hiring a fleet of ships to sail the seven seas
   b. asking the fish to swim to all parts of the world until they find it
   c. receiving it as a gift from the three ravens
   d. listening to the sparrows and learning its location — 9. ______

10. The moral of "The White Snake" is that
   a. acts of kindness may be repaid unexpectedly
   b. cruelty is always punished
   c. good deeds lead only to disaster
   d. happiness can be gained through magic — 10. ______

NAME ______________________ CLASS ________________ DATE ________ SCORE ________

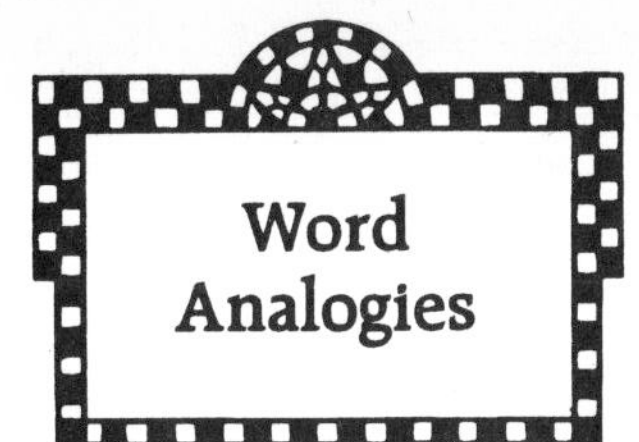

UNIT 1: WORLD MYTHS AND FOLKTALES

WORD ANALOGIES / Extending Vocabulary

Directions: In the space provided, write the letter of the pair of words with the relationship that is closest to that of the capitalized words. *(10 points each)*

1. ABODE : CABIN ::
   a. forest : tree
   b. vehicle : jeep
   c. bird : nest
   d. country : citizen — 1. ______

2. DIVERSIFIED : DIFFERENT ::
   a. few : numerous
   b. ordinary : unique
   c. similar : opposite
   d. identical : same — 2. ______

3. RECKONING : JUDGMENT ::
   a. modification : creation
   b. guilt : punishment
   c. appraisal : estimate
   d. confusion : understanding — 3. ______

4. LAMENTATION : MOURNFUL ::
   a. rage : angry
   b. apology : forgiven
   c. sorrow : happy
   d. pity : begging — 4. ______

5. MEAN : SHABBY ::
   a. rare : common
   b. middle : range
   c. valuable : costly
   d. copy : unique — 5. ______

6. ORATORY : LISTEN ::
   a. question : answer
   b. audience : hear
   c. poetry : poet
   d. essay : read — 6. ______

7. SOLDER : METAL ::
   a. hammer : wood
   b. glue : plastic
   c. heat : liquid
   d. stone : chisel — 7. ______

8. RESPLENDENT : JEWEL ::
   a. gritty : sandpaper
   b. smooth : surface
   c. wedding : diamond
   d. murky : transparent — 8. ______

9. AMIABLE : ALLY ::
   a. superior : opponent
   b. hostile : enemy
   c. polite : conversation
   d. generous : gratitude — 9. ______

10. REVERIE : PLEASURE ::
    a. inconvenience : discomfort
    b. laughter : entertainment
    c. nightmare : terror
    d. author : imagination — 10. ______

NAME ______________________ CLASS ______________________ DATE __________ SCORE __________

UNIT 1: WORLD MYTHS AND FOLKTALES

UNIT REVIEW TEST/Applying Skills I

A. Reading Comprehension. In the space provided, write the letter of the best answer to each question. *(8 points each)*

1. In "How the World Was Made," which animal obtains the ball of mud necessary to create the earth?
   a. the loon
   b. the turtle
   c. the coot
   d. the snow goose
   1.______

2. In the myth of "The Wooden People," the gods are
   a. perfect at creating things
   b. capable of making mistakes
   c. unwilling to admit their mistakes
   d. easy to please
   2.______

3. "How the World Was Made" explains several origins, including
   a. how dogs learned to bark
   b. the traits of the turtle
   c. how Maheo lost his power
   d. why animals distrust people
   3.______

4. In "Coyote and the Origin of Death," a trickster
   a. outwits the council and makes death permanent
   b. avoids death by building a large grass house
   c. lies to the council about his true feelings
   d. invents death, which angers the medicine men
   4.______

5. Which of these tasks does the hero Theseus complete?
   a. He kills the Minotaur.
   b. He wins Ariadne from the god Dionysus.
   c. He kills King Hades.
   d. He succeeds in getting Peirithous married to Persephone.
   5.______

6. A magical transformation that occurs in "Osiris and Isis" is
   a. Seth's change into a cat
   b. Nephthys' change into a gazelle
   c. Osiris' change into a frog
   d. Isis' change into a swallow
   6.______

(continued)

B. Identifying Characters. Each description below refers to a main character in one of the selections you have just read. Identify the character by choosing the letter of the best answer. Write the letter in the space provided. *(8 points each)*

7. He finds the queen's ring in the stomach of a duck.
   a. Maheo in "How the World Was Made"
   b. Coyote in "Coyote and the Origin of Death"
   c. The servant in "The White Snake"
   d. The grandfather in "Water Jar Boy"

   7. ______

8. She dies because her soul is not that of a human being.
   a. The beautiful princess in "The White Snake"
   b. Tomotada's wife in "Green Willow"
   c. The queen's child in "Osiris and Isis"
   d. Princess Aethra in "Theseus"

   8. ______

9. He reigns over a world of beauty and prosperity.
   a. Osiris in "Osiris and Isis"
   b. King Hades in "Theseus"
   c. Heart of Sky in "The Wooden People"
   d. Seth in "Osiris and Isis"

   9. ______

10. She carries the earth on her back.
    a. The Goddess Aphrodite in "Theseus"
    b. Isis in "Osiris and Isis"
    c. Grandmother Turtle in "How the World Was Made"
    d. The little coot in "How the World Was Made"

    10. ______

C. Composition. Choose *one* of these topics and write a brief essay on a separate piece of paper. *(20 points)*

1. Both "Green Willow" and "The White Snake" involve quests. Discuss how the two quests are similar and how they are different. You might consider such elements as the prize that the hero seeks, the problems that he encounters, and the reward that he receives at the end. Use details from each story to support your essay.

2. Folktales and myths often feature tricksters, characters who play tricks on others and act as anti-authority figures. "Coyote and the Origin of Death," "Osiris and Isis," and "Theseus" each have a character who is a trickster. Compare and contrast two of these tricksters. In your essay, you might want to focus on the motivations and character traits of the tricksters. Are they evil or just mischievous? Do they have any positive traits? What are the results of their actions? Use specific details from the stories to support your points.

NAME ______________ CLASS ______________ DATE ________ SCORE ________

UNIT 1: WORLD MYTHS AND FOLKTALES

CRITICAL THINKING AND WRITING/Applying Skills II

A. Reading a Folktale. Read the folktale below carefully. Then answer the questions that follow.

WATER JAR BOY

A Tewa Folktale

retold by

TRISTRAM POTTER COFFIN

The people were living at Sikyatki. There was a fine looking girl who refused to get married. Her mother made water jars all the time. One day as she was using her foot to mix some clay, she told her daughter to go on with this while she went for water. The girl tried to mix the clay on a flat stone by stepping on it. Somehow some of it entered her. This made her pregnant, and after a time she gave birth. The mother was angry about this, but when she looked she saw it was not a baby that had been born, but a little jar. When the mother asked where it came from the girl just cried. Then the father came in. He said he was very glad his daughter had a baby. When he found out that it was a water jar, he became very fond of it.

He watched it and saw it move. It grew, and in twenty days it had become big. It could go about with the other children and was able to talk. The children also became fond of it. They found out from his talk that he was Water Jar Boy. His mother cried, because he had no legs or arms or eyes. But they were able to feed him through the jar mouth.

When snow came the boy begged his grandfather to take him along with the men to hunt rabbits. "My poor grandson, you can't hunt rabbits; you have no arms or legs."

"Take me anyway," said the boy. "You are so old, you can't kill anything." His grandfather took him down under the mesa where he rolled along. Pretty soon he saw a rabbit track and followed it. Then a rabbit ran out, and he began to chase it. He hit himself against a rock. The jar broke, and up jumped a boy.

He was very glad his skin had been broken and that he was a big boy. He had lots of beads around his neck, earstrings of turquoise, a dance kilt[1] and moccasins, and a buckskin shirt. He was fine-looking and handsomely dressed. He killed four jackrabbits before sunset, because he was a good runner.

His grandfather was waiting for him at the foot of the mesa, but did not know him. He asked the fine looking boy, "Did you see my grandson anywhere?"

"No, I did not see him."

"That's too bad; he's late."

"'I didn't see anyone anywhere," said the boy. Then he said, "I am your grandson." He said this because his grandfather looked so disappointed.

"No, you are not my grandson."

[1]kilt: a garment like a skirt.

(continued)

"Yes, I am."

"You are only teasing me. My grandson is a round jar and has no arms and legs."

Then the boy said, "I am telling you the truth. I am your grandson. This morning you carried me down here. I looked for rabbits and chased one, just rolling along. Pretty soon I hit myself on a rock. My skin was broken, and I came out of it. I am the very one who is your grandson. You must believe me." Then the old man believed him, and they went home together.

When the grandfather came to the house with a fine-looking man, the girl was ashamed, thinking the man was a suitor. The old man said, "This is Water Jar Boy, my grandson." The grandmother then asked how the water jar became a boy, and the two men told her. Finally, the women were convinced.

The boy went about with the other boys of the village. One day he said to his mother, "Who is my father?"

"I don't know," she replied. He kept on asking, but it just made her cry. Finally he said, "I am going to find my father, tomorrow."

"You can't find him. I have never been with any man so there is no place for you to look for a father," she said.

"But I know I have one," the boy said. "I know where he lives. I am going to see him."

The mother begged him not to go, but he insisted. The next day she fixed food for him, and he went off toward the southwest to a place called Horse Mesa Point. There was a spring at this place. As he approached he saw a man walking a little way from the spring. He said to the boy, "Where are you going?"

"To the spring," the boy answered.

"Why are you going there?"

"I want to see my father."

"Who is your father?"

"He lives in this spring."

"Well, you will never find your father," said the man.

"Well, I want to go to the spring. My father is living in it," said the boy.

"Who is your father?" asked the man again.

"Well, I think you are my father."

"How do you know that?"

"I just know, that's all."

Then the man stared hard at the boy, trying to scare him. The boy just kept on saying, "You are my father." At last the man said, "Yes, I am your father. I came out of the spring to meet you." He put his arms around the boy's neck. He was very glad his boy had come, and he took him down to the spring.

There were many people living there. The women and the girls ran up to the boy and put their arms around him, because they were glad he had come. This way he found his father and his father's relatives. He stayed there one night. The next day he went to his own home and told his mother he had found his father.

Soon his mother got sick and died. The boy thought to himself, "It's no use for me to stay with these people," so he went to the spring. There he found his mother among the other women. He learned that his father was Red Water Snake. He told his boy that he could not live over at Sikyatki, so he made the boy's mother sick so she would die and come to live with him. After that they all lived together.

(continued)

B. Analyzing a Folktale. In the space provided, write the letter of the best answer to each question. *(6 points each)*

1. When does the girl become pregnant?
   a. soon after she marries
   b. while traveling far from home
   c. upon drinking from a magic spring
   d. while mixing clay on a flat stone

   1. ______

2. Water Jar Boy becomes a human being when
   a. his mother tells him the story of his birth
   b. a rabbit chases him
   c. his grandfather accidentally kicks him
   d. he runs into a rock and breaks

   2. ______

3. Which word best describes how his people feel about Water Jar Boy before he becomes a human being?
   a. angry
   b. suspicious
   c. fond
   d. uncomfortable

   3. ______

4. Once he becomes a human being, Water Jar Boy is
   a. confused and silent
   b. handsome and athletic
   c. ugly and clumsy
   d. shy and afraid

   4. ______

5. Before Water Jar Boy's father accepts him, Water Jar Boy must show
   a. talent
   b. love
   c. courage
   d. happiness

   5. ______

6. The fact that Water Jar Boy finds his father at the spring shows that water symbolizes, or stands for,
   a. death
   b. change
   c. courage
   d. rebirth

   6. ______

7. "Water Jar Boy" shares the following feature with other folktales.
   a. It includes supernatural events and transformations.
   b. It explains the origin of water.
   c. It was lost for centuries.
   d. It does not have much meaning.

   7. ______

(continued)

8. At the end of the story, Water Jar Boy has found
   a. his father and his father's relatives
   b. mortality
   c. how to be content even though he is alone
   d. that he no longer loves his mother

8. ______

9. The purpose of this story was probably to
   a. explain the origin of water jars
   b. explain the creation of the world
   c. teach a moral lesson
   d. explain the behavior of the gods

9. ______

10. Water Jar Boy is a quest hero in that he
    a. is scoffed at by his parents
    b. has an unusual birth and childhood
    c. feels he is better than the people at Sikyatki
    d. fails to overcome the obstacles in his path

10. ______

C. Writing About a Folktale. In "Water Jar Boy," a boy's quest leads to the discovery of his father, Red Water Snake. Write one paragraph about this quest. In your paragraph, explain (a) what characteristics of the hero lead to the successful conclusion of the quest and (b) what the hero finds at the end of the quest. Remember that myths and folktales often have symbolic meanings. In addition to his father, what else does Water Jar Boy find? *(40 points)*

____

____

____

____

____

____

____

____

____

____

____

____

UNIT 1: WORLD MYTHS AND FOLKTALES

UNIT INTRODUCTION TEST

(Textbook pages 2–7)

1. c	5. d	8. c
2. d	6. b	9. d
3. d	7. a	10. a
4. a		

HOW THE WORLD WAS MADE

retold by Alice Marriott and Carol K. Rachlin
(Textbook page 11)

REVIEW AND RESPONSE WORKSHEET

Reviewing the Selection

1. pleased
2. The coot is small, and it cannot fly or dive like the other birds.
3. Grandmother Turtle carries the earth on her back.
4. Maheo creates the first man with a rib bone from Maheo's right side.
5. He creates the first woman with a rib bone from his left side.

Reader's Response

Responses will vary. Students might mention the beauty and grace of the flying birds, the humbleness of the little coot, or the solemn slowness of Grandmother Turtle.

LANGUAGE SKILLS WORKSHEET

Punctuating and Capitalizing Dialogue

Exercise 1

Check marks should appear before items 2, 3, 4, 5, 8, and 9.

Exercise 2

1. The teacher said, "In the Greek story of the origin of the world, Chaos existed in the beginning."
2. "The children of Chaos," the teacher added, "were Night and Erebus, the place of death."
3. indirect quotation—no punctuation or capitalization necessary
4. "The next event was the creation of Light," the teacher went on. "The companion of Light was Day."
5. "What about the creation of people?" a student asked.

   "In one Greek story," the teacher responded, "it was the Titan Prometheus who created humans as they are today."

Exercise 3

Answers will vary. Check for correct punctuation and capitalization in the dialogue.

SELECTION TEST

Reading Comprehension

1. a	5. c	8. b
2. d	6. d	9. a
3. b	7. a	10. c
4. c		

(continued)

THE WOODEN PEOPLE *from the* POPOL VUH

translated by Dennis Tedlock
(Textbook page 18)

REVIEW AND RESPONSE WORKSHEET

1. c
2. The manikins are not competent and they do not honor their builder. He decides to destroy them in a great flood.
3. a
4. They were left behind after the flood as a reminder of the flawed manikins.

Reader's Response

Responses will vary. Students will most likely circle the adjectives *ugly, wooden, thoughtless, incompetent, ungrateful.*

LANGUAGE SKILLS WORKSHEET

Appositives and Appositive Phrases

Exercise 1

1. experiment, a cutout
2. Maker, Modeler, the Quiché Mayan god of creation
3. no appositive
4. humiliation, a great flood
5. One, Tearing Jaguar
6. dogs, the best friends of many people today
7. caves, a refuge from the ongoing destruction
8. no appositive
9. sign, monkeys
10. wooden people, mere manikins

Exercise 2

1. The Quiché Mayans had a god of creation, the Maker, Modeler.
2. "The Wooden People," a myth, tells the story of a mistake by the god of creation.
3. The manikins, mere bones and tendons at the end, got little sympathy even from their dogs.
4. Their everyday utensils, tortilla griddles and cooking pots, complained of sooty faces.
5. These human beings, worthless woodcarvings, would have to be replaced by a better design.

Exercise 3

The Popol Vuh, the Quiché Mayan book of creation, tells the story of how the Maker, Modeler creates a race of manikins, woodcarvings, who are disappointing to the gods. The Mayan father-god, Heart of Sky, decides to eliminate the wooden people in a great disaster, a flood. The wooden people are crushed, pounded down to bones and tendons by water and animals, including two jaguars, Crunching Jaguar and Tearing Jaguar. Even their dogs, faithful companions in the past, attack the wooden people, snarling that they will kill the poor woodcarvings, now friendless outcasts. Only one animal in the forest today, the monkey, has any features to remind people of the destroyed manikins.

SELECTION TEST

Reading Comprehension

1. c
2. a
3. c
4. b
5. a
6. b
7. b
8. b
9. a
10. d

(continued)

COYOTE AND THE ORIGIN OF DEATH

retold by Richard Erdoes and Alfonso Ortiz
(Textbook page 23)

REVIEW AND RESPONSE WORKSHEET

Reviewing the Selection

1. There is no more room for them.
2. in a large grass house
3. by shutting the door and keeping the spirit of the whirlwind out of the grass house
4. They are angry with him because he made death eternal.

Reader's Response

Responses will vary. Students who agree that the comparison makes sense are likely to say that the wind, like a person's spirit, is invisible but real. Some may feel that a gentle wind, rather than a whirlwind, would be a more appropriate comparison, unless the spirit of the dead person is restless or agitated.

SELECTION TEST

Reading Comprehension

1. c
2. d
3. a
4. b
5. b

THESEUS

retold by Robert Graves
(Textbook page 29)

REVIEW AND RESPONSE WORKSHEET

Reviewing the Selection

1. She tells Theseus to take a sword and sandals to his father, Aegeus, and to tell him he found them under a rock.
2. He will raise white sails in place of the black ones on his ship.
3. Ariadne
4. He cuts off the Minotaur's head and then follows a magic thread back to the entrance of the Labyrinth.
5. Theseus forgets to change the black sails to white, and Aegeus, thinking his son has been killed, jumps into the sea.

Reader's Response

Responses will vary.

LANGUAGE SKILLS WORKSHEET

Adjectives: Degrees of Comparison

Exercise 1

1. s oldest
2. c safer
3. p right
4. c shorter
5. p angry
6. s most powerful
7. c more glorious
8. p great
9. s bravest
10. s riskiest

Exercise 2

1. stronger
2. most notorious
3. more powerful
4. most brilliant
5. more splendid

Exercise 3

Minos of Crete was one of the <u>most successful</u> kings in Greek mythology. His wife enjoyed <u>greater</u> luxury than most people. Minos wanted his queen to live in absolutely the <u>grandest</u> palace he could provide. Therefore he hired Daedalus, the <u>most skillful</u> craftsman available, to build a palace at Knossos. But then <u>foolish</u> Minos angered Poseidon by refusing to sacrifice a white bull. The queen, too, was <u>more interested</u> in protecting the bull than in pleasing Poseidon. She hid the bull in a

(continued)

hollow wooden cow and observed it closely. When Poseidon learned of this deception, he imposed a more awful punishment on the queen than she could have imagined. He arranged for her to give birth to the Minotaur, the most horrible monster possible. To protect his kingdom from the monster, Minos called on Daedalus to build an even more elaborate construction than before: the Labyrinth.

SELECTION TEST

Reading Comprehension

1. d	5. d	8. a
2. b	6. c	9. a
3. c	7. a	10. a
4. d		

OSIRIS AND ISIS

retold by Padraic Colum
(Textbook page 35)

VOCABULARY ACTIVITY WORKSHEET

Developing Vocabulary

Responses will vary.

VOCABULARY TEST

A.

1. g	6. j
2. d	7. i
3. f	8. c
4. h	9. a
5. b	10. e

B. 11. reckoning
12. resplendent
13. divinity
14. diversified
15. oratory

REVIEW AND RESPONSE WORKSHEET

Reviewing the Selection

1. f	5. a	8. i
2. c	6. j	9. d
3. e	7. g	10. b
4. h		

Reader's Response

Responses will vary. Some students may point out the similarity between shutting a door and shutting the lid of a chest—both carry connotations of termination and finality.

LANGUAGE SKILLS WORKSHEET

Active and Passive Voice

Exercise 1

1. P	5. P	8. P
2. A	6. P	9. P
3. A	7. A	10. A
4. A		

Exercise 2

1. Re separated the Earth and the Sky.
2. People were shown by Osiris how to honor the gods.
3. A chest was made by Seth into which only Osiris would fit perfectly.
4. The cover on the chest was nailed by Seth's attendants.

(continued)

5. Then someone soldered the cover with melted lead.
6. In time, the bark of a tree covered the chest.
7. The chest was searched for everywhere by Isis.
8. A group of children told Isis about the tree.
9. However, someone had cut down the tree.
10. The queen was attracted by the fragrance from Isis's hand.

Exercise 3

The queen gave Isis her child to nurse. At night, Isis would put wood strips from the column on the fire. She would then place the child on the fire. The flames did not burn the baby, however. One night the queen snatched the child from the fire. Isis told the queen what she had been doing. If the child had been left in the fire for just two more nights, it would have gained immortality. Because the queen took it from the fire, the gods would give it a long life, but not immortality. When Isis revealed her divinity to the queen, the queen gave her the chest she had sought for so long.

SELECTION TEST

Reading Comprehension

1. c	5. b	8. b
2. b	6. a	9. d
3. a	7. d	10. b
4. c		

Green Willow

retold by Paul Jordan-Smith
(Textbook page 41)

VOCABULARY ACTIVITY WORKSHEET

Developing Vocabulary

Responses will vary.

VOCABULARY TEST

A.	1. c	**B.**	6. c
	2. d		7. b
	3. a		8. a
	4. e		9. a
	5. b		10. c

REVIEW AND RESPONSE WORKSHEET

Reviewing the Selection

Answers will vary. Here are some possible responses.

2. The old couple take Tomotada in.
3. Tomotada abandons his quest so as to be with Green Willow.
4. Green Willow confesses her secret and dies.

Reader's Response

Responses will vary. Some students might respond that a brief period of true love and happiness would be worth any price. Other students might discuss such ideas as adherence to duties and responsibilities, opportunities lost due to indulgence in fleeting pleasures, or the impermanence of happiness that is based on giving up future gains for present pleasures.

SELECTION TEST

Reading Comprehension

1. a	5. c	8. c
2. b	6. b	9. a
3. a	7. c	10. d
4. d		

(continued)

THE WHITE SNAKE

Jakob and Wilhelm Grimm
translated by Jack Zipes
(Textbook page 47)

REVIEW AND RESPONSE WORKSHEET

Reviewing the Selection

1. The servant is able to hear what various animals are saying to each other.
2. a. The fish bring him the gold ring.
   b. The ants put every grain of the millet back in the sack.
   c. The ravens obtain the golden apple.
3. When the princess receives the golden apple of the tree of life, she agrees to share her future with the servant.

Reader's Response

Responses will vary. Those who believe the princess is being fair and reasonable may (1) point out the importance of choosing the right marriage partner and (2) comment on the princess's understandable doubt that a servant is the best choice. Those who think the princess is being unfair and unreasonable may (1) mention that the princess keeps upping her demands and (2) suggest that she comes across as something of a snob.

LANGUAGE SKILLS WORKSHEET

Prepositions and Prepositional Phrases

Exercise 1

1. with high hopes / for adventure
2. among the reeds / in a pond
3. for them / from their trap
4. to an ant king / about people's horses
5. onto a different path / because of this
6. In a big city / for a husband
7. from the depths / of the sea
8. In spite of his first success / of other difficult tasks
9. on account of the animals' help / through his own efforts
10. from scorn / to love

Exercise 2

Answers may vary slightly.

1. The heroes of fairy tales are often people without social status but with good hearts.
2. Fairy-tale heroes often show kindness to people in distress.
3. Their kindness is frequently repaid through magic or by a last-minute rescue.
4. The servant in "The White Snake" discovers the needs of various animals.

Exercise 3

Answers may vary slightly.

The mother and father ravens are standing next to the nest and trying to push the baby ravens out of the nest. The unfortunate young ravens are lying on the ground and crying about their plight. The servant dismounts from his horse and proceeds to kill the horse with his sword. He leaves the horse's carcass for the young ravens and continues his journey on foot. After a long journey, he arrives at a big city where there is great deal of noise and a huge crowd in the streets. Here he learns that the king's daughter is looking for a husband. She insists on finding a man who is entirely without fear. The servant is so dazzled by the princess's beauty that he goes before the king and declares himself a suitor. The king and princess make success difficult for him, but he eventually triumphs over all obstacles.

(continued)

SELECTION TEST

Reading Comprehension

1. c
2. b
3. d
4. b
5. c
6. a
7. d
8. c
9. c
10. a

WORD ANALOGIES/Extending Vocabulary

1. b (abode : cabin :: vehicle : jeep)
   Relationship: class to species
   A *cabin* is a kind of *abode.* A *jeep* is a kind of *vehicle.*
2. d (diversified : different :: identical : same)
   Relationship: synonyms
   Diversified and *different* are synonyms meaning "varied." *Identical* and *same* are synonyms meaning "alike."
3. c (reckoning : judgment :: appraisal : estimate)
   Relationship: synonyms
   Reckoning and *judgment* are synonyms meaning "a settlement" or "an accounting." *Appraisal* and *estimate* are synonyms meaning "a decision about value or worth."
4. a (lamentation : mournful :: rage : angry)
   Relationship: object to characteristic (or quality)
   A *lamentation* has the characteristic of, or is associated with, being *mournful.* A *rage* is associated with being *angry.*
5. c (mean : shabby :: valuable : costly)
   Relationship: synonyms
   Mean and *shabby* are synonyms meaning "low in quality." *Valuable* and *costly* are synonyms meaning "of great value."
6. d (oratory : listen :: essay : read)
   Relationship: object to purpose (or characteristic)
   The purpose of *oratory* is to *listen* (to it). The purpose of an essay is to *read* (it).
7. b (solder : metal :: glue : plastic)
   Relationship: object to purpose
   A purpose of *solder* is its use on *metal.* A purpose of *glue* is its use on *plastic.*
8. a (resplendent : jewel :: gritty : sandpaper)
   Relationship: characteristic to object
   Resplendent expresses a characteristic of a *jewel. Gritty* expresses a characteristic of *sandpaper.*
9. b (amiable : ally :: hostile : enemy)
   Relationship: characteristic to person
   Amiable expresses a characteristic of an *ally. Hostile* expresses a characteristic of an *enemy.*
10. c (reverie : pleasure :: nightmare : terror)
    Relationship: cause-effect
    A *reverie* causes *pleasure.* A *nightmare* causes *terror.*

UNIT REVIEW TEST/Applying Skills I

A. Reading Comprehension

1. c
2. b
3. b
4. a
5. a
6. d

(continued)

B. Identifying Characters

7. c
8. b
9. a
10. c

C. Composition

1. Responses will vary. Some similarities are the testing of the heroes, the role of beautiful women, and the supernatural elements. A main difference is that the samurai in "Green Willow" fails to complete his quest, whereas the servant in "The White Snake" follows through faithfully on his.
2. Responses will vary. The tricksters are Coyote, Seth, and Hades. Students' paragraphs should concentrate on the differences between them in motivation, power, and results. They should identify whether each character is evil or just mischievous, describe the positive traits (if any) of each trickster, and explain the results of the tricksters' actions, citing specific details from the stories.

CRITICAL THINKING AND WRITING/ Applying Skills II

B. Analyzing a Folktale

1. d
2. d
3. c
4. b
5. c
6. d
7. a
8. a
9. c
10. b

C. Writing About a Folktale

Responses will vary. The best paragraphs will explain that characteristics of the hero such as kindness, loyalty, determination, and fearlessness led to the successful completion of the quest. They will also explain the fact that Water Jar Boy finds not only his father but also rebirth and immortality. Well-developed paragraphs will include specific details from the story, such as the actions and words of Water Jar Boy, to support explanations.

NOTES

NAME ______________________ CLASS ______________ DATE ________ SCORE ______

UNIT 2: THE AFRICAN LITERARY TRADITION

(Textbook pages 64–71)

INTRODUCTION/African Literature

Directions: In the space provided, write the letter of the best answer to each question. *(10 points each)*

1. The Nile River
   a. flooded frequently and unpredictably
   b. provided settlers only with water
   c. dried up during the rule of the pharaoh known as King Tut
   d. furnished the papyrus reeds Egyptians used to make paper — 1. ______

2. Egyptian society
   a. had a structure similar to a pyramid
   b. did not have a very large class of workers and peasants
   c. had no doctors or lawyers
   d. was not highly organized — 2. ______

3. Egyptian civilization
   a. lasted only a few centuries
   b. had three main eras, or periods
   c. produced the world's first democracy
   d. made little use of writing — 3. ______

4. The ancient Egyptians
   a. believed their pharaoh was an incarnation of the god Horus
   b. did not believe in an afterlife
   c. were a classless society
   d. ceremonially burned the body of the deceased pharaoh — 4. ______

5. The Book of the Dead was a kind of "traveler's guide" to
   a. the upper Nile valley
   b. the land of Kush
   c. the pyramids
   d. the afterlife — 5. ______

6. Most of the literature of ancient Egypt was
   a. closely related to religious beliefs
   b. purely for entertainment
   c. written for the lower classes
   d. not about religion — 6. ______

(continued)

7. The ancient civilizations of Africa
   a. were not very powerful
   b. never conquered Egypt
   c. included Kush and Aksum
   d. existed in complete isolation from the rest of the world

   7. ______

8. The ancient city of Timbuktu was
   a. the location of the largest pyramids
   b. the gateway to the Nile valley
   c. a center of trade and learning
   d. the capital of Egypt

   8. ______

9. An indigenous, or native, feature of African culture is
   a. oral literature
   b. Islam
   c. Christianity
   d. colonialism

   9. ______

10. A *griot* is best described as
    a. an instrument used to accompany oral performance
    b. the chief of a tribe
    c. a storyteller and historian
    d. a pharaoh

    10. ______

NAME ______________________ CLASS ______________ DATE ________ SCORE ______

THE GREAT HYMN TO THE ATEN

translated by Miriam Lichtheim (Textbook page 73)

REVIEWING THE SELECTION

Place a check mark before each item that is true of Aten when he is present on the earth.

_______ 1. He fills the land with beauty.

_______ 2. He has some limits.

_______ 3. The ships fare well on the sea.

_______ 4. He causes everyone to speak alike.

_______ 5. He causes water to drench the fields of the people.

_______ 6. He dispels the dark.

_______ 7. He causes the serpent to bite.

_______ 8. He dawns in the eastern lightland.

_______ 9. He is one of many gods.

_______ 10. He creates life.

Reader's Response

Although we no longer think of the sun as a god, can you think of ways that we worship the sun? Explain your answer in two or three sentences.

NAME ______________________ CLASS ________________ DATE ________ SCORE ______

NEW KINGDOM LOVE LYRICS

translated by William Kelly Simpson (Textbook page 81)

REVIEWING THE SELECTIONS

1. How is the speaker in "The Voice of the Wild Goose" like a wild goose? ________________

____

2. Why can't the speaker in "The Voice of the Wild Goose" perform regular tasks?

____

____

3. What might make the speaker in "Most Beautiful Youth Who Ever Happened" feel like someone "already in the grave"? ______________________________________

____

4. What brings joy to the speaker in "Most Beautiful Youth Who Ever Happened"? __________

____

5. Place a check mark before the item that best describes the theme of these poems.

   ______ a. Love is all joy.

   ______ b. Love is easy to walk away from.

   ______ c. Love can bring both joy and pain.

Reader's Response

In "The Voice of the Wild Goose," love is compared to a trap. Think about this comparison, and then complete both of these statements.

a. Love is like a trap because ____

____

b. Love is unlike a trap because ______________________________________

____

NAME ______________ CLASS ______________ DATE ________ SCORE ________

AFRICAN PROVERBS

(Textbook page 85)

REVIEWING THE SELECTIONS

"Translate" each of the following African proverbs by explaining its meaning in everyday English.

1. No one knows the story of tomorrow's dawn. ______________

2. Loose teeth are better than no teeth.[1] ______________

3. The man who has not carried loads himself does not know how heavy they are.[2] ______________

4. There is no hill that never ends.[3] ______________

5. Magic takes time.[4] ______________

Reader's Response

Choose one of the proverbs below and, on a separate sheet of paper, write a brief explanation of why you agree or disagree with the proverb's message. Draw on an example from your own life to support your opinion.

Those who love each other need only a small place.[5]
Words are easy, but real friendship is difficult.[6]
The polite lie is better than the forceful truth.[7]

NAME ______________________ CLASS ________________ DATE ________ SCORE ______

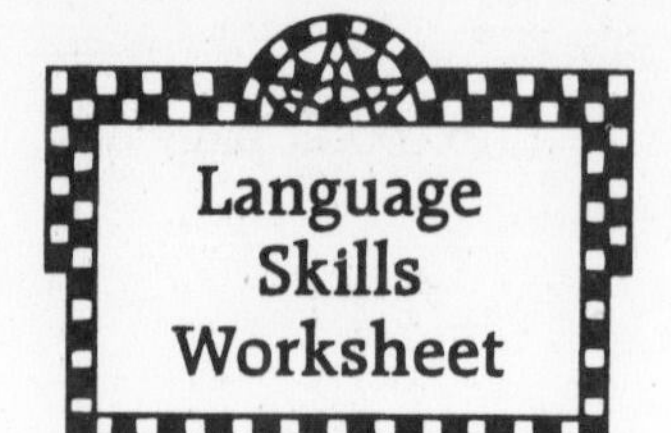

AFRICAN PROVERBS (Textbook page 85)

ADJECTIVE CLAUSES

A **clause** is a group of words with a subject and a verb that is used as part of a sentence. An **independent clause** can stand alone as a sentence. A **subordinate clause** (also called a **dependent clause**) cannot stand alone; it must be joined to an independent clause.

An **adjective clause** is a subordinate clause that modifies, or describes, a noun or pronoun.

EXAMPLE The man *who listens* is the one *who understands.*[1]

An adjective clause usually begins with one of the **relative pronouns**: *who, whom, whose, which,* and *that.* Sometimes, a **relative adverb** such as *when* or *where* may also begin an adjective clause. When you are using adjective clauses, follow these rules:

1. Place the adjective clause so that it closely follows the word it modifies.
2. Set the clause off from the rest of the sentence with commas unless it answers the question *Which one?*

EXAMPLES Giants, *who are large people,* are often featured in African literature. (Use commas to set off the clause.)

Giants *that do great things* appear in many African tales. (Do not use commas. The clause answers the question *Which giants?*)

Exercise 1. Identifying Adjective Clauses

Underline the adjective clause in each of the following sentences. Some of the sentences are African proverbs; other sentences are about proverbs.

EXAMPLE Proverbs, which are short, memorable sayings, exist in most world cultures.

1. Proverbs are sayings that express a culture's values.
2. A person who has only one set of clothing does not play in the rain.
3. In Africa, where people live close to the land, there are many proverbs about animals.
4. The sayings of Solomon, who was known for his wisdom, appear in the biblical book of Proverbs.
5. A tree does not fall on one who is not there.[2]

(continued)

6. During times when money is scarce, proverbs about thrift become popular.

7. Benjamin Franklin, whom people know as the author of *Poor Richard's Almanack*, composed many sayings in the form of proverbs.

8. A people whose literature was not written down passed proverbs along from generation to generation orally.

9. There is no hill that never ends.[3]

10. One who refuses you beans saves you from indigestion.[4]

Exercise 2. Using Adjective Clauses

Combine each pair of sentences below to form a proverb with an adjective clause. You may need to add, delete, or change words in order to make the combinations. There may also be more than one way to combine the sentences.

EXAMPLE People live in glass houses. They shouldn't throw stones.
People who live in glass houses shouldn't throw stones.

1. It is an ill wind. It blows no one any good.

____

____

2. Never trust someone. You have wronged someone.

____

____

3. It is a lazy bird. It won't build its own nest.

____

____

3. Proverbs from *Edeno Oo Lmaasai: Wisdom of the Maasai* by A. ol'Olisolo Massek and J. O. Sidai. Copyright © 1974 by **Transafrica Publishers.** Reprinted by permission of the publisher. 4. Proverbs from *Luganda Proverbs* by Ferdinand Walser. Copyright © 1982 by Dietrich Reimer Verlag. Reprinted by permission of ***Dietrich Reimer Verlag.***

(continued)

4. He likes to pull another into it. He is in the mud.

____

____

5. It is a watched pot. It never boils.

____

____

Exercise 3. Revising a Paragraph

Revise the following paragraph by changing some sentences into adjective clauses and combining them with other sentences. Add, delete, or change words as necessary. Not every sentence needs combining. Part of the paragraph has been revised for you as an example.

Benjamin Franklin did not always have a very high opinion of people. His *Poor Richard's Almanack* is still read today. One of his sayings is "Love your neighbor; yet don't pull down your hedge." The saying advises caution in dealing with others. Another example is in the saying "Three may keep a secret if two of them are dead." Franklin's opinion of people is low in that saying. In some sayings, he refers particularly to the institution of marriage. Franklin extends his mistrust to marriage, too. He writes, "Keep your eyes wide open before marriage, half shut afterward." Although Franklin did not always trust people, he was not bitter. He often used humor to express his feelings. One humorous proverb is "Fish and visitors smell in three days." The proverb is widely quoted today.

Benjamin Franklin, whose Poor Richard's Almanack is still read today, did not always have a high opinion of people.

____

____

____

____

____

____

____

____

____

NAME ______________ CLASS ______________ DATE ________ SCORE ________

SONG OF A MOTHER TO HER FIRSTBORN

translated by Jack H. Driberg

(Textbook page 90)

DEVELOPING VOCABULARY

Directions: Read carefully the explanation of each word. Then write a sentence of your own using that word. In your sentence, include clues to the word's meaning.

insolent (in'sə·lənt) ***adj.*** Disrespectful; rude. ▶ The word *insolent* is composed of Latin word parts meaning "not according to custom; immoderate." ■ The insolent trainee walked away while the instructor was speaking to her. **Page 91**

ORIGINAL SENTENCE ______________________________

____

quicken (kwik' ən) ***v.*** To come to life. ▶ The word comes from an Old English word meaning "alive." This old meaning appears in some translations of the Bible in the phrase "the quick and the dead." ■ In the movie *Frankenstein*, the monster starts to quicken after a jolt of electricity. **Page 92**

ORIGINAL SENTENCE ______________________________

____

oblation (ə·blā' shən) ***n.*** Gift or offering to God or a god. ▶ The noun *oblation* derives from a Latin verb meaning "to offer." ■ Making an oblation to a god or goddess is a feature of many religions. **Page 92**

ORIGINAL SENTENCE ______________________________

____

loins (loinz) ***n.*** The hips and lower abdomen, regarded as the region of strength and procreative power. ▶ This word is plural in form but singular in meaning. ■ The Egyptians wore short linen kilts about their loins. **Page 92**

ORIGINAL SENTENCE ______________________________

____

redemption (ri·demp' shən) ***n.*** A deliverance from sin and its punishments. ▶ This word comes from a Latin verb meaning "to get back, recover." ■ John Newton, the hymn writer, sought redemption after years of captaining a slave ship. **Page 92**

ORIGINAL SENTENCE ______________________________

____

NAME ______________________ CLASS ______________________ DATE __________ SCORE __________

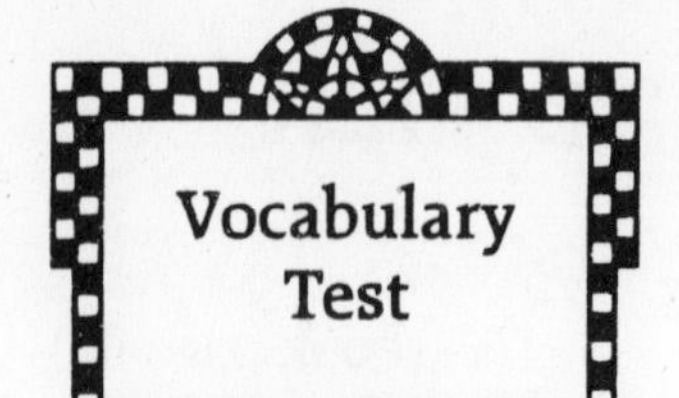

Song of a Mother to Her Firstborn

translated by Jack H. Driberg (Textbook page 90)

VOCABULARY TEST

A. Match each word in column I with the correct definition in column II. Place the letter of the definition you choose in the space provided. *(10 points each)*

I	II
______ 1. oblation	a. disrespectful; arrogant
______ 2. quicken	b. a deliverance from sin and its penalties
______ 3. redemption	c. an offering to God or a god
______ 4. loins	d. to come to life
______ 5. insolent	e. the hips and the lower abdomen

B. Complete each sentence below with the appropriate word from column I above. Write the word in the blank provided. *(10 points each)*

6. The people of this culture make an unusual ______________________ each year in memory of their ancestors.

7. The left side of the statue was slightly damaged from the ______________________ to the shoulder.

8. She was reprimanded for making ______________________ remarks to her commanding officer.

9. The dangerously weak heartbeat of the patient should ______________________ in response to the treatment.

10. A former thief, he sought ______________________ by helping other people.

NAME ____________ CLASS ____________ DATE ________ SCORE ________

Song of a Mother to Her Firstborn

translated by Jack H. Driberg

(Textbook page 90)

REVIEWING THE SELECTION

Circle the letter of the best answer for each question below.

1. What does the speaker in the poem predict her baby will grow up to be?
   a. a priest
   b. a great warrior
   c. a god

2. The naming of the baby
   a. takes place at birth
   b. is limited to such names as "Insolence" or "Worthless One"
   c. reflects the baby's good qualities

3. Which of the following does the mother list as gifts of the gods to her baby?
   a. insolence and greed
   b. beauty and strength
   c. a philosophical outlook and a placid nature

4. The mother says that the baby will make his father
   a. unhappy
   b. a better warrior
   c. immortal

Reader's Response

The mother in this poem feels that the naming of her baby is very important. In a sentence or two, tell how *you* would go about choosing a baby's name.

____

____

____

____

____

____

____

NAME ______________ CLASS ______________ DATE ________ SCORE ______

AFRICAN DILEMMA TALES

retold by A.W. Cardinall (Textbook page 95)

REVIEWING THE SELECTION

1. Circle the letter of the statement that best describes the endings of these two tales.
   a. Evil triumphs.
   b. The listener or audience is left to judge the actions of the characters.
   c. It is clear which character the storyteller likes best.

2. Circle the letter of the statement that best applies to "Wondrous Powers" and "The Five Helpers."
   a. They express the traditional values of an African culture.
   b. They are realistic.
   c. They are written in dialect.

3. Circle the letter of the statement that is true of dilemma tales.
   a. Dilemma tales are always told in the same words.
   b. There is only one right answer to the question posed in a dilemma tale.
   c. Dilemma tales are meant as tools to prompt discussion.

4. Circle the phrase that describes a folktale motif *not* found in one of these tales.

   a shape-changing snake
   a wicked queen
   bringing the dead to life
   magic powers

Reader's Response

What are your answers to the questions posed at the endings of the two tales? Write them on the lines below, and include a reason for each response.

1. Which of the sons in "Wondrous Powers" performed best, and why? ______________

____

2. Which man in "The Five Helpers" did best, and why? ______________

____

NAME ______________________ CLASS ________________ DATE ______ SCORE ______

TALK

retold by Harold Courlander (Textbook page 98)

REVIEWING THE SELECTION

The following people and things are all mentioned in "Talk." Write the word that fits best in each blank. You will use each word only once.

chief	farmer	village	dog	weaver
river	stool	head	yam	fisherman

A ______________ (1) goes to his field to dig up some yams and is amazed when a ______________ (2) tells him to leave it alone. When the farmer's ______________ (3), a tree branch, and a stone also speak to him, he runs away. The farmer meets a ______________ (4), who is startled in turn when the fish trap he is carrying on his ______________ (5) speaks. The two run off together and soon meet a ______________ (6) carrying a bundle of cloth. Later, they meet a man bathing in the ______________ (7). Finally, the farmer and his companions reach the main street of a ______________ (8). They go to talk to the ______________ (9). He hears their tale, scolds them, and sends them away. But his ______________ (10) has the last word in the story.

Reader's Response

At the very end of the story, the chief learns the truth about talking plants, animals, and objects. How do you imagine he reacts? Add a one- or two-sentence ending to the story, showing his reaction. You can use dialogue, if you wish.

____

____

____

____

NAME ______________________ CLASS ______________________ DATE __________ SCORE ________

TALK

retold by Harold Courlander

(Textbook page 98)

COMPOUND SENTENCES

A **compound sentence** consists of two or more simple sentences joined by a semicolon or by a comma and a **coordinating conjunction**. These are the most common coordinating conjunctions.

and   but   nor   or   for   yet

EXAMPLE The farmer planned to eat the yam, *but* the yam had other ideas.

Each part of a compound sentence must have its own subject and verb and must express a complete thought. Be careful not to confuse a compound sentence with a simple sentence that has a compound subject or a compound predicate.

EXAMPLES The cow said nothing, but the dog spoke up.
(compound sentence — two subjects, two verbs)
The fisherman and the weaver joined the farmer's flight.
(*not* a compound sentence — two subjects, one verb)
The farmer turned and looked at the cow in amazement.
(*not* a compound sentence — one subject, two verbs)

When joining two or more simple sentences into a compound sentence, be sure the sentences are closely related and of approximately equal importance.

EXAMPLES The farmer was startled, for his dog had never spoken before. (related ideas—good compound sentence)
The farmer became angry, and a yam is a sweet potato. (unrelated ideas—poor compound sentence)

Use a comma before *and, but,* and other coordinating conjunctions in a compound sentence.

Exercise 1. Identifying Compound Sentences

The following sentences are about the story "Talk." Identify each compound sentence by placing a check mark in the space provided.

______ 1. A farmer goes to his field for yams, but instead he gets a big surprise.

______ 2. First a yam speaks to him, and then his dog speaks.

______ 3. The farmer becomes angry and cuts a branch from a palm tree.

______ 4. The palm tree, the tree branch, and a stone all speak to the farmer.

______ 5. This is too much for the farmer, and he runs away.

(continued)

_______ 6. The farmer meets a fisherman and tells him his story.

_______ 7. The fisherman joins the farmer, for his fish trap has just spoken to him.

_______ 8. The two meet other people, and each in turn is frightened by a talking object.

_______ 9. The companions go to the village chief and tell him their story.

_______ 10. The farmer and his friends leave, and then the chief's stool speaks up.

Exercise 2. Writing Compound Sentences

The following sentences are about "Talk." Join each pair of simple sentences into a compound sentence, using *and, but, or,* or *for.* Remember to put a comma before the coordinating conjunction.

EXAMPLE A farmer goes to work in his field.
He gets a shock.
<u>A farmer goes to work in his field, and he gets a shock.</u>

1. The farmer questions the cow.
In fact, it was the yam that had been speaking.

____

____

2. The fisherman doubts the farmer's story.
Then his fish trap frightens him by speaking.

____

____

3. They meet a weaver and a man bathing in the river.
Both react in the same way as the fisherman.

____

____

4. The chief listens patiently.
He is probably used to hearing strange stories.

____

____

(continued)

NAME ______________ CLASS ______________ DATE ________ SCORE ________

5. Will the chief react differently to the talking stool? Will he run away, too?

____

____

Exercise 3. Revising a Paragraph

Revise the following paragraph, which consists of simple sentences about "Talk." Using coordinating conjunctions, combine the sentences that are closely related into compound sentences. Add a comma before each coordinating conjunction. Do not combine unrelated sentences.

"Talk" makes considerable use of repetition. This device adds to the humorous effect. Each person repeats the whole story each time. That is only one kind of repetition. Each person reacts to the story in the same way. Each new person listens to the story calmly. Each then reacts just like the farmer. We can therefore predict the chief's reaction. Repetition has made the pattern so familiar.

"Talk" makes considerable use of repetition, and this device adds to the humorous effect.

NAME ______________________________ CLASS ______________________ DATE __________ SCORE ________

TALK

retold by Harold Courlander (Textbook page 98)

READING COMPREHENSION

Directions: In the space provided, write the letter of the best answer to each question. *(10 points each)*

1. Why does the yam tell the farmer to leave it alone?
   a. The yam fears being eaten.
   b. The farmer has never weeded the yam.
   c. The yam wants to frighten the farmer.
   d. The farmer has disturbed the yam by stepping on it. 1. ______

2. Which of the following does *not* speak?
   a. the cow
   b. the farmer's dog
   c. a fish trap
   d. a bundle of cloth 2. ______

3. When the frightened farmer runs for his village,
   a. a palm tree falls on him
   b. a stone speaks to him
   c. he meets a fisherman
   d. a bundle of cloth attacks him 3. ______

4. How does the fisherman react when the farmer tells him about the talking objects?
   a. He calls the police.
   b. He tells the farmer to see a doctor.
   c. He becomes angry and hits the farmer.
   d. He acts unimpressed. 4. ______

5. While running, the farmer and the fisherman meet
   a. another talking yam
   b. a gazelle
   c. a merchant coming from the village
   d. a weaver with a bundle of cloth on his head 5. ______

6. How does the farmer explain why he is running?
   a. He points to the talking yam.
   b. He asks the fisherman to describe things.
   c. He tells his listeners what each object said to him.
   d. He is too frightened to talk. 6. ______

(continued)

7. The last person the farmer and his companions meet on their way to the village is
   a. a man bathing in the river
   b. the chief
   c. a high servant of the Ashanti king
   d. a medicine man

   7. ______

8. The word that best describes the chief's reaction to the story of the farmer and his companions is
   a. fear
   b. approval
   c. excitement
   d. disbelief

   8. ______

9. The last object to speak is
   a. the river
   b. a bundle of cloth
   c. the chief's stool
   d. a tree in the village

   9. ______

10. This tale is ironic—that is, it contains unexpected or incongruous events—because
    a. a stool thinks it fantastic that a yam can talk
    b. the farmer believes a yam can talk
    c. the chief does not believe a yam can talk
    d. the farmer eats the yam after all

    10. ______

NAME ______________________ CLASS ____________________ DATE ________ SCORE ______

from SUNDIATA

D. T. Niane
translated by G. D. Pickett

(Textbook page 105)

DEVELOPING VOCABULARY

Directions: Read carefully the explanation of each word. Then write a sentence of your own using that word. In your sentence, include clues to the word's meaning.

rampart (ram′ pärt′) ***n.*** An embankment of earth, usually supporting a wall, that encircles a castle or fort for defense against attack. ▶ The plural form of this word appears in the first stanza of "The Star-Spangled Banner." ▪ The invaders tried in vain to climb over the well-defended rampart. **Page 111**

ORIGINAL SENTENCE ____

____

implore (im·plôr′) ***v.*** To beg or plead for. ▶ This word comes from a Latin word meaning "to weep or cry out." ▪ "I implore you," cried Anna, "to listen to my plea!" **Page 114**

ORIGINAL SENTENCE ____

____

nascent (nas′ ənt) ***adj.*** Coming into existence; in the process of being born. ▶ This word comes from a Latin word meaning "to be born." ▪ The nascent democracies of Eastern Europe face many problems. **Page 109**

ORIGINAL SENTENCE ____

____

efface (ə·fās′) ***v.*** To rub out. ▶ This word comes from Latin word parts meaning "from the face." ▪ It took workers a day to efface the graffiti on the walls. **Page 107**

ORIGINAL SENTENCE ____

____

(continued)

impregnable (im·preg′ nə·bəl) ***adj.*** Not capable of being entered by force. ▶ The prefix *im-* means "not"; the seldom-used adjective *pregnable* means "able to be captured." ▪ The king considered his castle impregnable because of its moats, turrets, and massive walls. **Page 113**

ORIGINAL SENTENCE ______________________________

____

comprise (kəm·prīz′) ***v.*** To consist of; be composed of. ▶ English speakers of the 1400s borrowed this form of an Old French verb. ▪ The fairgrounds comprise twenty acres of land with a large grandstand. **Page 113**

ORIGINAL SENTENCE ______________________________

____

affront (ə·frunt′) ***n.*** An open or intentional offense or insult. ▶ This word comes from a French verb meaning "to encounter face to face." ▪ The travelers took the host's rude remark about their country as an affront. **Page 106**

ORIGINAL SENTENCE ______________________________

____

deploy (dē·ploi′) ***v.*** To position forces systematically over an area. ▶ The word *deploy* is from the same root as *display.* ▪ His plan was to deploy fifty archers on a small hill where they could shoot over the ramparts. **Page 111**

ORIGINAL SENTENCE ______________________________

____

raze (rāz) ***v.*** To make level with the ground; destroy. ▶ This word comes from a Latin verb meaning "to scrape," as does our word *razor.* ▪ The city had to raze several old buildings to make room for the new performing arts center. **Page 115**

ORIGINAL SENTENCE ______________________________

____

rout (rout) ***n.*** An utter and overpowering defeat. ▶ Although *rout* and *route* come from the same French and Latin roots, they have very different meanings. ▪ Cutting off the enemy's escape route turned the withdrawal into a rout. **Page 112**

ORIGINAL SENTENCE ______________________________

____

NAME ______________________ CLASS ______________________ DATE __________ SCORE __________

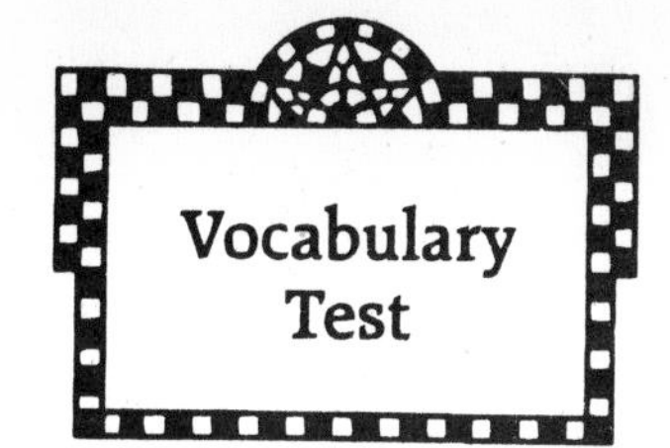

from SUNDIATA

D. T. Niane

translated by G. D. Pickett

(Textbook page 105)

VOCABULARY TEST

A. Match each word in column I with the correct definition in column II. Place the letter of the definition you choose in the space provided. *(7 points each)*

I	II
______ 1. rout	a. to position forces
______ 2. efface	b. to level; destroy
______ 3. comprise	c. an intentional insult
______ 4. rampart	d. an overpowering defeat
______ 5. deploy	e. not capable of being taken by force
______ 6. implore	f. to consist of
______ 7. nascent	g. to beg for
______ 8. affront	h. coming into existence
______ 9. raze	i. to erase; to rub out
______ 10. impregnable	j. an embankment for defense

B. Read the sentences below. Write *C* if the italicized word is used correctly and *I* if it is used incorrectly. *(6 points each)*

______ 11. A person would be happy to receive an *affront* at a party.

______ 12. If an abandoned building is a fire hazard, the owner may be ordered to *raze* it.

______ 13. A good general will *deploy* troops according to a carefully thought out plan.

______ 14. A *nascent* democracy might be too old and weak to survive.

______ 15. A criminal is likely to *implore* punishment.

NAME ______________________ CLASS ______________________ DATE __________ SCORE ________

from SUNDIATA

D. T. Niane
translated by G. D. Pickett

(Textbook page 105)

REVIEWING THE SELECTION

The three main events of this excerpt from *Sundiata* are outlined in the boxes below. All of the verbs are missing. Fill each blank with the appropriate verb from the list below.

captures	lifts	routs
deprives	makes	uproots
grazes	razes	walks

Sundiata first (1)______________________ at the age of seven, (2)______________________ an iron bar, and (3)______________________ the baobab tree.

At Krina, Sundiata (4)______________________ Soumaoro with a special arrow, (5)______________________ him of his power, and (6)______________________ him in battle.

Sundiata's army (7)______________________ the city of Sosso, (8)______________________ it to the ground, and (9)______________________ Sundiata the master of the world.

Reader's Response

Your feelings about the characters in *Sundiata* may change as the story unfolds. Write a word or phrase that describes how you felt at the following points in the story.

1. When Sundiata brings the baobab tree to his mother ______________________
____
2. When Soumaoro feels his powers leave him ______________________
____
3. When Sundiata orders the destruction of Sosso ______________________
____

NAME ______________________ CLASS ______________________ DATE __________ SCORE __________

from SUNDIATA

D. T. Niane
translated by G. D. Pickett

(Textbook page 105)

SIMPLE VERB TENSES

Verbs change form to show the time of the action or idea they express. The time expressed by a verb is called its **tense**. The three simple tenses are the **present tense**, the **past tense**, and the **future tense**. Follow these rules in using the simple tenses.

1. Use the present tense to express an action or idea that happens in the present.

EXAMPLE Sundiata *sits* on his useless legs.

2. Use the past tense to express action or an idea that happened in the past and does not continue into the present. The past tense is usually formed by adding *-d* or *-ed.*

EXAMPLE Sundiata's father *died* during Sundiata's boyhood.

3. Use the future tense to express action or an idea that will happen in the future. Form the future tense with *will.*

EXAMPLE Sundiata *will rule* wisely.

4. When explaining events in a story, use the present tense unless the characters themselves refer to events in the past or the future.

EXAMPLES Sundiata *captures* the city of Sosso. (present tense)
Sundiata says that he *will capture* the city of Sosso. (future tense)

5. Use tenses consistently. Do not switch tenses unless you have a good reason for doing so.

EXAMPLES The young Sundiata *seems* helpless, but he *surprised* everyone. (There is no reason for the shift from present tense to past tense.)
Mali *is* a less-industrialized nation today, but it *was* very powerful six hundred years ago. (The tense shift reflects the shift in thought from modern times to the past.)

Exercise 1. Identifying Verb Tenses

The following sentences are about the excerpt from *Sundiata.* In the blank before each of the sentences, write the letter that identifies the tense of the verb in italics.

a. present b. past c. future

EXAMPLE __a__ *Sundiata* is a blend of fact and legend.

______ 1. "Sundiata *will become* a great leader of his people," the mysterious hunter predicts.

______ 2. Few people except Sassouma *took* the prophecy seriously.

______ 3. Sassouma often *ridiculed* young Sundiata.

(continued)

______ 4. Sundiata *wonders* why his mother is so worried about him.

______ 5. Sassouma's son *walked* when he was just an infant.

______ 6. At Sundiata's request, Balla Fasséké *hurries* away to order an iron rod.

______ 7. "I *shall bring* my mother the whole tree," Sundiata decides.

______ 8. "*Will* Sundiata *lift* the iron bar?" the onlookers wonder.

______ 9. Sundiata *rises* to his feet in triumph.

______ 10. The son of Sogolon *acquires* instant popularity.

Exercise 2. Using Verb Tenses Consistently

The following sentences are about the excerpts from *Sundiata.* In each of the sentences, underline the verb form in parentheses that is in the same tense as the verb in italics.

EXAMPLE When the evil sorcerer-king *invades* Mali, Sundiata (will challenge, challenges) him.

1. Sundiata *pitched* his camp at Dayala while Soumaoro (advances, advanced) as far as Krina.
2. That night, Sundiata and Soumaoro *exchange* boasts and (vow, vowed) to defeat each other in battle.
3. A soothsayer predicts that Soumaoro *will die* and Sundiata (prevails, will prevail).
4. An arrow with a cock's spur *nicks* Soumaoro, which (takes, took) away Soumaoro's powers.
5. Long after the battle, death *hovered* over the bloody plain at Krina as soldiers (died, will die) from their wounds.

(continued)

Exercise 3. Revising a Paragraph

Some of the underlined verbs in the following paragraph about *Sundiata* are used correctly. Others make an unnecessary shift in tense. Remember that in writing about literature, you will usually use the present tense. (This is often called the **literary present**.) You will change tense only when the meaning in a sentence clearly requires it. Cross out each verb form below that is incorrect and write the correct form above it. The first correction is shown as an example.

Sundiata is an epic hero of Mali who overcomes many obstacles and regained his father's throne. Until he reaches the age of seven, Sundiata does nothing remarkable. Indeed, he seemed either dull or lazy to most people, including the spiteful Sassouma. "He never amounts to anything" is the general view. But finally, for his mother's sake, he walks for the first time—and what a walk it was! He lifts a heavy iron bar, stood up, and goes to fetch a young baobab tree. This triumph wins Sundiata popularity and shows that Sassouma's long-standing hatred achieves nothing. Much later, when Sundiata learns that Soumaoro, the king of a neighboring country, has invaded Mali, he gathers an army and fought him. Sundiata gains a great victory, destroyed Soumaoro's magical powers, and razed his great city. He regains his father's throne. Few doubt that Sundiata has a long and successful reign in the years to come.

NAME ______________________ CLASS ______________________ DATE __________ SCORE __________

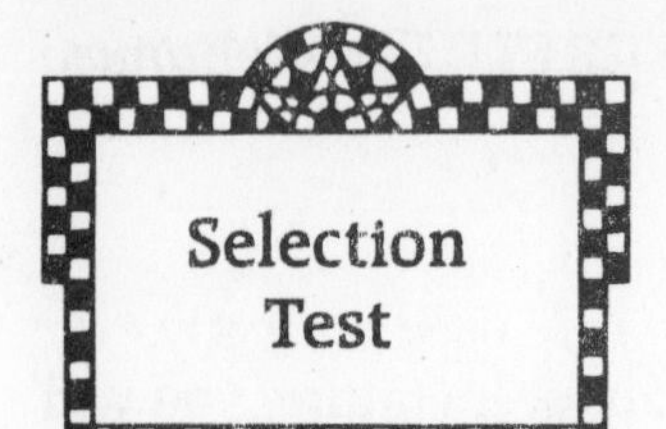

from SUNDIATA

D. T. Niane

translated by G. D. Pickett

(Textbook page 105)

READING COMPREHENSION

Directions: In the space provided, write the letter of the best answer to each question. *(10 points each)*

1. After the death of Sundiata's father, Sundiata's family
   a. is treated cruelly
   b. is treated respectfully
   c. is banished
   d. never expects help from anyone
   1. ______

2. The child Sundiata
   a. is the son of King Maghan Kon Fatta
   b. does not like his mother
   c. walks at an early age
   d. uses an iron rod as a crutch
   2. ______

3. Sogolon's special request of her son is
   a. for her son to kill his father
   b. for her son to kill her
   c. for her son to bring her the baobab tree and its roots
   d. for her son to leave the country
   3. ______

4. Sundiata is able to walk with the aid of
   a. a baobab tree
   b. a magic potion
   c. an iron rod
   d. crutches
   4. ______

5. Sundiata decides to challenge Soumaoro when he hears that Soumaoro
   a. has challenged Sundiata to a duel
   b. has killed Sundiata's best friend
   c. has killed King Maghan Kon Fatta
   d. has invaded Mali
   5. ______

6. Nana Triban tells Sundiata that the way to defeat Soumaoro is
   a. to touch him with a cock's spur
   b. to scare him with a cock's crow
   c. to kill him with an arrow of iron
   d. to let her kill the evil sorcerer-king
   6. ______

(continued)

7. The capital city of Soumaoro's kingdom is
   a. Krina
   b. Sosso
   c. Niger
   d. Dayala

   7.______

8. When Soumaoro is losing in battle, he sees
   a. a great eagle
   b. a lion
   c. a great black bird
   d. some buffalo

   8.______

9. At the end of the story, the city of Sosso is
   a. made Sundiata's new capital
   b. restored to its original glory
   c. left as a place for passersby to rest
   d. razed to the ground

   9.______

10. Sundiata is best known to his people as
   a. a child who performed great feats as an infant
   b. a strong but arrogant leader
   c. a strong, just leader
   d. a leader with a violent temper

   10.______

NAME ______________________ CLASS ______________________ DATE ________ SCORE 

UNIT 2: THE AFRICAN LITERARY TRADITION

WORD ANALOGIES/Extending Vocabulary

Directions: In the space provided, write the letter of the pair of words with the relationship that is closest to that of the capitalized words. *(10 points each)*

1. RAZE : DESTROY ::
   a. ruin : strengthen
   b. create : alter
   c. plan : complete
   d. build : construct

   1.______

2. ROUT : DEFEAT ::
   a. hero : soldier
   b. triumph : victory
   c. battle : won
   d. failure : successful

   2.______

3. AFFRONT : INSULT ::
   a. compliment : praise
   b. flattery : gossip
   c. request : order
   d. affection : respect

   3.______

4. DEPLOY : TROOPS ::
   a. declare : peace
   b. allocate : funds
   c. arrest : detain
   d. deposit : invest

   4.______

5. IMPLORE : URGE ::
   a. discourage : persuade
   b. trust : doubt
   c. demand : request
   d. accuse : deny

   5.______

6. EFFACE : REMOVE ::
   a. surrender : defeat
   b. disguise : disappear
   c. advance : retreat
   d. erase : delete

   6.______

7. QUICKEN : ENERGIZE ::
   a. pacify : soothe
   b. relax : lively
   c. increase : full
   d. revive : quiet

   7.______

8. INSOLENT : POLITE ::
   a. bashful : famous
   b. insincere : dishonest
   c. rude : courteous
   d. civil : friendly

   8.______

9. REDEMPTION : SINNER ::
   a. guilt : blame
   b. priest : forgiveness
   c. relief : sufferer
   d. performer : applause

   9.______

10. RAMPART : INVASION ::
    a. flood : dam
    b. splint : arm
    c. vaccine : disease
    d. harbor : anchor

    10.______

NAME ______________________ CLASS ______________________ DATE __________ SCORE ________

UNIT 2: THE AFRICAN LITERARY TRADITION

UNIT REVIEW/Applying Skills I

A. Reading Comprehension. In the space provided, write the letter of the best answer to each question. *(8 points each)*

1. "The Great Hymn to the Aten" shows the speaker's belief in
   a. Islam
   b. one god
   c. a moon goddess
   d. no gods at all
   1. ______

2. Which of the following African proverbs is similar in meaning to "One man's meat is another man's poison"?
   a. The man who listens is one who understands.[1]
   b. He whom one loves never does anything wrong.[2]
   c. What is bad luck for one man is good luck for another.
   d. Loose teeth are better than no teeth.[3]
   2. ______

3. In "The Voice of the Wild Goose," one of the New Kingdom love lyrics, the speaker compares love to
   a. a trap
   b. a daffodil
   c. a wild goose
   d. the Nile
   3. ______

4. The speaker in "Song of a Mother to Her Firstborn" tells her baby that he will bring his father
   a. money
   b. grief
   c. immortality
   d. melon seeds
   4. ______

5. In "Talk," the farmer and those he meets are frightened by ordinary objects that
   a. hurl spears
   b. speak
   c. vanish
   d. change into snakes
   5. ______

6. Before the battle in *Sundiata*, the hero and his enemy Soumaoro exchange
   a. boasts
   b. compliments
   c. headdresses
   d. wooden arrows
   6. ______

(continued)

B. Identifying Characters. Each description below refers to a main character in one of the selections you have just read. Identify the character by choosing the letter of the best answer. Write the letter in the space provided. *(8 points each)*

7. He lights up the sky to behold the fruit of his creation.
   a. Sundiata, the epic hero
   b. the farmer in "Talk"
   c. Soumaoro Kanté, the sorcerer-king of Sosso
   d. Aten, the Egyptian sun god

   7. ______

8. He is brought back to life by his three sons
   a. the father in "Wondrous Powers: Mirror, Sandals, and a Medicine Bag"
   b. the pharaoh in "The Great Hymn to the Aten"
   c. Soumaoro, the sorcerer-king in *Sundiata*
   d. Aten, the Egyptian sun god

   8. ______

9. He accuses his visitors of telling wild stories and threatens to punish them for disturbing the peace.
   a. Soumaoro, Sundiata's enemy, in *Sundiata*
   b. the chief of the village in "Talk"
   c. the leopard in an African proverb
   d. the speaker in "The Voice of the Wild Goose"

   9. ______

10. He uproots a baobab tree for his mother.
    a. King Maghan Kon Fatta, Sundiata's father
    b. Sundiata, the epic hero
    c. Soumaoro, Sundiata's enemy
    d. the farmer in "Talk"

    10. ______

C. Composition. Choose *one* of the following topics and write at least one paragraph about it, using a separate sheet of paper if necessary. *(20 points)*

1. In what ways is Sundiata a "typical" epic hero? What traits does he share with other epic heroes in world literature?

2. In "Song of a Mother to Her Firstborn," the mother tells her baby that he is very important to the family, and particularly to the father. Explain what she means by this. Give examples.

____

____

____

____

____

NAME ______________________ CLASS ______________ DATE ________ SCORE ______

UNIT 2: THE AFRICAN LITERARY TRADITION

CRITICAL THINKING AND WRITING/Applying Skills II

A. Reading a Story. Read the following story carefully. Then answer the questions that follow.

THE MAN AND THE MUSKRAT

A Fipa Folktale

translated by

ROY WILLIS

There was a certain hunter who used to go out with his dog searching for game to bring back to his wife and children. One day he said: "I'm going deep into the bush because game has become very scarce these days." He set off with his bow, arrows, spear, and dog.

When he had gone some way, he heard a voice saying, "Oh, you, hunter, help me over the crossroads, and I will help you another day."

He looked round without seeing who had spoken to him, then stopped, and said, "Who is it who's talking? Speak again, so that I can see what you are."

Then he heard again: "Oh, sir, help me over the crossroads and I'll help you some other time—I, a muskrat."

The man looked down and saw the animal, and said, "I would help you across the road only you stink so and will make me smell likewise."

The muskrat replied, "Oh no, sir, just help me across the road, because if I don't get over I shall die. If you do help me, I will save you one day."

The man said, "What! You who are so small will save me who am so big? Whatever could beat me that you would be able to cope with? You're lying, you little animal!"

The muskrat replied, "Oh, no sir, just lift me with your bow if you're afraid I will make you stink, and throw me so that I fall on the other side of the path, and one day I will rescue you from a great trouble!"

The gentleman took his bow and lifted the muskrat over the path, dropping him on the other side.

"Thank you very much for having pity on me," said the muskrat. Then both went their separate ways. That was all that happened on that day.

In the evening, the man returned home and told his wife about his encounter with the muskrat and what it had told him. His wife said scornfully, "What nonsense! How could a rat help you!" The husband replied, "Well, I thought that, too, when he said he would save me one day, but that's what he promised." And the father slept until morning. That day he stayed in the village, saying that the next day he would go hunting in the bush. When darkness returned, he slept again.

Came the morning, he said to his wife, "Oh, wife, prepare some food so that I can eat, because today I am going farther than I have ever gone before."

His wife heated some relish, grilled some flour, and prepared millet porridge. Her

(continued)

husband ate and was satisfied. Then he took his customary hunting equipment, called his dog, and set out.

He kept going until he had covered a great distance. It was the wet season, at that time, and the sky was heavy with rain, with vast clouds obscuring the view. He said to himself, "Yes, today I'm going to get soaked, but what can I do?"

He thought, "Just let me find somewhere to shelter"—the man would have died for sure, if he hadn't exerted himself—and after that he killed three guinea fowl.

He kept going and then, luckily, he noticed a cave and got inside with his dog just as the rain began pelting down. Well, there hidden in the darkness was the muskrat, too.

Now, it happened that a certain lion, who had also been hunting, was himself seeking shelter from the rain, and he came to that very cave. The man glanced up and saw the lion had come in. Fear gripped him, and his dog began to bark, but the man silenced him by holding his muzzle. Then he said, "Yes, O Lion, you may eat me, but I want to say that I am not a thief, I have not stolen people's goods, nor taken from their granaries, neither have I ever killed anyone. I am just a man of the bush, a poor man with wife and children, and like you, I was looking for food, and the rain has brought you here, so now you can eat me."

Then the lion began to roar, until the tears fell from the man's eyes, plop, plop, plop. He gripped his weapons with manly courage, but the lion set to roaring even more, until the cave shook and seemed about to collapse.

Then the lion said to the man, "Oh, sir, give your dog those guinea fowl there, and when he has eaten, you can eat the dog, and finally I'll eat you. What do you say?" The gentleman, whose insides had by this time turned to water, said, "Yes, today I'm going to die because of this hunting business of mine!"

The lion told him again, "You, sir, give your dog the guinea fowl, and when he has eaten, then you eat the dog, and then I'll eat you. How about it?"

At that moment, they heard a voice coming from somewhere in the cave, saying, "Yes, sir, give the dog those guinea fowl, and when he has eaten, you can eat the dog, and Mr. Lion can eat you, and when he has eaten, I'll eat *him*." When the muskrat had finished saying this, he added, "Well, my boys of the royal bodyguard, what do you say?"

And the termites in the cave wall replied, *"Mmmmmmm."*

At this, the lion and the man were amazed, wondering who was speaking in there. Then they heard again, "You sir, give the dog the guinea fowl, and you eat the dog, and the lion will eat you, and then I will eat the lion. All right, men of the royal bodyguard?" The termites replied, *"Mmmmmmm."*

Now, the lion was thinking more about being eaten than about eating anyone else, and the man said to him, "Hold up the cave so it doesn't collapse, and I'll go and cut some timber so we can shore it up." The lion agreed. The man then left, with the lion still holding up the cave, thinking it would fall. The man hurried off as fast as he could go, and his dog likewise, and they didn't stop until they reached home.

One day, he met the muskrat again, and the rat said, "Did you know who it was speaking in the cave, saying, 'Oh, sir, give the dog the guinea fowl and you eat the dog and the lion can eat you, then I'll eat the lion?' Did I not say I would save you when you helped me across the path? And indeed I scared the lion and rescued you."

The man thanked him very much, then went home and told his wife, and they were all happy.

(continued)

B. Analyzing a Story. In the space provided, write the letter of the best answer to each question. *(6 points each)*

1. Why is the hunter reluctant to help the muskrat?
   a. He is in a hurry to begin hunting.
   b. He thinks the muskrat will bite him.
   c. He wants to avoid getting the muskrat's smell on him.
   d. He thinks the muskrat is lying about his plight. 1. ______

2. When the hunter tells his wife about the muskrat's promise, she
   a. is very impressed
   b. asks for more details
   c. says that muskrats don't talk
   d. thinks the promise is nonsense 2. ______

3. What does the muskrat say to frighten the lion?
   a. He threatens to eat the lion.
   b. He says that termites will destroy the cave.
   c. He tells the lion that lightning will strike him.
   d. He claims that the hunter has magic powers. 3. ______

4. The *Mmmmmmm* of the termites is an example of **onomatopoeia**—the imitation in language of a natural sound. Which of these is also onomatopoeic?
   a. "The lion told him again"
   b. "the tears fell . . . plop, plop, plop"
   c. "O Lion, you may eat me"
   d. "Fear gripped him" 4. ______

5. **Irony** is the contrast between what is expected and what actually happens. It is ironic that
   a. a lion is frightened by a muskrat
   b. a dog is trapped in a cave with his master
   c. termites make the sound *Mmmmmmm*
   d. a man is frightened by a lion 5. ______

6. Which of the following features of oral literature occurs in this story?
   a. dancing
   b. call-and-response
   c. repetition
   d. singing 6. ______

(continued)

7. The beginning of this tale arouses the reader's curiosity about
   a. how the hunter will escape the lion
   b. how the muskrat can keep its promise
   c. whether the hunter will find any game
   d. whether the hunter's wife will believe the muskrat story

   7. ______

8. The **character** of the hunter is revealed mainly through
   a. what others say about him
   b. his clothing and appearance
   c. what he says and does
   d. his inner thoughts

   8. ______

9. The **climax,** or highest emotional point of the plot, occurs when
   a. the hunter lifts the muskrat over the path
   b. the hunter goes into the cave
   c. the lion tells the hunter to prepare to be eaten
   d. the hunter tells his wife what happened

   9. ______

10. The **moral** of the tale is that
    a. a good deed may be repaid
    b. taking refuge in a cave is dangerous
    c. termites can be helpful as well as destructive
    d. muskrats, like people, can feel gratitude

    10. ______

C. Writing About a Story. At the end of the story, the muskrat tells the hunter that he rescued him by scaring the lion. Ask yourself: Is the muskrat's help the only thing that saves the hunter? Look back at the story and decide for yourself. Using the evidence you find in the story, write *one* paragraph beginning like this: "The muskrat's help is (or is not) the only thing that saves the hunter. This is clear because. . . ." *(40 points)*

____

____

____

____

____

____

____

____

____

____

UNIT 2: THE AFRICAN LITERARY TRADITION

UNIT INTRODUCTION TEST

(Textbook pages 64–71)

1. d	5. d	8. c
2. a	6. a	9. a
3. b	7. c	10. c
4. a		

THE GREAT HYMN TO THE ATEN

translated by Miriam Lichtheim
(Textbook page 73)

REVIEW AND RESPONSE WORKSHEET

Reviewing the Selection

Check marks should appear before items 1, 3, 5, 6, 8, and 10.

Reader's Response

Responses will vary. Students might mention the extent to which Americans flock to the beaches and other sunny areas and even the use of suntanning salons to promote the "healthy" glow of the sun.

NEW KINGDOM LOVE LYRICS

translated by William Kelly Simpson
(Textbook page 81)

REVIEW AND RESPONSE WORKSHEET

Reviewing the Selections

1. Both the speaker and the wild goose are caught in a trap. (The speaker's trap is love.)
2. Love prevents the speaker from doing work.
3. Not having the lover near at night makes the speaker feel like someone dead, or in the grave.
4. The lover's well-being brings the speaker joy.
5. c

Reader's Response

Responses will vary. These are some possibilities.

Love is like a trap because

it catches a person by surprise
it changes one's behavior
it puts one's future at least partly in another's hands
it limits one's choices

Love is unlike a trap because

the consequences are not pain or death but may be happiness
we struggle to escape from a trap, but we don't always try to escape from love

AFRICAN PROVERBS

(Textbook page 85)

REVIEW AND RESPONSE WORKSHEET

Reviewing the Selections

Responses will vary. These are sample responses.

1. You can't predict the future.
2. Something that's imperfect is better than nothing at all.
3. You can't understand someone else's problems unless you've experienced them yourself.
4. A bad situation eventually ends.
5. What seems effortless on the surface ("magic") has taken a lot of time.

(continued)

Reader's Response

Responses will vary.

LANGUAGE SKILLS WORKSHEET

Adjective Clauses

Exercise 1

1. that express a culture's values
2. who has only one set of clothing
3. where people live close to the land
4. who was known for his wisdom
5. who is not there
6. when money is scarce
7. whom people know as the author of *Poor Richard's Almanack*
8. whose literature was not written down
9. that never ends
10. who refuses you beans

Exercise 2

Combined sentences may vary slightly. These are sample responses.

1. It is an ill wind that blows no one any good.
2. Never trust someone whom you have wronged.
3. It is a lazy bird that won't build its own nest.
4. He who is in the mud likes to pull another into it.
5. It is a watched pot that never boils.

Exercise 3

Revised paragraphs will vary. This is a sample revision.

Benjamin Franklin, whose *Poor Richard's Almanack* is still read today, did not always have a high opinion of people. One of his sayings that advises caution in dealing with others is "Love your neighbor; yet don't pull down your hedge." Another example that shows Franklin's low opinion of people is the saying "Three may keep a secret if two of them are dead." Franklin also has sayings about the institution of marriage, which he mistrusts, such as the saying, "Keep your eyes wide open before marriage, half shut afterward." Although Franklin did not always trust people, he was not bitter. He often used humor to express his feelings. One humorous proverb, which is widely quoted today, is "Fish and visitors smell in three days."

Song of a Mother to Her Firstborn

translated by Jack H. Driberg
(Textbook page 90)

VOCABULARY ACTIVITY WORKSHEET

Developing Vocabulary

Responses will vary.

VOCABULARY TEST

A.
1. c
2. d
3. b
4. e
5. a

B.
6. oblation
7. loins
8. insolent
9. quicken
10. redemption

REVIEW AND RESPONSE WORKSHEET

Reviewing the Selection

1. b 2. c 3. b 4. c

Reader's Response

Responses will vary. Students are likely to give one of these reasons for their choice: (1) to honor a relative, a friend, or a famous person; (2) to maintain a family tradition; (3) to give the child a name with favorable associations.

(continued)

African Dilemma Tales

Retold by A.W. Cardinall
(Textbook page 95)

REVIEW AND RESPONSE WORKSHEET

Reviewing the Selection

1. b 2. a 3. c 4. a wicked queen

Reader's Response

Accept all responses that name a character in each tale and that give a coherent reason. Possible responses follow:

1. All were equal, because their father couldn't have been saved if any of their magic objects were missing.
2. The healer, because without him, all the previous helpers' efforts would have been in vain.

Talk

retold by Harold Courlander
(Textbook page 98)

REVIEW AND RESPONSE WORKSHEET

Reviewing the Selection

1. farmer
2. yam
3. dog
4. fisherman
5. head
6. weaver
7. river
8. village
9. chief
10. stool

Reader's Response

Responses will vary. Encourage students to use their imaginations. Their response could be as simple and straightforward as "The chief fainted" or "The chief ran away to join the farmer's band." Or it could be more unusual: "Yes, Stool, I'm afraid our secret is out," or, "Well, Stool, I confess I've heard a yam talk, but a fish trap?—ridiculous!"

LANGUAGE SKILLS WORKSHEET

Compound Sentences

Exercise 1

1. CS
2. CS
3. N
4. N
5. CS
6. N
7. CS
8. CS
9. N
10. CS

Exercise 2

Responses will vary.

1. The farmer questions the cow, but, in fact, it was the yam that had been speaking.
2. The fisherman doubts the farmer's story, but then his fish trap frightens him by speaking.
3. They meet a weaver and a man bathing in the river, and both react in the same way as the fisherman.
4. The chief listens patiently, for he is probably used to hearing strange stories.
5. Will the chief react differently to the talking stool, or will he run away, too?

Exercise 3

Responses will vary.

"Talk" makes considerable use of repetition, and this device adds to the humorous effect. Each person repeats the whole story each time, but that is only one kind of repetition. Each person reacts to the story in the same way. Each new person listens to the story calmly, but each then reacts just like the farmer. We can therefore predict the chief's reaction, for repetition has made the pattern so familiar.

SELECTION TEST

Reading Comprehension

1. b
2. a
3. c
4. d
5. d
6. c
7. a
8. d
9. c
10. a

(continued)

from SUNDIATA

D. T. Niane
translated by G. D. Pickett
(Textbook page 105)

VOCABULARY ACTIVITY WORKSHEET

Developing Vocabulary

Responses will vary.

VOCABULARY TEST

A. 1. d 6. g
2. i 7. h
3. f 8. c
4. j 9. b
5. a 10. e

B. 11. I 14. I
12. C 15. I
13. C

REVIEW AND RESPONSE WORKSHEET

Reviewing the Selection

1. walks 4. grazes 7. captures
2. lifts 5. deprives 8. razes
3. uproots 6. routs 9. makes

Reader's Response

Responses will vary. Here are a few possibilities.
1. delight, satisfaction
2. sympathy, pity (or perhaps enjoyment, acceptance)
3. disapproval, perplexity (or perhaps good riddance)

LANGUAGE SKILLS WORKSHEET

Simple Verb Tenses

Exercise 1

1. c 2. b 3. b
4. a 7. c 9. a
5. b 8. c 10. a
6. a

Exercise 2

1. advanced 4. takes
2. vow 5. died
3. will prevail

Exercise 3

Sundiata is an epic hero of Mali who overcomes many obstacles and regains his father's throne. Until he reaches the age of seven, Sundiata does nothing remarkable. Indeed, he seems either dull or lazy to most people, including the spiteful Sassouma. "He never will amount to anything" is the general view. But finally, for his mother's sake, he walks for the first time—and what a walk it is! He lifts a heavy iron bar, stands up, and goes to fetch a young baobab tree. This triumph wins Sundiata popularity and shows that Sassouma's long-standing hatred achieved nothing. Much later, when Sundiata learns that Soumaoro, the king of a neighboring country, has invaded Mali, he gathers an army and fights him. Sundiata gains a great victory, destroys Soumaoro's magical powers, and razes his great city. He regains his father's throne. Few doubt that Sundiata will have a long and successful reign in the years to come.

SELECTION TEST

Reading Comprehension

1. a 5. d 8. c
2. a 6. a 9. d
3. c 7. b 10. c
4. c

(continued)

WORD ANALOGIES/Extending Vocabulary

1. d (raze : destroy : : build : construct)
Relationship: synonyms
Raze and *destroy* are synonyms meaning "to level." *Build* and *construct* are synonyms meaning "to form" or "to put together." The analogy is strengthened by the fact that *raze* and *build* are antonyms, as are *destroy* and *construct.*
2. b (rout : defeat :: triumph : victory)
Relationship: synonyms
A *rout* is an overpowering defeat. A *triumph* is an overpowering victory.
3. a (affront : insult :: compliment : praise)
Relationship: synonyms
Affront and *insult* are synonyms sharing the meaning "an intentional offense." *Compliment* and *praise* are synonyms sharing the meaning "an intentional act of courtesy." The analogy is strengthened by the fact that *affront* and *compliment* are antonyms, as are *insult* and *praise.*
4. b (deploy : troops :: allocate : funds)
Relationship: action to object
One *deploys,* or positions according to plan, *troops.* One *allocates,* or distributes according to a plan, *funds.*
5. c (implore : urge :: demand : request)
Relationship: differ by degree
To *implore,* "beg," suggests a kind of desperation and is stronger than to *urge.* To *demand* suggests an exercise of greater authority than to *request.*
6. d (efface : remove :: erase : delete)
Relationship : synonyms
All four words are synonyms sharing the meaning "to wipe out" or "to obliterate."
7. a (quicken: energize :: pacify : soothe)
Relationship: cause-effect
The effect of acting to *quicken* someone is to revive or *energize* that person. The effect of acting to *pacify* someone is to calm or *soothe* that person.
8. c (insolent : polite :: rude : courteous)
Relationship: antonyms
Insolent, "disrespectful," is an antonym of *polite. Rude* and *courteous* are also antonyms. The relationship is strengthened by the fact that *insolent* and *rude* are synonyms, as are *polite* and *courteous.*
9. c (redemption : sinner :: relief : sufferer)
Relationship: action-agent
A *sinner* seeks *redemption,* "deliverance from sin." A *sufferer* seeks *relief.*
10. c (rampart : invasion :: vaccine : disease)
Relationship: object to purpose
The purpose of a *rampart,* "an earthern embankment," is to prevent an *invasion.* The purpose of a *vaccine* is to prevent a *disease.*

UNIT REVIEW TEST/Applying Skills I

A. Reading Comprehension

1. b
2. c
3. a
4. c
5. b
6. a

B. Identifying Characters

7. d
8. a
9. b
10. b

C. Composition

1. Responses will vary. Students should make two or more of the following points:
   - Sundiata has an unusual childhood, but shows signs of greatness.
   - Sundiata possesses unusual powers.

(continued)

- Sundiata goes into exile and returns as a leader of his people.
- Sundiata embodies the highest value of his culture.

2. Responses will vary. Students should specify the son's role in ensuring his father's immortality by giving one or more of the following examples:
   - The son will preserve his father's soul by tending his shrine.
   - The son will keep his father's name alive as he makes sacrifice and oblation each year.
   - The son will continue his father's line (lines 61–63).

CRITICAL THINKING AND WRITING/
Applying Skills II

B. Analyzing a Story

1. c	3. a	5. a	7. b	9. c
2. d	4. b	6. c	8. c	10. a

C. Writing About a Story

Answers will vary. Some students may argue that the muskrat's efforts are the only thing that save the hunter. They may support their argument with the muskrat's statement and with the observation that it is the muskrat, together with the sound of the termites, that permits the hunter's escape. The sentence "Now, the lion was thinking more about being eaten than about eating anyone else" is good evidence for this view. Perceptive readers will note, however, that (a) the muskrat without the termites would probably not have succeeded, and, more importantly, (b) the hunter helps his own cause by convincing the lion that the cave is about to fall in on them. This gives him the opportunity to leave the cave to "cut some timber" to use in shoring it up, thus permitting his escape. The better answer is probably that the muskrat provides the opportunity, and the hunter has the wit to use it. Either position can be reasonably argued.

NOTES

NAME ______________________ CLASS ______________ DATE ________ SCORE ________

UNIT 3: THE ANCIENT MIDDLE EAST

(Textbook pages 128–135)

INTRODUCTION/The Literature of Ancient Mesopotamia

Directions: In the space provided, write the letter of the best answer to each question. *(10 points each)*

1. The ancient Sumerians
   a. lived in walled city-states
   b. had one powerful, central government
   c. based their economy mostly on art
   d. did not develop a very high level of culture — 1. ______

2. The Sumerians settled in Mesopotamia sometime between
   a. 500 and 400 B.C.
   b. 20,000 and 15,000 B.C.
   c. A.D. 300 and 400
   d. 5,000 and 4,000 B.C. — 2. ______

3. The natural resource of Mesopotamia that was most important to the Sumerians was
   a. stone
   b. river mud
   c. lumber
   d. papyrus — 3. ______

4. *Cuneiform* is
   a. an Egyptian invention
   b. a mathematical formula
   c. a system of writing achieved by pressing a stylus, or stick, into soft clay
   d. a type of building — 4. ______

5. The ziggurats are a good example of the Sumerians' advanced understanding of
   a. government
   b. agriculture
   c. architecture
   d. medicine — 5. ______

6. When the Babylonians conquered the Sumerians, they
   a. destroyed all traces of Sumerian writings
   b. preserved Sumerian writings in the Library of Nineveh
   c. adapted the Sumerians' script to their own Semitic language
   d. made Gilgamesh their king — 6. ______

(continued)

7. Which of the following statements is true of ancient Mesopotamia?
   a. The ancient culture of the Sumerians was destroyed by the Egyptians.
   b. Many different groups of people successively invaded the area.
   c. The Akkadian empire was the last great empire of Mesopotamia.
   d. No one reads the literature of the Mesopotamians today. 7. ______

8. The Babylonian Code of Hammurabi can best be described as a
   a. religious ceremony
   b. set of strict laws
   c. multi-layered class system
   d. document limiting the powers of Hammurabi 8. ______

9. The city of Nineveh, with its great library, was built by a warlike group from Asia Minor called the
   a. Assyrians
   b. Sumerians
   c. Babylonians
   d. Hittites 9. ______

10. The Hanging Gardens of Babylon
    a. were built before the great flood
    b. were recognized by the Greeks as one of the Seven Wonders of the Ancient World
    c. were destroyed in the Gulf War
    d. were built by King Gilgamesh 10. ______

NAME ______________________ CLASS ________________ DATE ________ SCORE ________

from the EPIC OF GILGAMESH

translated by N. K. Sandars (Textbook page 139)

DEVELOPING VOCABULARY

Directions: Read carefully the explanation of each word. Then write a sentence of your own using that word. In your sentence, include clues to the word's meaning.

somber (säm'bər) ***adj.*** Melancholy, depressed. ▶ This word comes from the prefix *sub-*, "under," and the Latin word *umbra*, meaning "shade." ▪ His somber face mirrored the misery he felt inside. **Page 140**

ORIGINAL SENTENCE ____

____

incantation (in'kan·tā'shən) ***n.*** The recitation of magical words to cast a spell or perform magic. ▶ Incantations can be either spoken or sung. ▪ In the play *Macbeth*, the witches performed an incantation while stirring a boiling pot. **Page 141**

ORIGINAL SENTENCE ____

____

ominous (äm'ə·nəs) ***adj.*** Seeming to threaten evil or misfortune; sinister. ▶ *Ominous* and *omen* both come from an Indo-European root meaning " to announce." ▪ There was something ominous about the foggy, silent streets. **Page 141**

ORIGINAL SENTENCE ____

____

deluge (del'yōōj') ***n.*** A great flood. ▶ This word is based on a Latin word, *diluere*, meaning "to wash away." ▪ After the dam broke, the city was awash in a deluge. **Page 142**

ORIGINAL SENTENCE ____

____

allot (ə·lät') ***v.*** To distribute or apportion by random chance. ▶ *Allot* and *lottery* both came into English from Old French. ▪ Facing student protest, administrators changed the system used to allot football tickets. **Page 144**

(continued)

ORIGINAL SENTENCE ____

____

consign (kən·sīn′) ***v.*** To assign to an undesirable, objectionable position or place; relegate. ▶ The Latin *signum*, "a mark," is the root of *consign*. ▪ The captives were consigned to forced labor. **Page 148**

ORIGINAL SENTENCE ____

____

transgression (tranz·gresh′ən) ***n.*** The act of overstepping or breaking a law. ▶ A person who commits a transgression is called a *transgressor*. ▪ Truancy is a transgression of school rules. **Page 148**

ORIGINAL SENTENCE ____

____

pestilence (pes′tə·ləns) ***n.*** Any disease, especially one of epidemic proportions, such as bubonic plague. ▶ *Pestilence* and *pest* both come from the Latin word *pestis*, meaning "plague." ▪ Malaria is a pestilence that still exists in many parts of the world. **Page 148**

ORIGINAL SENTENCE ____

____

sluice (slo͞os) ***n.*** A gate or valve used in opening or closing an artificial passage for water. ▶ Sluice is related to *exclude*; both come from a Latin word meaning " to shut out." ▪ Dam operators use sluices both to let water in and to hold it back. **Page 150**

ORIGINAL SENTENCE ____

____

slough (sluf) ***v.*** To get rid of or throw off. ▶ The English word *slough* was borrowed from a Middle German word meaning "snakeskin." ▪ The sunburned skin on my arm sloughed off in patches. **Page 151**

ORIGINAL SENTENCE ____

____

NAME ______________________ CLASS ______________________ DATE __________ SCORE __________

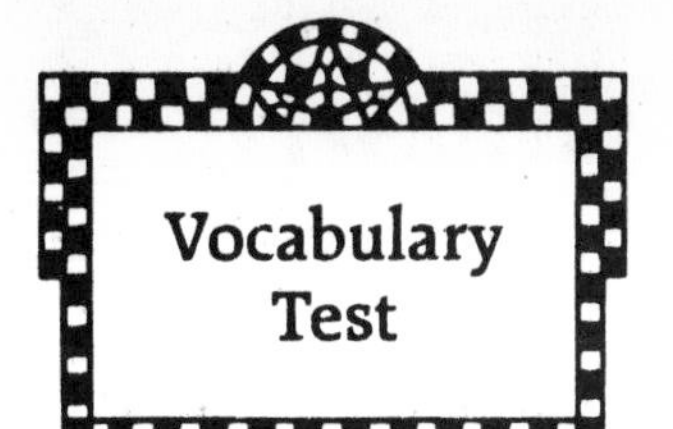

from the EPIC OF GILGAMESH

translated by N. K. Sandars (Textbook page 139)

VOCABULARY TEST

A. Match each word in column I with the correct definition in column II. Place the letter of the definition you choose in the space provided. *(7 points each)*

I	II
______ 1. allot	a. disease, plague
______ 2. consign	b. great flood
______ 3. deluge	c. to distribute by random chance
______ 4. incantation	d. floodgate
______ 5. ominous	e. recitation of magical words
______ 6. pestilence	f. to overstep or break a law
______ 7. slough	g. threatening, sinister
______ 8. sluice	h. to get rid of or throw off
______ 9. somber	i. melancholy, depressed
______ 10. transgress	j. to assign to an undesirable position

B. Complete the following paragraph by filling in each blank with one of the words below. Use each word only once. *(6 points each)*

consigned somber deluge incantations ominous

The mood of the people was ______________________ as they looked up at the ______________________ black clouds in the sky. For days, the village had suffered unending rain. The prayers and ______________________ of the holy man had gone unanswered. A(n) ______________________ was inevitable. The people shivered at the thought of the awful damage and wondered why the gods had ______________________ them to this fate.

NAME ______________ CLASS ______________ DATE ________ SCORE ________

from the EPIC OF GILGAMESH

translated by N. K. Sandars (Textbook page 139)

REVIEWING THE SELECTION

1. Enkidu wants to die in battle. How does he actually die? ______________________________

____

2. Circle the letter of the sentence that describes what happens to Gilgamesh.
   a. He finds eternal life.
   b. He journeys through the mountains of Mashu.
   c. He brings Enkidu back to life.

3. Circle the letter of the sentence that tells what happens because of the flood.
   a. Utnapishtim and his wife are destroyed.
   b. Utnapishtim becomes immortal.
   c. The world enters a new golden age.

4. Circle the letter of the sentence that tells what happens when Gilgamesh finds the flower that will restore lost youth.
   a. He wins back all his former strength.
   b. He restores the youth of his friend Enkidu.
   c. He loses the flower to a serpent in a well.

Reader's Response

How do you respond to Gilgamesh as an epic hero? Place a check mark before each of the following qualities of Gilgamesh that you admire. What else about Gilgamesh do you find appealing?

______ great friendship with Enkidu

______ courage in face of hardships

______ wisdom

______ knowledge about life and death

____

____

____

____

NAME ______________________ CLASS ______________________ DATE __________ SCORE __________

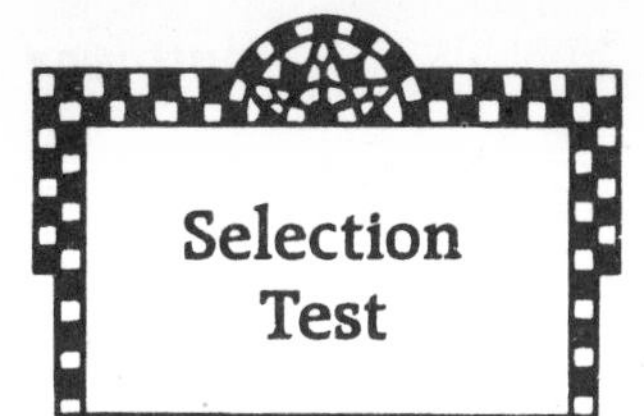

from the EPIC OF GILGAMESH

translated by N. K. Sandars (Textbook page 139)

READING COMPREHENSION

Directions: In the space provided, write the letter of the best answer to each question. *(10 points each)*

1. Who is Gilgamesh?
   a. a legendary Sumerian king and superhuman hero
   b. half serpent and half man
   c. a king of the Hebrews
   d. an ordinary man who has great adventures 1. ______

2. What does Enkidu's dream foretell?
   a. his own death
   b. the gods' downfall
   c. a great flood
   d. a mighty battle 2. ______

3. What does Gilgamesh hope to find at the end of his quest?
   a. his father
   b. a new friend
   c. everlasting life
   d. power to destroy the gods 3. ______

4. What does Siduri, the maker of wine, advise Gilgamesh to do?
   a. continue his journey
   b. climb over the mountains
   c. swim across the ocean
   d. be content with life as a mortal 4. ______

5. What event brings Utnapishtim his eternal life?
   a. an earthquake
   b. a flood
   c. a hurricane
   d. a drought 5. ______

6. According to Utnapishtim, why did the gods once try to destroy humanity?
   a. The gods wanted greater power.
   b. People had become as strong as the gods.
   c. People made too much noise, disturbing the gods' rest.
   d. People had become too timid. 6. ______

(continued)

7. How does Utnapishtim test Gilgamesh's resolve to find everlasting life?
   a. by instructing Gilgamesh to resist sleep for six days and seven nights
   b. through a duel between Gilgamesh and Enkidu
   c. by tempting Gilgamesh with promises of wealth and glory
   d. by challenging Gilgamesh to wrestle with Urshanabi   7. ______

8. What, according to Utnapishtim, will restore lost youth?
   a. new clothes
   b. a boat
   c. the apple of the tree of life
   d. a special plant   8. ______

9. What happens to Gilgamesh's secret of youth?
   a. He drowns before he can grasp it.
   b. A serpent snatches it away.
   c. Since Gilgamesh fails his test, Utnapishtim refuses to tell him how to obtain it.
   d. He succeeds in grasping it, and brings it to his people.   9. ______

10. At the end of the epic, Gilgamesh is
    a. a bitter old man
    b. known for his wisdom
    c. going on another journey
    d. hated by his subjects   10. ______

NAME ______________________ CLASS ______________ DATE ________ SCORE ________

UNIT 3: THE ANCIENT MIDDLE EAST

(Textbook pages 154–159)

INTRODUCTION/Hebrew Literature

Directions: In the space provided, write the letter of the best answer to each question. *(10 points each)*

1. Canaan, homeland of the early Hebrews, was located
   a. between the Jordan River and the Mediterranean Sea, in the Fertile Crescent
   b. in West Africa
   c. east of Babylon
   d. between the city of Ur and the Arabian Peninsula — 1. ______

2. The Hebrew patriarchs, or founding fathers, were
   a. Solomon and David
   b. Abraham, Isaac, and Jacob
   c. Israel, Saul, and Moses
   d. Joshua and the leaders of the twelve tribes — 2. ______

3. The Book of Exodus tells how the Hebrews left Egypt and then received
   a. enough grain to survive a great drought
   b. the Ten Commandments
   c. God's promise that the Egyptians would become their slaves
   d. a homeland in Babylon — 3. ______

4. After the Hebrews returned to Canaan, judges loosely held the twelve tribes together until 1020 B.C., when Israel was united and gained great power under
   a. Moses
   b. Joshua
   c. King Saul
   d. King David — 4. ______

5. King David gained control over the Philistines and established the capital city of
   a. Judah
   b. Samaria
   c. Jerusalem
   d. Palestine — 5. ______

(continued)

6. Solomon's Temple of Jerusalem, built between 970 and 925 B.C., was important because
   a. it was a symbol of spiritual unity
   b. it gave rise to disagreements that split the Hebrew kingdom
   c. it attracted the attention and admiration of the powerful Romans
   d. it was the central place of worship for the Palestinians — 6. ______

7. What happened after the twelve tribes of Israel split into two kingdoms?
   a. They saw themselves as two separate peoples spiritually.
   b. Both kingdoms were conquered by Assyrians.
   c. Both kingdoms disappeared without a trace.
   d. The northern kingdom of Israel was conquered by the Assyrians. — 7. ______

8. In 586 B.C., the Chaldean king Nebuchadnezzar
   a. invaded Babylon but was defeated
   b. conquered Israel
   c. destroyed the Temple of Jerusalem
   d. was defeated by Judah — 8. ______

9. After their bitter period of slavery in Babylon, the Hebrews
   a. were released by Cyrus the Great of Persia
   b. were released by Alexander the Great of Macedonia
   c. lost their culture and never returned to Jerusalem
   d. became an independent nation until 167 B.C. — 9. ______

10. Which of the following sentences states a major difference between the Hebrews and most of their neighbors in the Middle East?
    a. The Hebrews believed that human beings could also be divine.
    b. The Hebrews believed that their God would protect them even if they disobeyed the law.
    c. When the Hebrews lost their homeland, they lost any sense of spiritual unity.
    d. The Hebrews worshiped one god. — 10. ______

NAME ______________ CLASS ______________ DATE ________ SCORE ________

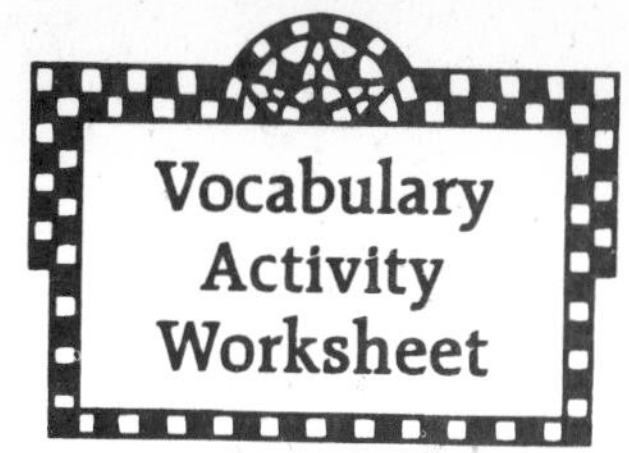

IN THE BEGINNING *from* GENESIS

King James Bible

(Textbook page 163)

DEVELOPING VOCABULARY

Directions: Read carefully the explanation of each word. Then write a sentence of your own using that word. In your sentence, include clues to the word's meaning.

dominion (də·min′ yən) ***n.*** Rule or power to rule. ▶ This word comes from the Latin *dominus*, meaning "lord" or "master." ▪ The Revolutionary War was fought to free Americans from the dominion of England. **Page 164**

ORIGINAL SENTENCE ______________________________

____

replenish (ri·plen′ ish) ***v.*** To make full or complete again. ▶ The prefix *re-*, "again," is joined to the French *plein*, "full," to create this word. ▪ When we inhale, we replenish our lungs with fresh air. **Page 165**

ORIGINAL SENTENCE ______________________________

____

subdue (səb·do͞o′) ***v.*** To conquer; prepare land for the cultivation of crops. ▶ The prefix *sub-*, "under," plus the Latin *ducere*, "to lead," form this word. ▪ Kim found she had to subdue her fears before she could perform in public. **Page 165**

ORIGINAL SENTENCE ______________________________

____

beguile (bē·gīl′) ***v.*** To deceive. ▶ *Beguile* comes from the Middle English noun *guile*, meaning "crafty or deceitful cunning." ▪ He was a smooth talker who could beguile others with his charm. **Page 167**

ORIGINAL SENTENCE ______________________________

____

enmity (en′mə·tē) ***n.*** Hostility. ▶ This word is related to an Old French word meaning "enemy." ▪ Her arrogant behavior only increased the enmity of her rival. **Page 167**

ORIGINAL SENTENCE ______________________________

____

NAME ______________ CLASS ______________ DATE ________ SCORE ________

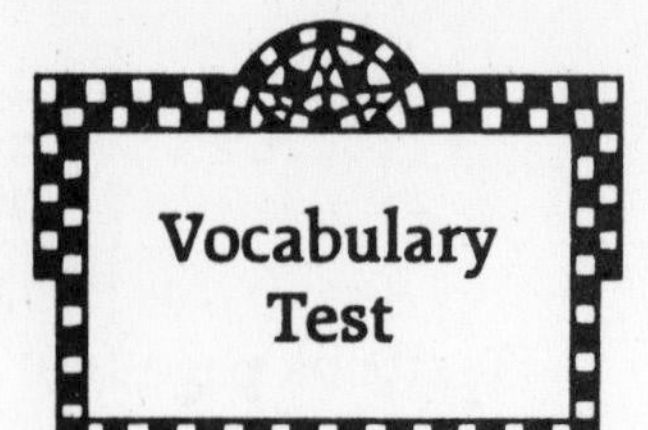

IN THE BEGINNING *from* GENESIS

King James Bible (Textbook page 163)

VOCABULARY TEST

A. Match each word in column I with the correct definition in column II. Place the letter of the definition you choose in the space provided. *(10 points each)*

	I	II
______	1. beguile	a. hostility
		b. to make full or complete again
______	2. dominion	c. to deceive
		d. to conquer
______	3. enmity	e. power to rule
______	4. replenish	
______	5. subdue	

B. In the space provided, write the letter of the word or phrase closest in meaning to the word in italics. *(10 points each)*

______ 6. The contest was bitterly waged, and you could almost feel the *enmity* between the two football teams.
a. sportsmanship b. competition c. bad feelings

______ 7. As much as he hated airplanes, Nick tried hard to *subdue* his fear of flying.
a. bring under control b. heighten c. hide

______ 8. She often used sneaky tactics to *beguile* others.
a. trick b. convince c. help

______ 9. King Henry VIII had total *dominion* over his subjects, even the ability to condemn them to death.
a. corruption b. authority c. nerve

______ 10. At dinner, it was my job to *replenish* the water glasses when they were empty.
a. polish b. refill c. wash

NAME ______________________ CLASS ______________ DATE ________ SCORE ______

IN THE BEGINNING *from* GENESIS

King James Bible

(Textbook page 163)

REVIEWING THE SELECTION

1. God spends six days creating the heavens and the earth. What happens on the seventh day?

____

2. In the garden of Eden, God first creates Man. Why does he then create Woman? ________

____

3. How does God know that Adam and Eve have eaten of the tree of knowledge? __________

____

4. God punishes Eve for her disobedience by increasing her sorrow. What are the other ways that he punishes Adam and Eve? ______________________

____

Reader's Response

Eden before the Fall is regarded as a paradise, but the Bible does not describe the paradise in detail. Write down a list of words and phrases that tell what you feel the garden of Eden must have been like before the Fall.

____

____

____

____

____

____

____

____

NAME ______________________ CLASS ______________ DATE ________ SCORE ______

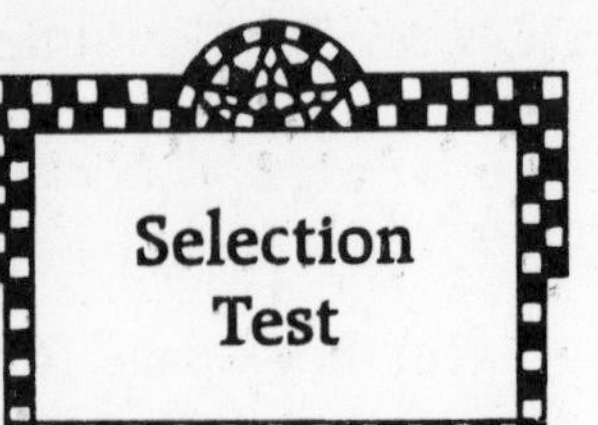

IN THE BEGINNING *from* GENESIS

King James Bible

(Textbook page 163)

READING COMPREHENSION

Directions: In the space provided, write the letter of the best answer to each question. *(10 points each)*

1. Which of these describes the Book of Genesis?
   a. It contains the *Epic of Gilgamesh.*
   b. It was written by one person.
   c. It explains many of the basic beliefs of the Jewish people.
   d. It is the first book written on papyrus. 1. ______

2. In the Book of Genesis, what does God create on the first day?
   a. dry land
   b. Adam and Eve
   c. animals and trees
   d. day and night 2. ______

3. To which living creatures does God give the most power?
   a. cattle
   b. man and woman
   c. birds and fish
   d. all of the above 3. ______

4. From what does God create Adam?
   a. Eve's rib
   b. dust
   c. a plant
   d. a star 4. ______

5. What place does God set aside for Adam and Eve to inhabit?
   a. the mountains
   b. Havilah
   c. the garden of Eden
   d. the Nile 5. ______

6. Why does God create Eve?
   a. to build a temple
   b. to rule over Adam
   c. to name the animals and the plants
   d. to be a companion to Adam 6. ______

(continued)

7. What does the serpent persuade Eve to do?
   a. eat from the tree of knowledge of good and evil
   b. eat animal flesh
   c. drink from sacred waters
   d. build a wall around the garden of Eden

7. ______

8. How does God know that Adam and Eve have disobeyed him?
   a. The serpent tells God.
   b. They become ashamed of being naked.
   c. They move away from the garden.
   d. They boast of their deed.

8. ______

9. What does God do to the serpent?
   a. kills it
   b. forgives it and gives it one more chance
   c. makes it the lowliest of all animals
   d. drives it from the garden with a flaming sword

9. ______

10. What punishment do Adam and Eve suffer for disobeying God?
   a. the pain of childbirth
   b. sorrow and death
   c. banishment from the garden of Eden
   d. all of the above

10. ______

NAME ______________________ CLASS ______________ DATE ________ SCORE ________

NOAH AND THE FLOOD *from* GENESIS

Jewish Publication Society of America (Textbook page 171)

DEVELOPING VOCABULARY

Directions: Read carefully the explanation of each word. Then write a sentence of your own using that word. In your sentence, include clues to the word's meaning.

terminate (tur'mə·nāt') ***v.*** To end. ▶ This verb is derived from the Latin word *terminus*, meaning "boundary" or "end." ▪ Most people terminate a letter by signing their name. **Page 171**

ORIGINAL SENTENCE ____

____

covenant (kuv'ə·nənt) ***n.*** A binding or solemn agreement. ▶ This word is related to the word *convene*, which means "to meet." ▪ Many neighborhoods require residents to sign a covenant to maintain their property properly. **Page 171**

ORIGINAL SENTENCE ____

____

subside (səb·sīd') ***v.*** To sink to a lower level. ▶ This word is based on the Latin prefix *sub-*, "down," and the verb *sidere*, "to settle." ▪ After a week of rain, it took another week before the river water completely subsided. **Page 173**

ORIGINAL SENTENCE ____

____

reckoning (rek'ən·ing) ***n.*** The settlement or accounting of rewards or punishments for an action. ▶ This word implies an accounting for previous conduct. ▪ Many people believe that there will be a day of reckoning. **Page 174**

ORIGINAL SENTENCE ____

____

abound (ə·bound') ***v.*** To be plentiful. ▶ *Abound* comes from an Old French word meaning "to overflow." ▪ Wild animals used to abound in the jungles and plains of Africa. **Page 174**

ORIGINAL SENTENCE ____

____

NAME ______________ CLASS ______________ DATE ________ SCORE ________

NOAH AND THE FLOOD *from* GENESIS

Jewish Publication Society (Textbook page 171)

VOCABULARY TEST

A. Match each word in column I with the correct definition in column II. Place the letter of the definition you choose in the space provided. *(10 points each)*

	I	II
______	1. abound	a. to sink to a lower level
		b. settlement of accounts
______	2. covenant	c. to end
		d. to be plentiful
______	3. reckoning	e. agreement, promise
______	4. subside	
______	5. terminate	

B. Complete the following paragraph by filling in each blank with one of the words below. You will use each word only once. *(10 points each)*

covenant subside
abounded reckoning
terminate

Our volleyball team lost again, and no wonder! Volleyball fans ______________ in our huge school, but we had little confidence in the team. At last we realized that the day of ______________ had arrived. We made a ______________ with each other that we would get behind the team. During the next game, we cheered as loudly as we could. I thought the noise would never ______________. Finally, when the game was just about to ______________, our team jumped into the lead, and we won. I guess it proves that a team is only as good as its fans.

NAME ______________________ CLASS ________________ DATE ________ SCORE ______

NOAH AND THE FLOOD *from* GENESIS

Jewish Publication Society of America (Textbook page 171)

REVIEWING THE SELECTION

Directions: For each of the following items, circle the letter of the phrase that best completes the sentence.

1. God decides to cause a flood because
   a. God is angry with one man—Noah
   b. God believes that the world suffers from overpopulation
   c. the earth has become corrupt and lawless
   d. God believes he erred in the creation of the plant kingdom and wants to start over

2. Noah is instructed to make an ark
   a. so that he and his family, along with representatives of the animal kingdom, will survive the flood
   b. to keep dry the tablets bearing the Lord's sacred covenant
   c. to save mammals, birds, and insects, but not snakes
   d. with room for himself and his family, excluding his sons' wives

3. After forty days and forty nights,
   a. the ark reaches dry land on top of a mountain
   b. the dove comes back with an olive leaf in its beak
   c. a wind blows, and the water level begins to subside
   d. the rain stops, but the floodwaters remain

4. When dry ground reappears after the flood, Noah
   a. comes out of the ark but keeps the animals inside until it is safer
   b. decrees that any animal or human that kills its own kind must be punished
   c. builds an altar and prepares burnt offerings
   d. tells his family that they may eat any animal or plant on the earth

Reader's Response

The story of Noah offers an explanation for the rainbow: it appears with rainclouds to remind God of his promise not to destroy the earth by flood. Imagine a purpose for some other natural phenomenon, such as the colors of the sunset or the varied shapes of snowflakes. On a separate piece of paper, briefly describe the phenomenon and explain the purpose you imagine it serves.

NAME ______________________ CLASS ________________ DATE ________ SCORE ______

NOAH AND THE FLOOD *from* GENESIS

Jewish Publication Society of America (Textbook page 171)

READING COMPREHENSION

Directions: In the space provided, write the letter of the best answer to each question. *(10 points each)*

1. Why does God send the great flood?
   a. to reduce the size of the population
   b. to punish people for their wickedness
   c. to show his power
   d. to destroy every one of his creations — 1.______

2. Which of the following pieces of information did God give to Noah?
   a. how to make the ark
   b. where the ark would land when the rain stopped
   c. which bird to use to test for dry land
   d. how to make the flood stop — 2.______

3. Who or what does God allow to survive the disaster?
   a. pairs of all animals
   b. Noah and his sons
   c. Noah's wife and his sons' wives
   d. all of the above — 3.______

4. How old is Noah when the flood begins?
   a. 600 years old
   b. 60 years old
   c. 950 years old
   d. 20 years old — 4.______

5. How long does it rain?
   a. ten days
   b. forty days
   c. one year
   d. two years — 5.______

6. The ark
   a. leaks badly
   b. can be seen in a museum today
   c. is broken up in the flood
   d. comes to rest on mountains — 6.______

(continued)

7. The dove is important because
   a. it shows Noah that some birds are still alive
   b. it shows God's covenant with Noah
   c. it shows Noah that there is dry land
   d. it shows Noah that not all God's creatures are wicked — 7. ______

8. What does Noah do to thank God?
   a. He promises never to build another ark.
   b. He builds an altar and makes burnt offerings.
   c. He frees all the animals.
   d. He sends a rainbow to God. — 8. ______

9. What promise does God give Noah?
   a. He will never again destroy the earth by flood.
   b. Noah will live forever.
   c. Noah's sons will father many children.
   d. God will always destroy all evil people by means of a flood. — 9. ______

10. What does God create to show he will keep the covenant?
    a. the sun
    b. the rainbow
    c. the moon
    d. the North Star — 10. ______

NAME ______________ CLASS ______________ DATE ________ SCORE ________

THE BOOK OF RUTH

King James Bible

(Textbook page 178)

DEVELOPING VOCABULARY

Directions: Read carefully the explanation of each word. Then write a sentence of your own using that word. In your sentence, include clues to the word's meaning.

sojourn (sō' jərn) ***v.*** To stop and dwell in a place temporarily. ▶ This word derives from the Latin *sub-*, "under," and *diurnus*, "day." ▪ Scott sojourned in France for a month before returning to England. **Page 178**

ORIGINAL SENTENCE ______________________________

____

tarry (tar' ē) ***v.*** To stay in a place, especially in expectation; delay; linger. ▶ This verb derives from the Latin *tardus*, "slow," which also produced the English word *tardy*. ▪ The frightened child did not tarry in his walk home after dark. **Page 178**

ORIGINAL SENTENCE ______________________________

____

entreat (en·trēt') ***v.*** To ask sincerely and urgently; beg. ▶ *Entreaty*, which means "an appeal, supplication, or prayer," is the noun form of this word. ▪ The subjects entreated the king to lower taxes. **Page 179**

ORIGINAL SENTENCE ______________________________

____

afflict (ə ·flikt') ***v.*** To cause pain or suffering to. ▶ This verb is similar to *inflict*, which means "to cause pain by striking or beating." ▪ Pneumonia afflicts many elderly people every year. **Page 179**

ORIGINAL SENTENCE ______________________________

____

kindred (kin' drid) ***n.*** Family; kinfolk. ▶ The adjective form, which is spelled the same, means "of like nature," as in the phrase "kindred spirits." ▪ Elliot, who was suspicious of strangers, felt most at home among his kindred. **Page 180**

(continued)

ORIGINAL SENTENCE ______________________________

____

sheaf (shēf) ***n.*** A quantity of cut stalks of grain and the like, bundled together. ▶ This word derives from the Indo-European root *skeup*, which means "bundle or clump." *Sheaf* can refer in general to a collection of things gathered together, especially papers. ▪ The reaper put a sheaf of cornstalks into the loading truck. **Page 180**

ORIGINAL SENTENCE ______________________________

____

nativity (nə·tiv′ ə·tē) ***n.*** Birth and, particularly, the circumstances surrounding a birth. ▶ A *nativity* scene, often seen around Christmas, is a depiction of the birth of Jesus. ▪ The astronaut expressed regret that he was not present for his child's nativity. **Page 180**

ORIGINAL SENTENCE ______________________________

____

recompense (rek′ əm·pens′) ***v.*** To pay for; compensate. ▶ The noun *recompense* means "repayment or reward." ▪ The insurance company recompensed the family for the loss of their house. **Page 180**

ORIGINAL SENTENCE ______________________________

____

suffice (sə·fīs′) ***v.*** To meet or satisfy a need; to be sufficient. ▶ The Latin verb *sufficere*, "to provide or suffice," produced this word. Its adjective form, *sufficient*, means "as much as is needed." ▪ The couple decided that one large steak would suffice for both of them. **Page 181**

ORIGINAL SENTENCE ______________________________

____

reproach (ri·prōch′) ***v.*** To scold, reprimand, or censure, especially in a way that produces shame. ▶ *Reproachful* means "full of or expressing blame," while *reproachable* means "worthy of blame." ▪ The mother reproached her husband for his harsh treatment of their son. **Page 181**

ORIGINAL SENTENCE ______________________________

____

NAME ______________________ CLASS ____________________ DATE ________ SCORE ________

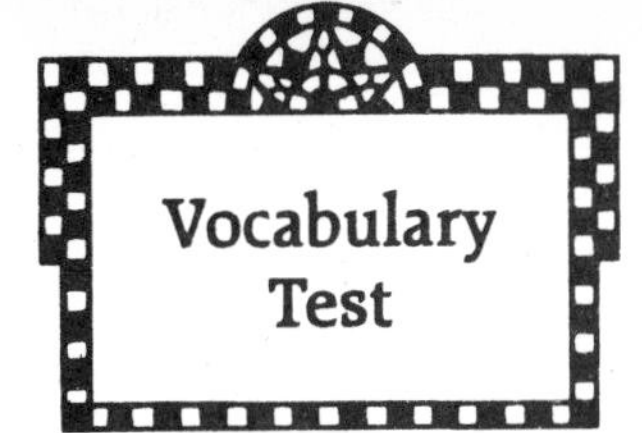

THE BOOK OF RUTH

King James Bible (Textbook page 178)

VOCABULARY TEST

A. Match each word in column I with the correct definition in column II. Place the letter of the definition you choose in the space provided. *(7 points each)*

I	II
______ 1. afflict	a. to scold or reprimand
______ 2. entreat	b. to delay; linger
______ 3. kindred	c. to pay for; compensate
______ 4. recompense	d. birth
______ 5. reproach	e. to beg; plead
______ 6. sheaf	f. to inflict pain upon
______ 7. sojourn	g. to stop and dwell in a place temporarily
______ 8. suffice	h. to satisfy a need
______ 9. tarry	i. family or kinfolk
______ 10. nativity	j. a bundle of stalks

B. In the space provided, write the letter of the word or phrase closest in meaning to the word in italics. *(6 points each)*

______ 11. The parents thought a single telephone would *suffice* for the whole family.
a. be enough b. be too little c. be too much

______ 12. The mother told her son not to *tarry* or he might be late for school.
a. hide b. show off c. linger

______ 13. Cheryl *reproached* herself for forgetting her father's birthday gift.
a. commended b. scolded c. thanked

______ 14. Because of all the complications, the family viewed Jiana's *nativity* as a miracle.
a. birth b. death c. anniversary

______ 15. The little girl *entreated* her mother for more time to play the electronic game.
a. wanted to ask b. refused to ask c. begged

NAME ______________________ CLASS ______________________ DATE __________ SCORE __________

THE BOOK OF RUTH

King James Bible (Textbook page 178)

REVIEWING THE SELECTION

1. Naomi's husband and two sons die in the foreign land of ______________________.

   Then she has only her two daughters-in-law, Orpah and ______________________.

2. Circle the letter of the best completion of the sentence. When Naomi and Ruth return to Bethlehem,
   a. no one recognizes them
   b. the barley harvest is just starting
   c. many relatives of Naomi's husband offer them food
   d. Naomi urges Ruth to go back to her native land

3. Ruth gathers leftover grain in the fields of Boaz. What does Boaz tell her when he learns

   what she is doing?____

   ____

4. Circle the letter of the best completion of the sentence. In order to seal the agreement that Boaz, and not the nearer kinsman, will marry Ruth, the nearer kinsman
   a. raises his right hand
   b. calls five elders as witnesses
   c. takes off his shoe
   d. removes his head covering

Reader's Response

Great news! The company you work for is publishing a modern translation of The Book of Ruth, and you've been chosen to design the cover! Your assignment is to plan the cover art and to choose a new title that reflects the story's theme. In the space below, using words, illustrations, or both, describe the cover and title you will create.

NAME ______________________ CLASS ______________________ DATE __________ SCORE __________

The Book of Ruth

King James Bible (Textbook page 178)

COORDINATING CONJUNCTIONS

A **conjunction** joins words, groups of words, or sentences. A **coordinating conjunction** joins equal parts of a sentence. Coordinating conjunctions include *and, or, for, but, nor, yet,* and *so.*

EXAMPLES The story of Ruth is one of devotion *and* compassion.
(joins two words)
The story of Ruth can be viewed as a lesson *or* as a short story.
(joins two groups of words)
The story of Ruth teaches a lesson, *but* it is also an entertaining story.
(joins two sentences)

Follow these rules when using coordinating conjunctions in sentences.

1. Conjunctions connect two or more similar or "equal" expressions—two verbs, two nouns, two phrases, two clauses.
2. The conjunctions *and, but, or,* and *nor* can join words, phrases, and clauses.
3. The conjunctions *for, so,* and *yet* usually join clauses.
4. Unless sentences are very short, use a comma before a coordinating conjunction that joins two sentences.

Exercise 1. Identifying Coordinating Conjunctions

Underline the coordinating conjunctions in each of the following sentences about the Book of Ruth. Look for conjunctions that join words, groups of words, and sentences. The number in parentheses indicates how many coordinating conjunctions you should find.

EXAMPLE I enjoyed this story, <u>but</u> Ruth's problems <u>and</u> hardships made me sad. (2)

1. Ruth's husband dies, yet she refuses to part with his mother. (1)
2. Naomi tries to urge Ruth and Orpah to return to their own families, but Ruth refuses. (2)
3. Naomi and Ruth have no husbands to support them, nor do they have any skills for earning a living. (2)
4. Boaz says he admires Ruth because she is kind and faithful to Naomi and because she does not pursue young men, rich or poor. (3)
5. The kinsman refuses to marry Ruth, for he fears that he will jeopardize his son's inheritance. (1)
6. It is tradition that if a man dies without a son, the man's brother, uncle, or other male relative will marry the man's widow. (1)
7. At first, Boaz says he cannot marry Ruth, but after he and the kinsman make a deal, he changes his mind. (2)
8. Ruth and Naomi have little food or money, yet Ruth manages to feed them both. (3)

(continued)

9. Naomi sends Ruth to lie at Boaz's feet, and Boaz reacts just as Naomi had hoped. (1)
10. As it turns out, Ruth and Boaz's son will be very important, for he will become the grandfather of David, the greatest king of Israel, yet no one could have known that this would happen. (3)

Exercise 2. Combining Sentences with Coordinating Conjunctions

Combine each group of short, related sentences about The Book of Ruth into one sentence by inserting one or more coordinating conjunctions. You may need to change, add, or delete words in the original sentences.

EXAMPLE The Book of Ruth has characters, a setting, a plot, and a theme. It might be considered a short story.

The Book of Ruth has characters, a setting, a plot, and a theme, so it might be considered a short story.

1. After the deaths of her husband and sons, Naomi wants to leave Moab. She decides to return to Bethlehem. Ruth goes with her.

____

____

2. Ruth could have chosen to return to her own people. She chooses to stay with Naomi.

____

____

3. Ruth has no skills. She is willing to gather bits of grain. This gives Naomi and Ruth food to eat.

____

____

4. Boaz tells his servant to let Ruth take all the grain she wants. He admires her goodness. He admires her kindness to Naomi.

____

____

(continued)

5. Boaz is surprised to see Ruth lying at his feet. He allows her to stay. He tells her that he will find her a husband.

____

____

Exercise 3. Revising a Paragraph

Revise the following paragraph. Focus on using coordinating conjunctions to combine sentences. You may add or change words, move words around, or make other changes that you think will improve the paragraph. (Not every sentence needs revision.) Remember that a comma usually comes before a coordinating conjunction that joins two sentences. Part of the beginning has been revised as a sample.

Loyalty is important, but it ~~Loyalty~~ does not always come easily. It's hard to hang in there when your best friend is in trouble. Others may turn their backs on your friend. You may want to stand up. You may want to fight for your friend's good name. You have your own reputation and welfare to protect. What do you do? You can't very well ignore the situation. You can't ignore your friend forever. Do you help your friend? Do you turn your back, hoping that things will get better? It may help to put yourself in your friend's place. This way you can better understand your friend's feelings. Ask yourself what you would want your friend to do if the situation were reversed. You might have been the one in trouble. Then let your conscience be your guide.

NAME ______________________ CLASS ______________________ DATE __________ SCORE __________

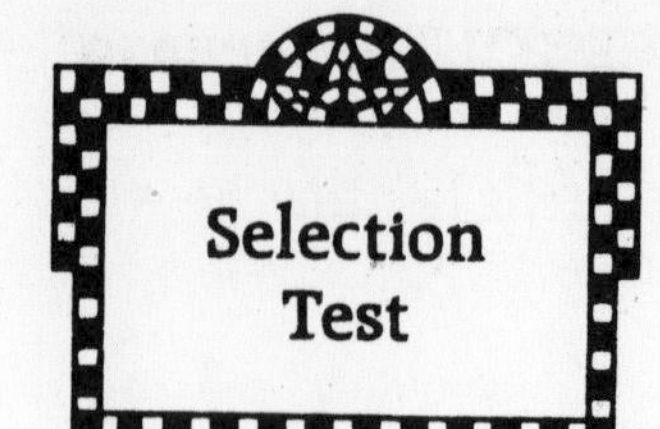

The Book of Ruth

King James Bible

(Textbook page 178)

READING COMPREHENSION

Directions: In the space provided, write the letter of the best answer to each question. *(10 points each)*

1. Who is Naomi?
   a. Ruth's mother-in-law
   b. Ruth's natural mother
   c. Ruth's sister
   d. a stranger that Ruth meets in Moab

   1. ______

2. Why does Naomi want to leave Moab after her husband and sons die?
   a. to find a new husband
   b. to get a job
   c. to return to Bethlehem
   d. to escape the famine in Moab

   2. ______

3. Why does Naomi try to discourage Ruth from returning with her to Bethlehem?
   a. She has never cared for her daughter-in-law.
   b. She is afraid that Ruth will be sold into slavery.
   c. She believes that Ruth is cursed by God.
   d. Naomi has no other son to offer Ruth in marriage.

   3. ______

4. What important decision does Ruth make?
   a. to return to her own people
   b. to live with Orpah
   c. to remain faithful to her religion as a Moabite
   d. to follow Naomi

   4. ______

5. Why does Ruth go into the fields?
   a. to gather grain for herself and Naomi
   b. to cry out a curse against God
   c. to meet other women her age
   d. to meet other men her age

   5. ______

6. Why does Boaz give special favors to Ruth?
   a. He wants to see more women working in the fields.
   b. Ruth has been kind to Naomi.
   c. Naomi asks him to.
   d. Ruth begs for special favors.

   6. ______

(continued)

7. Why does Naomi believe Boaz should marry Ruth?
   a. Boaz is rich.
   b. Boaz is a kinsman.
   c. Ruth is talented and beautiful.
   d. Boaz is from Moab. 7.______

8. Why does Boaz first tell Ruth he cannot marry her?
   a. There is another kinsman more closely related to Ruth.
   b. He does not love her.
   c. Her virtue is questionable.
   d. Another has already asked to marry her. 8.______

9. At the end of the story, Naomi
   a. becomes the nurse of Boaz and Ruth's child
   b. returns to Moab
   c. marries a kinsman
   d. is punished by God 9.______

10. The Book of Ruth offers an important lesson in
    a. the problems relatives can bring
    b. the terrible effects of famine
    c. the dangers of blind loyalty
    d. the virtues of love and compassion 10.______

NAME ______________________ CLASS ______________________ DATE __________ SCORE ________

from the BOOK OF PSALMS

King James Bible (Textbook page 187)

DEVELOPING VOCABULARY

Directions: Read carefully the explanation of each word. Then write a sentence of your own using that word. In your sentence, include clues to the word's meaning.

minister (min'is·tər) ***n.*** A person or thing serving as the agent of some higher power. ▶ The Latin word *minister* was often used to refer to an attendant or servant. ▪ Politicians act as ministers to the people. **Page 188**

ORIGINAL SENTENCE ______________________________

____

rebuke (ri·byo͞ok') ***v.*** To reprimand or scold. ▶ This word is related to the Old French *buche*, which means "stick or club." To *rebuke* someone is to give that person a verbal beating. ▪ Mr. Johnson rebuked his son for forgetting to feed the dog. **Page 188**

ORIGINAL SENTENCE ______________________________

____

manifold (man'ə·fōld') ***adj.*** Many and diverse. ▶ This word comes from the Old English word with the same meaning, *manigfeald*. ▪ The caretaker, who was always busy, had manifold duties. **Page 190**

ORIGINAL SENTENCE ______________________________

____

meditation (med'ə·tā' shən) ***n.*** Solemn reflection on spiritual matters. ▶ A *meditation* can also refer to a thoughtful essay or sermon, as in Descartes' *Meditations*. ▪ Lindsay needed a time for meditation as an escape from her stressful life. **Page 191**

ORIGINAL SENTENCE ______________________________

____

consume (kən·so͞om') ***v.*** To destroy; burn. ▶ *Consume* can also mean "use up," "devour," or "absorb completely." ▪ In a matter of seconds, the forest fire consumed thousands of trees. **Page 191**

ORIGINAL SENTENCE ______________________________

____

NAME ______________________ CLASS ______________________ DATE ________ SCORE ________

from the BOOK OF PSALMS

King James Bible (Textbook page 187)

VOCABULARY TEST

A. Match each word in column I with the correct definition in column II. Place the letter of the definition you choose in the space provided. *(10 points each)*

I	II
______ 1. manifold	a. solemn reflection
______ 2. minister	b. many and diverse
______ 3. rebuke	c. to reprimand or scold
______ 4. consume	d. to destroy
______ 5. meditation	e. one serving as an agent of some power

B. In the space provided, write the letter of the word or phrase closest in meaning to the word in italics. *(10 points each)*

______ 6. A period of *meditation* helps some people gather their thoughts for the day.
a. contemplation b. recreation c. education

______ 7. The civil servant views herself as a *minister* of the government.
a. student b. taskmaster c. representative

______ 8. The books in the library are *manifold*, including both fiction and nonfiction.
a. of different kinds b. easy to read c. bound

______ 9. A fire may *consume* everything in its path.
a. release b. do away with c. drench

______ 10. Even though she is my best friend, I had to *rebuke* her for what I believed was wrong.
a. praise b. reprimand c. laugh at

NAME ______________________ CLASS ______________________ DATE __________ SCORE __________

PARABLES

New English Bible

(Textbook page 199)

DEVELOPING VOCABULARY

Directions: Read carefully the explanation of each word. Then write a sentence of your own using that word. In your sentence, include clues to the word's meaning.

prodigal (präd′i·gəl) ***adj.*** Carelessly wasteful. ▶ This adjective comes from the Latin *prodigere*, which literally means "to drive away." ▪ Jack was always broke because of his prodigal spending. **Page 199**

ORIGINAL SENTENCE ____

____

squander (skwän′dər) ***v.*** To spend wastefully or extravagantly. ▶ This word is probably a variation of the British *squander*, which meant "to scatter." ▪ In less than a year, Fred squandered the money his aunt left him. **Page 199**

ORIGINAL SENTENCE ____

____

retort (ri·tôrt′) ***v.*** To reply in a quick, sharp manner. ▶ This word is derived from the Latin *retorquere*, which means "to twist back." ▪ When asked to be careful, Peter retorted, "Do you think I'm trying to hurt myself?" **Page 200**

ORIGINAL SENTENCE ____

____

capacity (kə·pas′i·tē) ***n.*** Ability or talent. ▶ This word derives from the Latin adjective *capax*, meaning both "roomy" and "capable." ▪ He divided his fortune among his sons according to their capacity. **Page 202**

ORIGINAL SENTENCE ____

____

forfeit (fôr′fit) ***v.*** To lose, give up, or be deprived of because of some crime or failure. ▶ This word is derived from the Latin words *foris*, "beyond," and *facere*, "to do." When you go beyond lawful limits, you are often required to forfeit something. ▪ The owner had to forfeit all his land because he had never paid taxes. **Page 202**

ORIGINAL SENTENCE ____

____

NAME ______________________ CLASS ______________________ DATE __________ SCORE __________

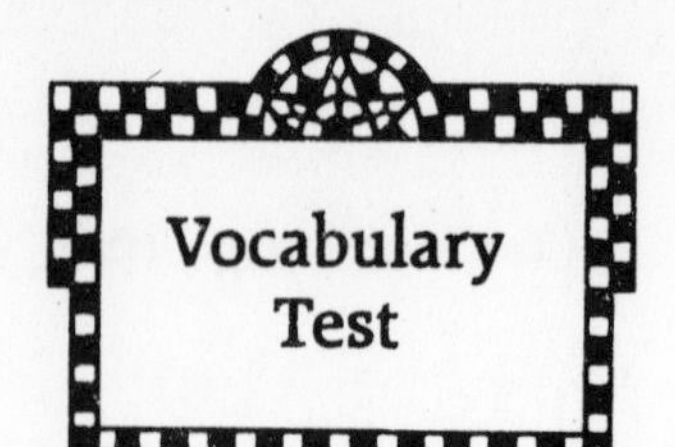

PARABLES

New English Bible (Textbook page 199)

VOCABULARY TEST

A. Match each word in column I with the correct definition in column II. Place the letter of the definition you choose in the space provided. *(10 points each)*

	I	II
______	1. capacity	a. carelessly wasteful
______	2. forfeit	b. to spend wastefully or extravagantly
______	3. prodigal	c. ability or talent
______	4. retort	d. to lose or give up
______	5. squander	e. to reply quickly and sharply

B. From the words listed below, choose the word that best completes the sentence. Write the word. *(10 points each)*

prodigal forfeit capacity retorted squandered

6. Even the best person has the ______________________ to do evil in certain situations.

7. The team had to ______________________ the game because it didn't have enough players.

8. The young heirs ______________________ their fortune on bad investments.

9. Members of the wiser, older generation typically criticize their children for their

   ______________________ habits.

10. When the policeman asked the thief why he stole the ring, the brash criminal

    ______________________, "Why not?"

NAME ______________________ CLASS ______________________ DATE __________ SCORE __________

PARABLES

New English Bible

(Textbook page 199)

REVIEWING THE SELECTION

1. The prodigal son leaves home with money. What happens to it?

____

2. Why does the elder brother of the prodigal son become angry at their father?

____

3. Circle the letter of the sentence that tells how Jesus explains the parable of the sower.
   a. The sower sows the word of God, but the word takes root only in some of those who hear it.
   b. Seed that falls on rocky ground will produce a strong yield.
   c. Only people who live by farming the soil can understand parables.

4. The man with five bags of gold invests it. What does the man with only one bag of gold do with it? ____

Reader's Response

In "The Talents," the master gives one man's bag of gold to another man who already has ten bags of gold. Complete this paragraph:

The master's decision is fair [or unfair] because _______________________

____

____

____

____

____

____

____

NAME ____________ CLASS ____________ DATE ________ SCORE ________

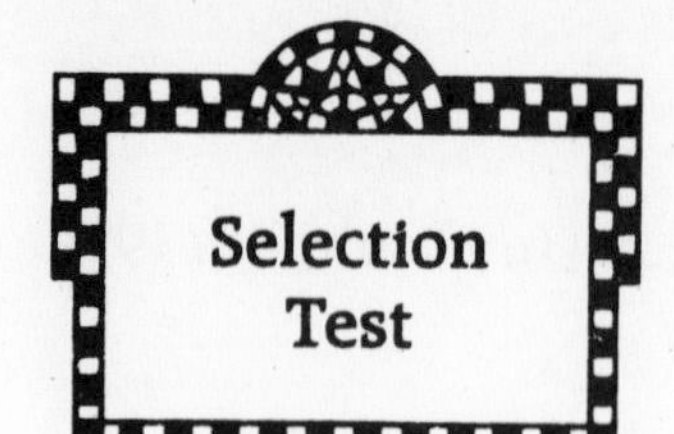

PARABLES

New English Bible

(Textbook page 199)

READING COMPREHENSION

Directions: In the space provided, write the letter of the best answer to each question. *(10 points each)*

1. What do all parables have in common?
   a. They are written in verse.
   b. They teach lessons.
   c. They are about animals.
   d. They are extremely difficult to understand.

   1. ______

2. What does the prodigal son ask his father to do?
   a. give him his share of the property
   b. give him all of the property
   c. give his share to the poor
   d. give his share to his brothers

   2. ______

3. What is the prodigal son's attitude when he returns home?
   a. arrogant
   b. angry
   c. lighthearted
   d. humble

   3. ______

4. What happens when the prodigal son returns home?
   a. His older brother joyfully kills a calf in his honor.
   b. His father celebrates his return.
   c. His father tells him that he cannot stay.
   d. The older son leaves home in protest.

   4. ______

5. What is the lesson implied in "The Prodigal Son"?
   a. We are our brothers' keepers.
   b. The love of money is the root of all evil.
   c. Enjoy life while you are young.
   d. Repent, and you will be forgiven.

   5. ______

6. In "The Sower," what do the seeds represent?
   a. fruit
   b. corn
   c. the word of God
   d. the evil of Satan

   6. ______

(continued)

7. In "The Sower," to what does Jesus liken the birds on the footpath?
   a. Satan
   b. thistles
   c. rocky soil
   d. God

   7. ______

8. According to the parable "The Sower," people who are the most blessed are those who
   a. accept the word at first but eventually forget about it
   b. renounce the word when they are persecuted
   c. hear the word and welcome it
   d. continually question the word

   8. ______

9. In "The Talents," what does the master do to the man who hides his talents?
   a. doubles his money
   b. punishes him
   c. rewards him
   d. gives him another chance

   9. ______

10. What lesson is implied in "The Talents"?
    a. If you have money, don't spend it all in one place.
    b. Use the gifts that you are given.
    c. Some talents are more valuable than others.
    d. Do not take gifts from others.

    10. ______

NAME ______________________ CLASS ______________________ DATE __________ SCORE __________

UNIT 3: THE ANCIENT MIDDLE EAST

WORD ANALOGIES / Extending Vocabulary

Directions: In the space provided, write the letter of the pair of words with the relationship that is closest to that of the capitalized words. *(10 points each)*

1. ALLOT : SHARES ::
   a. spend : shopper
   b. distribute : portions
   c. budget : balance
   d. hire : employer
   1. ______

2. OMINOUS : THREATENING ::
   a. promising : encouraging
   b. familiar : alien
   c. courageous : dangerous
   d. isolated : calm
   2. ______

3. SLOUGH : SKIN ::
   a. rake : trees
   b. wound : bandage
   c. shed : fur
   d. plant : food
   3. ______

4. SOMBER : CHEERFUL ::
   a. serious : interesting
   b. gloomy : bright
   c. pleasant : calm
   d. sad : mournful
   4. ______

5. FORFEIT : LOSS ::
   a. win : defeat
   b. deny : right
   c. carry : burden
   d. gain : profit
   5. ______

6. KINDRED : RELATIVE ::
   a. parent : child
   b. mammal : animal
   c. friend : companion
   d. job : worker
   6. ______

7. TARRY : WAIT ::
   a. depart : linger
   b. relax : work
   c. wander : settle
   d. hasten : rush
   7. ______

8. FAULT : REPROACH ::
   a. approve : shame
   b. confess : guilt
   c. merit : praise
   d. punish : reward
   8. ______

9. SQUANDER : SAVE ::
   a. rich : wealthy
   b. waste : preserve
   c. dishonest : sly
   d. elaborate : useful
   9. ______

10. RETORT : RESPOND ::
    a. question : inquire
    b. reply : ask
    c. guess : know
    d. insult : respect
    10. ______

NAME ______________________ CLASS ______________________ DATE __________ SCORE __________

UNIT 3: THE ANCIENT MIDDLE EAST

UNIT REVIEW TEST/Applying Skills I

A. Reading Comprehension. In the space provided, write the letter of the best answer to each question. *(8 points each)*

1. In the *Epic of Gilgamesh*, Gilgamesh loses his last chance for immortality when
   a. the snake eats the plant
   b. he gets caught in the great flood
   c. he sleeps for six days and seven nights
   d. Utnapishtim refuses to help him
   1. ______

2. "In the Beginning" explains
   a. how Adam convinced Eve to eat the forbidden fruit
   b. why God decided to destroy all living creatures
   c. why humans do not have everlasting life
   d. why the serpent is a powerful animal
   2. ______

3. In "Noah and the Flood," Noah knows the water has subsided when
   a. the dove brings back an olive leaf
   b. the raven flies over the ark
   c. he opens the ark and sees dry land
   d. the dove speaks to him and tells him it has seen dry land
   3. ______

4. In The Book of Ruth, Naomi is Ruth's
   a. mother
   b. sister-in-law
   c. sister
   d. mother-in-law
   4. ______

5. Which of these words best describes the prodigal son's father?
   a. negligent
   b. stern
   c. forgiving
   d. spiteful
   5. ______

6. In "The Talents," which of the men does the master punish?
   a. the one who turned five bags of gold into ten
   b. the one who buried his gold
   c. the one who turned two bags of gold into four
   d. all of them
   6. ______

(continued)

B. Identifying Characters. Each description below refers to a main character in one of the selections you have just read. Identify the characters by choosing the letter of the best answer. Write the letter in the space provided. *(8 points each)*

7. He has a horrifying dream of the underworld.
   a. Enkidu in the *Epic of Gilgamesh*
   b. Boaz in The Book of Ruth
   c. Noah in "Noah and the Flood"
   d. the brother in "The Prodigal Son" 7. ______

8. She marries a wealthy man who owns many grain fields.
   a. Siduri in the *Epic of Gilgamesh*
   b. Eve in "In the Beginning"
   c. Ruth in The Book of Ruth
   d. The narrator in Psalm 23 8. ______

9. He describes a time when the Earth is flooded.
   a. Utnapishtim in the *Epic of Gilgamesh*
   b. The narrator in Psalm 23
   c. Shem in "Noah and the Flood"
   d. Gilgamesh in the *Epic of Gilgamesh* 9. ______

10. These people weep in exile and hang up their harps on trees.
    a. Adam and Eve in "In the Beginning"
    b. Gilgamesh and Enkidu in the *Epic of Gilgamesh*
    c. The Jews exiled in Babylon in Psalm 137
    d. Naomi and Orpah in The Book of Ruth 10. ______

C. Composition. Choose *one* of these topics and write a brief essay on a separate sheet of paper. *(20 points)*

1. A *covenant* is a solemn or binding agreement. In both "In the Beginning" and "Noah and the Flood," God makes a covenant with people. Describe and discuss each of these covenants. You might consider the circumstances under which the covenants were made, whether they were honored by the people involved, and the results of each covenant. Use details from each story to support your essay.

2. In these stories, you read about two diverse personalities—Gilgamesh and Ruth. Both had something to achieve. Compare and contrast these two characters. You might consider the motives of each character. What mattered to them? How did they approach their individual problems? Why did one succeed and one fail? Use details from each story to support your essay.

NAME ______________________________ CLASS ______________________ DATE ________ SCORE ________

UNIT 3: THE ANCIENT MIDDLE EAST

CRITICAL THINKING AND WRITING/Applying Skills II

A. Reading a Parable. Read the New Testament parable below carefully, and then answer the questions that follow.

THE PARABLE OF THE GOOD SAMARITAN

King James Bible

And, behold, a certain lawyer stood up, and tempted him, saying, Master, what shall I do to inherit eternal life?

He said unto him, What is written in the law? how readest thou?

And he answering said, Thou shalt love the Lord thy God with all thy heart, and with all thy soul, and with all thy strength, and with all thy mind; and thy neighbor as thyself.

And he said unto him, Thou hast answered right; this do, and thou shalt live.

But he, willing to justify himself, said unto Jesus, And who is my neighbor?

And Jesus answering said, A certain man went down from Jerusalem to Jericho, and fell among thieves, which stripped him of his raiment, and wounded him, and departed, leaving him half dead.

And by chance there came down a certain priest that way; and when he saw him, he passed by on the other side.

And likewise a Levite, when he was at the place, came and looked on him, and passed by on the other side.

But a certain Samaritan, as he journeyed, came where he was; and when he saw him, he had compassion on him.

And went to him, and bound up his wounds, pouring in oil and wine, and set him on his own beast, and brought him to an inn, and took care of him.

And on the morrow when he departed, he took out two pence, and gave them to the host, and said unto him, Take care of him; and whatsoever thou spendest more, when I come again, I will repay thee.

Which now of these three, thinkest thou, was neighbor unto him that fell among the thieves?

And he said, He that showed mercy on him. Then said Jesus unto him, Go, and do thou likewise.

—Luke 10:25-37

(continued)

B. Analyzing a Parable. In the space provided, write the letter of the best answer to each question. *(6 points each)*

1. The man going from Jerusalem to Jericho is
   a. thrown from his mule
   b. stricken with a deadly disease
   c. attacked by robbers
   d. left homeless by a famine

   1. ______

2. Both the priest and the Levite, upon seeing the man,
   a. refuse to look at him
   b. look at him, then go by
   c. assume he is dead
   d. ask the innkeeper to help him

   2. ______

3. The Samaritan tells the innkeeper that he will
   a. pay all the man's expenses
   b. come back and get the man
   c. take the man with him the next day
   d. split the man's expenses with the innkeeper

   3. ______

4. The lesson implied by this parable is that people should
   a. love God with all their heart and soul
   b. know how to take care of an injured person
   c. care for the welfare of others
   d. know the names of all their neighbors

   4. ______

5. When Jesus refers to "neighbor," he means
   a. any person in trouble
   b. any person who lives nearby
   c. any person who shares one's religious beliefs
   d. any person one recognizes

   5. ______

6. The main thing the lawyer wants to know is
   a. the law of God
   b. who the Samaritan is
   c. what to do if he sees an injured person
   d. how to gain eternal life

   6. ______

7. Which character trait does the Samaritan show?
   a. selfishness
   b. hypocrisy
   c. greed
   d. mercy

   7. ______

(continued)

8. Samaritans were considered inferior people in Jesus' time. The fact that a person considered inferior behaves even more kindly than a priest is an example of
   a. metaphor
   b. parallelism
   c. imagery
   d. irony

   8. ______

9. Jesus says that others can be good neighbors by
   a. following the example of the Samaritan
   b. making friends of enemies
   c. following the example of the priest and the Levite
   d. punishing those who hurt others

   9. ______

10. The twentieth-century equivalent to the response of the priest and the Levite would be to say,
    a. "we tried to help, but it did no good"
    b. "we didn't want to get involved"
    c. "we didn't see him"
    d. all of the above

    10. ______

C. Writing About a Parable. *(40 points)* Parables are stories that illustrate ideas. How does the parable of "The Good Samaritan" illustrate the precept, "Love thy neighbor as thyself"? Find evidence in the parable to support your ideas.

Directions: Using evidence you have found in the parable, write *one* paragraph. You might start with a statement such as: "The Good Samaritan shows love for his neighbor

when he ______________________________

First of all, he ______________________________

____

____

____

____

____

____

____

____

____

Unit 3: The Ancient Middle East

UNIT INTRODUCTION TEST

INTRODUCTION/The Literature of Ancient Mesopotamia

(Textbook pages 128–135)

1. a	5. c	8. b
2. d	6. c	9. a
3. b	7. b	10. b
4. c		

from the Epic of Gilgamesh

translated by N. K. Sandars
(Textbook page 139)

VOCABULARY ACTIVITY WORKSHEET

Developing Vocabulary

Responses will vary.

VOCABULARY TEST

A.	1. c	5. g	8. d
	2. j	6. a	9. i
	3. b	7. h	10. f
	4. e		

B. somber, ominous, incantations, deluge, consigned

REVIEW AND RESPONSE WORKSHEET

Reviewing the Selection

1. He dies as the result of an illness.
2. b
3. b
4. c

Reader's Response

Responses will vary. Students may mention his strength and perseverance in carrying out his quest. Since he is only two-thirds divine, some may find his human weaknesses appealing, as when he cannot stay awake even to gain everlasting life.

SELECTION TEST

Reading Comprehension

1. a	5. b	8. d
2. a	6. c	9. b
3. c	7. a	10. b
4. d		

UNIT INTRODUCTION TEST

INTRODUCTION/Hebrew Literature

(Textbook pages 154–159)

1. a	5. c	8. c
2. b	6. a	9. a
3. b	7. d	10. d
4. c		

In the Beginning *from* Genesis

King James Bible
(Textbook page 163)

VOCABULARY ACTIVITY WORKSHEET

Developing Vocabulary

Responses will vary.

VOCABULARY TEST

A.	1. c	**B.**	6. c
	2. e		7. a
	3. a		8. a
	4. b		9. b
	5. d		10. b

(continued)

REVIEW AND RESPONSE WORKSHEET

Reviewing the Selection

1. God ends his work and rests. He also blesses and sanctifies that day.
2. He creates Woman so that Man will not be alone and so that Man will have a helpmate.
3. Because Adam and Eve are ashamed of their nakedness, God knows they have knowledge.
4. Eve is to have sorrow in childbirth and to be ruled over by her husband. Adam is also to know sorrow, pain, and death.

Reader's Response

Responses will vary.

SELECTION TEST

Reading Comprehension

1. c	5. c	8. b
2. d	6. d	9. c
3. b	7. a	10. d
4. b		

NOAH AND THE FLOOD *from* GENESIS

Jewish Publication Society of America

(Textbook page 171)

VOCABULARY ACTIVITY WORKSHEET

Developing Vocabulary

Responses will vary.

VOCABULARY TEST

A. 1. d 2. e 3. b 4. a 5. c

B. abounded, reckoning, covenant, subside, terminate

REVIEW AND RESPONSE WORKSHEET

Reviewing the Selection

1. c	3. d
2. a	4. c

Reader's Response

Responses will vary.

SELECTION TEST

Reading Comprehension

1. b	5. b	8. b
2. a	6. d	9. a
3. d	7. c	10. b
4. a		

THE BOOK OF RUTH

King James Bible

(Textbook page 178)

VOCABULARY ACTIVITY WORKSHEET

Developing Vocabulary

Responses will vary.

VOCABULARY TEST

A.

1. f	5. a	8. h
2. e	6. j	9. b
3. i	7. g	10. d
4. c		

B.

11. a	14. a
12. c	15. c
13. b	

REVIEW AND RESPONSE WORKSHEET

Reviewing the Selection

1. Moab, Ruth
2. b

(continued)

3. He tells her to glean only in his fields, stay close to his reapers, and share their food and drink, because he admires her virtue.
4. c

Reader's Response

Responses will vary.

LANGUAGE SKILLS WORKSHEET

Coordinating Conjunctions

Exercise 1.

1. Ruth's husband dies, yet she refuses to part with his mother.
2. Naomi tries to urge Ruth and Orpah to return to their own families, but Ruth refuses.
3. Naomi and Ruth have no husbands to support them, nor do they have any skills for earning a living.
4. Boaz says he admires Ruth because she is kind and faithful to Naomi and because she does not pursue young men, rich or poor.
5. The kinsman refuses to marry Ruth, for he fears that he will jeopardize his son's inheritance.
6. It is tradition that if a man dies without a son, the man's brother, uncle, or other male relative will marry the man's widow.
7. At first, Boaz says he cannot marry Ruth, but after he and the kinsman make a deal, he changes his mind.
8. Ruth and Naomi have little food or money, yet Ruth manages to feed them both.
9. Naomi sends Ruth to lie at Boaz's feet, and Boaz reacts just as Naomi had hoped.
10. As it turns out, Ruth and Boaz's son will be very important, for he will become the grandfather of David, the greatest king of Israel, yet no one could have known that this would happen.

Exercise 2.

Responses will vary. Students' responses should be similar to the following.

1. After the deaths of her husband and sons, Naomi wants to leave Moab, so she decides to return to Bethlehem, and Ruth goes with her.
2. Ruth could have chosen to return to her own people, but she chooses to stay with Naomi.
3. Ruth has no skills, but she is willing to gather bits of grain, and this gives Naomi and Ruth food to eat.
4. Boaz tells his servant to let Ruth take all the grain she wants, for he admires her goodness and her kindness to Naomi.
5. Boaz is surprised to see Ruth lying at his feet, but he allows her to stay, and he tells her he will find her a husband.

Exercise 3.

Responses will vary. Students' responses may be similar to the following.

Loyalty is important, but it does not always come easily. It's hard to hang in there when your best friend is in trouble, or when others turn their backs on him or her. You may want to stand up and fight for your friend's good name, yet you have your own reputation and welfare to protect. What do you do? You can't very well ignore the situation, nor can you ignore your friend forever. Do you help your friend, or do you turn your back on him or her, hoping that things will get better? It may help to put yourself in your friend's place, so you can better understand your friend's feelings. Ask yourself what you would want your friend to do if the situation were reversed and you were the one in trouble. Then let your conscience be your guide.

(continued)

SELECTION TEST

Reading Comprehension

1. a 5. a 8. a
2. c 6. b 9. a
3. d 7. b 10. d
4. d

from the BOOK OF PSALMS

King James Bible
(Textbook page 187)

VOCABULARY ACTIVITY WORKSHEET

Developing Vocabulary

Responses will vary.

VOCABULARY TEST

A. 1. b 2. e 3. c 4. d 5. a

B. 6. a 7. c 8. a 9. b 10. b

REVIEW AND RESPONSE WORKSHEET

Reviewing the Selection

1. c
2. because the Lord is with him
3. beasts; ships; leviathan or whale
4. sing and be happy
5. Jerusalem, their home

Reader's Response

Responses will vary.

PARABLES

New English Bible
(Textbook page 199)

VOCABULARY ACTIVITY WORKSHEET

Developing Vocabulary

Responses will vary.

VOCABULARY TEST

A. 1. c 2. d 3. a 4. e 5. b

B. 6. capacity 7. forfeit 8. squandered 9. prodigal 10. retorted

REVIEW AND RESPONSE WORKSHEET

Reviewing the Selection

1. He squanders the money in reckless living.
2. The elder son thinks the prodigal son is being honored for his wasteful living; he is also angered because his father never held a party for him.
3. a
4. He hides it in a hole in the ground.

Reader's Response

Responses will vary. Students who think the decision is fair may say that the man with one bag deserved to lose it because of his short-sightedness. Those who think the decision is unfair could argue that the man thought he was doing the right thing and is now being condemned for it.

SELECTION TEST

Reading Comprehension

1. b 5. d 8. c
2. a 6. c 9. b
3. d 7. a 10. b
4. b

(continued)

WORD ANALOGIES/Extending Vocabulary

1. b (allot : shares :: distribute : portions)
   Relationship: action to object
   One acts to *allot*, or "give out," *shares* (pieces), as one acts to *distribute*, or "give out," *portions* (pieces).
2. a (ominous : threatening :: promising : encouraging)
   Relationship: synonyms
   Ominous and *threatening* are synonyms meaning "sinister." *Promising* and *encouraging* are synonyms meaning "pleasing or desirable." The analogy is strengthened by the fact that *ominous* and *promising* are antonyms, as are *threatening* and *encouraging*.
3. c (slough : skin :: shed : fur)
   Relationship: action to object
   A reptile acts to *slough*, "cast off," *skin*. An animal acts to *shed*, "cast off," *fur*.
4. b (somber : cheerful :: gloomy : bright)
   Relationship: antonyms
   Somber, "sad," is an antonym of *cheerful*. *Gloomy*, "dark," is an antonym of *bright*. The analogy is strengthened by the fact that *somber* and *gloomy* are synonyms of each other, as are *cheerful* and *bright*.
5. d (forfeit : loss :: gain : profit)
   Relationship: action to result
   The result of a *forfeit* is a *loss*. The result of a *gain* is a *profit*.
6. c (kindred : relative :: friend : companion)
   Relationship: synonyms
   Kindred and *relative* are synonyms meaning "kinfolk." *Friend* and *companion* are also synonyms.
7. d (tarry : wait :: hasten : rush)
   Relationship: synonyms
   Tarry and *wait* are synonyms meaning "to delay." *Hasten* and *rush* are also synonyms. The analogy is strengthened by the fact that *tarry* and *hasten* are antonyms, as are *wait* and *rush*.
8. c (fault : reproach :: merit : praise)
   Relationship: Cause and effect
   When one finds *fault*, one *reproaches*, or reprimands. When one finds *merit*, one *praises*.
9. b (squander : save :: waste : preserve)
   Relationship: antonyms
   Squander, "to spend recklessly," is an antonym of *save*. *Waste* and *preserve* are also antonyms. The analogy is strengthened by the fact that *squander* and *waste* are synonyms, as are *save* and *preserve*.
10. a (retort : respond :: question : inquire)
    Relationship: synonyms
    Retort and *respond* are synonyms meaning "reply." *Question* and *inquire* are synonyms meaning "ask."

UNIT REVIEW TEST/Applying Skills I

A. Reading Comprehension

1. a	3. a	5. c
2. c	4. d	6. b

B. Identifying Characters

7. a	9. a
8. c	10. c

C. Composition

1. Answers will vary. Students may point out that in both stories, God provides humans with an abundance, provided they follow his will. In "In the Beginning," humans break God's covenant by eating the fruit of the tree of knowledge of good and evil and are punished by losing their immortality. In "Noah and the Flood," God's covenant *follows* his punishing flood—he vows never to destroy the earth by flood again. His rainbow serves as a sign of this covenant. Students may interpret God's punishment in "Noah and the Flood" as a continuation of his disappointment with humanity since its fall from grace in Eden.

(continued)

2. Answers will vary. Students may point out that Gilgamesh's goal is motivated mainly by self-interest; although he is deeply moved by Enkidu's death, it is his own death he hopes to avoid. Ruth's goal—to stay with Naomi—does not seem to be in her own best interest. Yet it is her very selflessness that inspires the benevolence of Boaz. Ironically, in spite of Gilgamesh's great strength, it is his human frailty—as he fails Utnapishtim's test of sleep and again as he loses his grasp of the youth-giving plant—that undoes him. On the other hand, the seemingly vulnerable Ruth, because of her inner strength, triumphs over her misfortunes.

CRITICAL THINKING AND WRITING/
Applying Skills II

B. Analyzing a Parable

1. c
2. b
3. a
4. c
5. a
6. d
7. d
8. d
9. a
10. b

C. Writing About a Parable

Responses will vary, but the students should note that the Samaritan administers first aid, takes the traveler to an inn, cares for him through the night, and assumes responsibility for him until he's sure that the traveler will be well enough to leave.

NOTES

NAME ______________________ CLASS ________________ DATE ______ SCORE ______

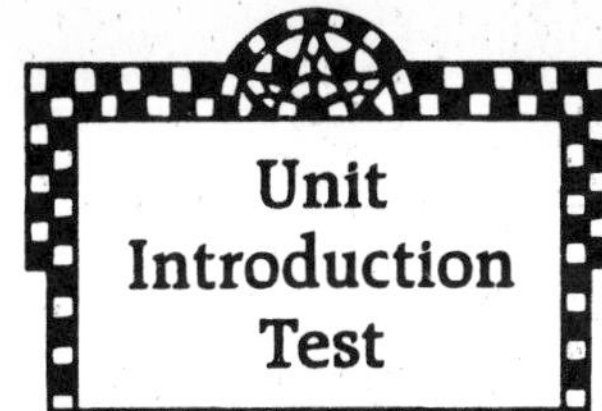

UNIT 4: GREEK AND ROMAN LITERATURES

(Textbook pages 214–223)

INTRODUCTION/Greek Literature

Directions: In the space provided, write the letter of the best answer to each question. *(10 points each)*

1. The achievements of the ancient Greeks grew largely from their love of
   a. pleasure
   b. emotions
   c. knowledge
   d. warfare
   1. ______

2. Greek civilization began in
   a. Athens
   b. Crete
   c. Troy
   d. Sparta
   2. ______

3. A significant invention of the Epic Age was
   a. the alphabet
   b. the wheel
   c. athletic contests
   d. the calendar
   3. ______

4. Athens was the first city-state to
   a. require physical training for all boys and girls
   b. establish a democratic government
   c. record its war victories
   d. be controlled by a dictator
   4. ______

5. According to Greek religion,
   a. the gods controlled humans like puppets
   b. the gods existed on high mountains
   c. the gods were not very powerful
   d. a person controlled his or her own fate
   5. ______

6. The Athenian stage produced great Greek dramas of which type(s)?
   a. romance
   b. tragedy and comedy
   c. history
   d. mystery
   6. ______

(continued)

7. Who is considered to be the first Western historian?
   a. Herodotus
   b. Pericles
   c. Plato
   d. Socrates

7. ______

8. The Golden Age of Athens fostered
   a. the rise of Greek drama
   b. historical writings
   c. both of the above
   d. none of the above

8. ______

9. The Greek word for "philosopher" literally means
   a. critic
   b. great leader
   c. lover of wisdom
   d. smart

9. ______

10. After the decline of Athens, Greek culture and knowledge
    a. became extinct
    b. had limited impact on history
    c. was outlawed by the Romans
    d. was spread to the West by Alexander the Great and the Romans

10. ______

NAME ______________________ CLASS ________________ DATE ________ SCORE ______

from the ILIAD, *from* BOOK 1

Homer

translated by Robert Fitzgerald

(Textbook page 229)

DEVELOPING VOCABULARY

Directions: Read carefully the explanation of each word. Then write a sentence of your own using that word. In your sentence, include clues to the word's meaning.

revere (ri·vēr′) ***v.*** To have great respect and love for. ▶ The title *Reverend,* which designates members of the clergy, derives from this word. ▪ Because Jason was taught from an early age to revere his grandparents, he never failed to write or call them regularly. **Page 230**

ORIGINAL SENTENCE ____

____

assent (ə·sent′) ***v.*** To agree. ▶ Do not confuse this word with *assert,* which means "to declare firmly." ▪ The club members voted to assent to the president's proposal, and they passed it immediately. **Page 230**

ORIGINAL SENTENCE ____

____

formidable (fôr′·mə·də·bəl) ***adj.*** Producing fear or horror. ▶ A secondary definition of this word means "awe-inspiring." ▪ The runner barely made it up the formidable hill near the end of the race. **Page 232**

ORIGINAL SENTENCE ____

____

faction (fak′shən) ***n.*** A split within an organization or country; internal conflict. ▶ President Lincoln used this word to describe the Civil War. ▪ Faction within European soccer leagues is so intense that fights often break out. **Page 235**

ORIGINAL SENTENCE ____

____

(continued)

execration (ek′si·krā′shən) ***n.*** The act of cursing or speaking abusively of a person or thing. ▶ An early use of this word meant "a curse." ▪ Mr. Gardner's execration of his political opponent was so intense that TV stations would not carry his remarks. **Page 237**

ORIGINAL SENTENCE ______________________________

renounce (ri·nouns′) ***v.*** To purposefully give up a claim, right, way of living, and so forth; repudiate or disown. ▶ This word derives from the Latin word meaning "to protest against." ▪ At the press conference, the mayor renounced her membership in the controversial country club. **Page 238**

ORIGINAL SENTENCE ______________________________

prowess (prou′is) ***n.*** Bravery; courage. ▶ This word derives from the Old French word meaning "gallant or brave." ▪ The rescue workers demonstrated great prowess in saving victims of the disaster. **Page 239**

ORIGINAL SENTENCE ______________________________

relent (ri·lent′) ***v.*** To yield. ▶ The prefix *re–* here means "again," and the base word derives from the Latin word for "bend." ▪ Only after hours of persuasion did Mr. Martinez relent and let his daughter join the rock band. **Page 239**

ORIGINAL SENTENCE ______________________________

loath (lōth, lō͟th) ***adj.*** Reluctant. ▶ This word is usually followed by an infinitive. ▪ She was so loath to study the chart of chemical symbols that she put it off until the last minute. **Page 241**

ORIGINAL SENTENCE ______________________________

appease (ə·pēz′) ***v.*** To pacify or quiet by giving what is demanded. ▶ The root word here comes from the Old French for "peace," and the prefix *a–* means "to." ▪ To appease her mother, Eleanor came home early. **Page 243**

ORIGINAL SENTENCE ______________________________

NAME ______________________ CLASS ________________ DATE ________ SCORE ______

from the ILIAD, *from* BOOK 1

Homer
translated by Robert Fitzgerald (Textbook page 229)

VOCABULARY TEST

Directions: In the space provided, write the letter of the word or phrase closest in meaning to the word in italics. *(10 points each)*

1. *appease:* a. to annoy b. to pacify or quiet c. to speak quietly d. using good manners 1. ______
2. *assent:* a. to agree b. to fight c. to complain d. to avoid 2. ______
3. *renounce:* a. to introduce b. to join c. to give up a claim to or association with d. to show support 3. ______
4. *faction:* a. division of a whole number b. a piece of trivia c. internal conflict in a group d. a war hero 4. ______
5. *loath:* a. reluctant b. enthusiastic c. lazy d. brave 5. ______
6. *formidable:* a. big in size b. producing fear or horror c. sneaky d. having athletic talent 6. ______
7. *execration:* a. recommendation b. exile c. military maneuver d. speaking abusively of a person or thing 7. ______
8. *revere:* a. to hold in contempt b. to move backward c. to love or respect d. to study or inspect 8. ______
9. *prowess:* a. bravery or courage b. sword fight c. thief d. secretive 9. ______
10. *relent:* a. to save b. to promise c. to borrow d. to yield 10. ______

NAME ______________ CLASS ______________ DATE ________ SCORE ______

from the ILIAD, *from* BOOK 1

Homer

translated by Robert Fitzgerald

(Textbook page 229)

REVIEWING THE SELECTION

1. Who are Agamemnon and Achilles?

____

____

2. Why is Book 1 titled "The Quarrel"?

____

____

3. Why does Achilles hand Briseis over to Agamemnon's men?

____

____

4. For what does Achilles ask his mother, Thetis, to pray to Zeus?
   a. for Zeus to take the side of the Trojans, bringing defeat to Agamemnon
   b. for Zeus to send a lightning bolt down on Agamemnon
   c. for Zeus to mediate in a debate between Agamemnon and Achilles

Reader's Response

The selection does not mention Briseis' feelings when Agamemnon's men come for her. How do you imagine she feels about being first abducted from her home, then being passed from Achilles to Agamemnon? Write two or three sentences explaining your answer.

____

____

____

____

____

NAME ______________________ CLASS ______________________ DATE __________ SCORE __________

from the ILIAD, *from* BOOK 1

Homer

translated by Robert Fitzgerald

(Textbook page 229)

READING COMPREHENSION

Directions: In the space provided, write the letter of the best answer to each question. *(10 points each)*

1. Book 1 follows the conventions of Homer's epics when it
   a. begins with a quarrel
   b. begins in the middle of the action
   c. leaves out parts
   d. deals with historical fact

   1. ______

2. The quarrel that opens Book 1 is between
   a. Zeus and Apollo
   b. Agamemnon and Achilles
   c. Chryses and his daughter, Chryseis
   d. Athena and Hera

   2. ______

3. Chryses begs Agamemnon and Achilles to
   a. stop fighting
   b. keep fighting
   c. release his daughter
   d. sail back to Argos

   3. ______

4. Chryses is a
   a. military leader
   b. king
   c. soldier
   d. priest

   4. ______

5. All the men agree to Chryses' request except
   a. Agamemnon
   b. Achilles
   c. Apollo
   d. Calchas

   5. ______

6. To punish the Greeks, Apollo sends
   a. a fierce wind that destroys their ships
   b. lightning
   c. a huge fire
   d. a terrible plague

   6. ______

(continued)

7. What does Apollo want the Greeks to do?
   a. pray for forgiveness
   b. return Chryses' daughter without ransom
   c. surrender
   d. sail for home

   7. ______

8. Agamemnon agrees to Apollo's request on the condition that
   a. Agamemnon can replace the girl Chryseis with another of his choosing
   b. Achilles take over the army
   c. the gods promise them a safe journey home
   d. Chryses give them his blessing

   8. ______

9. Achilles is talked out of killing Agamemnon by
   a. Apollo
   b. the army
   c. Athena
   d. Agamemnon

   9. ______

10. What does Achilles lose to Agamemnon?
    a. his prize, the girl Briseis
    b. his fighting ships
    c. his army
    d. his children

    10. ______

NAME ______________ CLASS ______________ DATE ________ SCORE ________

from the ILIAD, *from* BOOKS 22 *and* 24

Homer

translated by Robert Fitzgerald

(Textbook page 246)

DEVELOPING VOCABULARY

Directions: Read carefully the explanation of each word. Then write a sentence of your own using that word. In your sentence, include clues to the word's meaning.

resolute (rez'ə·lo͞ot) ***adj.*** Having a decided purpose; determined. ▶ The noun form of this word is *resolution,* which means "the state of being resolute." ■ "I am resolute about sticking to my exercise plan," Bianca declared. **Page 248**

ORIGINAL SENTENCE ____

____

bereave (bē·rēv') ***v.*** To deprive of something or someone. ▶ The past participle of this verb is *bereft.* ■ The careless driver was about to bereave the family of their only child, but he managed to get control of the car in time. **Page 248**

ORIGINAL SENTENCE ____

____

implacable (im·plā'kə·bəl, -plak'-) ***adj.*** Not capable of being pacified or quieted. ▶ The prefix *im–* here means "not." ■ The baby in the stroller was implacable; he would not stop crying. **Page 251**

ORIGINAL SENTENCE ____

____

ponderous (pän'dər·əs) ***adj.*** Heavy or massive. ▶ The Latin root for this word means "weight." ■ The huge stack of lumber was a ponderous load for the carpenter to carry. **Page 257**

ORIGINAL SENTENCE ____

____

defile (dē·fīl') ***v.*** To profane; show disrespect or contempt. ▶ The prefix *de–* here means "down," and the Latin root means "to trample." ■ Vandals defiled the public buildings with their graffiti. **Page 260**

ORIGINAL SENTENCE ____

____

(continued)

felicity (fə·lis'i·tē) ***n.*** Joy; gladness. ▶ The plural form of this word is *felicities.* ▪ Their wedding day held nothing but great felicity. **Page 267**

ORIGINAL SENTENCE ______________________________

____

flout *v.* To scoff or jeer at; scorn. ▶ Do not confuse this word with *flaunt,* which means "to show off." ▪ "Why do you always have to flout the rules and get into trouble?" the lifeguard asked. **Page 269**

ORIGINAL SENTENCE ______________________________

____

deft *adj.* Skillful and quick. —*deftly,* **adv.** ▶ The original meaning of this word was "gentle or meek." ▪ Her deft jumps and spins helped figure skater Kristi Yamaguchi win an Olympic gold medal. **Page 271**

ORIGINAL SENTENCE ______________________________

____

allay (a·lā') ***v.*** To relieve (fears, for example); pacify; calm. ▶ A synonym for this word is *relieve.* ▪ The child's teddy bear helped to allay his fears of the dark room. **Page 272**

ORIGINAL SENTENCE ______________________________

____

shroud *v.* 1. To wrap a corpse in burial cloth. 2. To hide or conceal. ▶ This word is also a noun, meaning "a burial cloth." ▪ The heavy fog was about to shroud the highway completely, making driving extremely dangerous. **Page 276**

ORIGINAL SENTENCE ______________________________

____

NAME ______________ CLASS ______________ DATE ________ SCORE ________

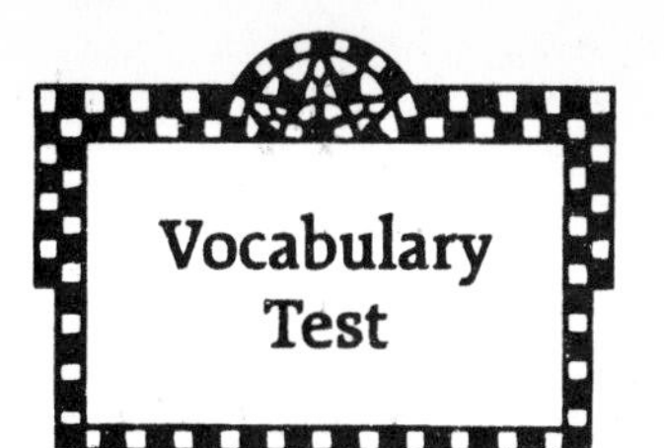

from the ILIAD, *from* BOOKS 22 *and* 24

Homer

translated by Robert Fitzgerald

(Textbook page 246)

VOCABULARY TEST

Directions: Complete the following paragraph by circling the correct word in the pair. *(10 points each)*

Detective Minsky looked at the (ponderous/resolute) stack of citizens' complaints on her desk with distaste. She knew that most of them referred to the recent wave of mischief at the cemetery. A band of revelers had (flouted/allayed) authority, jumped the fence, and left the debris of their party behind, (shrouding/defiling) the graves tended to lovingly by (allayed/bereaved) family members. Yesterday Detective Minsky had been able to (defile/allay) one citizen's fear that the police would not push to end the disturbances. But the anger of another gentleman had been (implacable/deft). (Bereaved/Resolute) in her determination to end the mystery, Detective Minsky turned to the clues gathered at the scene of the mischief. She felt assured that her (deft/defiled) reasoning abilities would soon point her in the direction of the guilty parties—and nothing would be a source of greater (felicity/flout) than this. Detective Minsky worked for a few more hours, then left for the crime scene in search of more clues. She was confident that, (allayed/shrouded) by the cloak of night, she would be inconspicuous.

NAME ______________________ CLASS __________________ DATE ________ SCORE ______

from the ILIAD, *from* BOOKS 22 *and* 24

Homer

translated by Robert Fitzgerald (Textbook page 246)

REVIEWING THE SELECTION

1. The father and mother of Hector, the Trojan hero, beg him to come inside the town to safety. Why does Hector refuse?

   ____

   ____

2. Alone, Achilles charges toward Hector, who stands outside the walls of Troy. What occurs next?
   a. Athena helps Achilles to kill Hector.
   b. Hector thinks his favorite brother has come to help him.
   c. Achilles runs from Hector's deadly spear.

3. Hector asks that his body be returned to the Trojans for a proper funeral. How does Achilles respond?

   ____

   ____

4. Draw a line from each name to the correct phrase.

a. Priam	is eventually buried by the Greeks with proper rites.
b. Patroclus	helps Hector's father to enter the Greek camp.
c. Hermes	weeps with Hector's father.
d. Achilles	pleads on his knees for the return of Hector's body.

Reader's Response

Homer begins the *Iliad* by calling it a song of ruinous anger. Think about an experience that you have had with "ruinous anger," either one you have experienced personally or one in history or politics that you have learned about through reading or through TV or the movies. What was the event, and what were its results? Write several sentences explaining your answer.

____

____

____

NAME ______________________ CLASS ______________________ DATE __________ SCORE __________

from the ILIAD, BOOKS 22 and 24

Homer

translated by Robert Fitzgerald (Textbook page 246)

READING COMPREHENSION

Directions: In the space provided, write the letter of the best answer to each question. *(10 points each)*

1. Where is Hector when the Trojans retreat behind the city walls?
   a. in the main Trojan camp
   b. beside the city
   c. in his house
   d. outside the city walls 1. ______

2. Who is chasing Hector?
   a. Apollo
   b. Achilles
   c. Priam
   d. Patroclus 2. ______

3. Achilles delivers the fatal blow to Hector's
   a. heart
   b. face
   c. throat
   d. back 3. ______

4. What is Hector's dying plea to Achilles?
   a. to let Hector's parents have his body
   b. to kill him quickly
   c. to return his body to the ships
   d. to end the war 4. ______

5. It is especially important that Priam be allowed to bury his son Hector because
   a. Hector was Priam's only son, and he deserves a great funeral
   b. Achilles' friend Patroclus requests Hector's funeral
   c. the Greeks will elect a new leader if Agamemnon does not bury Hector
   d. the soul of a dead Greek or Trojan will not find rest if the body is not given burial 5. ______

6. Achilles at first refuses to bury Hector because
   a. Hector betrayed him
   b. Hector killed Achilles' great friend Patroclus
   c. it was Hector who stole Helen and began the Trojan War
   d. Achilles is simply a bad sport 6. ______

(continued)

7. After Achilles kills Hector, he
   a. cuts off his head
   b. drags him three times around the walls of Troy
   c. gives him back to Hector's wife
   d. burns him in a boiling vat of oil

   7.______

8. Hecuba is
   a. Agamemnon's wife
   b. Priam's wife
   c. Hector's wife
   d. Achilles' wife

   8.______

9. When Priam appeals to Achilles for his son Hector's body, Achilles
   a. has him thrown out of camp
   b. has him killed
   c. has him taken prisoner
   d. takes pity on him

   9.______

10. A character flaw of Achilles is his
   a. strength
   b. weakness in battle
   c. anger and rage
   d. misjudgment of his opponents in battle

   10.______

NAME ______________________ CLASS ______________________ DATE __________ SCORE __________

from the ILIAD

Homer

translated by Robert Fitzgerald

(Textbook page 229)

TRANSITIONAL EXPRESSIONS

Transitional expressions are words and phrases that connect ideas and show the relationships between them. Different types of transitional expressions show different relationships.

1. Transitions linking related or similar ideas:

also	for example	likewise
and	for instance	moreover
another	further, furthermore	of course
besides	in a like manner	similarly
equally important	in the same fashion	too

EXAMPLE Homer tells how the gods and goddesses sometimes cause problems for humans. *For example*, the Greek goddess of Discord was responsible for the Trojan War.

2. Transitions showing dissimilar or contradictory ideas:

although	even if	on the contrary
and yet	however	otherwise
as if	in spite of	provided that
but	instead	still
conversely	nevertheless	yet

EXAMPLE The gods tended to meddle in human affairs; the war might not have started, *however*, if young Prince Paris of Troy had not been so willing to be bribed.

3. Transitions showing a cause-and-effect relationship:

as	for this reason	so
as a result	hence	then
because	if	therefore
consequently	if . . . then	thus
for	since	

EXAMPLE *Because* Aphrodite promised Paris the most beautiful woman in the world, Paris awarded Aphrodite the golden apple.

4. Transitions signaling a summary or conclusion:

as a result	in fact	in summary
in any event	in other words	on the whole
in conclusion	in short	to sum up

EXAMPLE Paris kidnapped Helen, who was the world's most beautiful woman. *As a result* of his action, the Greeks sailed to Troy to retrieve her, and the Trojan War began.

(continued)

Exercise 1. Identifying Transitional Expressions

Underline the transitional expressions (words or phrases) in the following sentences. The sentences are based on details in Homer's *Iliad.* (Some sentences may have more than one transitional expression.)

1. Although Achilles and Agamemnon are fighting the Trojans together, they still end up in a terrible argument.
2. Agamemnon, commander of the Greek forces, takes Chryseis, the daughter of the Trojan priest Chryses, for his own, and that action leads to the quarrel.
3. Chryses wants his daughter back, so he begs the Greeks to take his ransom.
4. In spite of the agreement of the whole army, Agamemnon will not return Chryseis, so the gods take action.
5. Since the gods take pity on Chryses, they send a plague on the Greek army.
6. The plague kills the Greeks' pack animals and dogs; moreover, it kills many soldiers, too.
7. As a result, Achilles suggests that they ask a priest how they have angered the gods.
8. Calchas agrees to give the answer provided that Achilles promises to protect him.
9. Of course, Achilles promises to protect Calchas.
10. Furthermore, he promises specifically to protect him from Agamemnon.

Exercise 2. Writing with Transitional Expressions

Think how the ideas in each of the following sets of sentences about Homer's *Iliad* are related to each other. Then use transitions to combine each set of sentences into one logical sentence. Use a variety of transitions in your sentences. Change words as needed to make the combinations. (There is more than one way to combine each set of sentences.)

EXAMPLE Homer's poem includes epic conventions.
It is important to know what these conventions are.

Because Homer's poem includes epic conventions,
it is important to know what these conventions are.

1. The invocation that begins the poem is a formal plea to the Muse for help. The invocation states the poem's theme.

____

____

2. Homer uses *in medias res.* The poem starts in the middle of the action.

____

____

(continued)

3. *In medias res* means the reader might not know what happened previously. Homer uses flashbacks to show previous actions.

____

____

4. There were poets before Homer who created poems in the oral traditions. Homer is among the first poets whose work was recorded in writing.

____

____

5. Certain features of Homer's epic poems were widely imitated. Virgil used these features in the *Aeneid.* John Milton used these features in *Paradise Lost.*

____

____

Exercise 3. Revising a Paragraph

Revise the following paragraph by using transitions to show relationships between ideas. Add, delete, or change words and combine sentences as needed. One way to clarify the relationship among the first three sentences is shown as an example. (Hint: Not every line needs changing.)

Because, and

The *Iliad* is an extremely long poem. was recited orally. It was probably difficult to maintain the poem's metrical structure. Homer uses devices such as the *stock epithet.* The stock epithet is a word or phrase that is repeatedly used to describe a character. Hector, the Trojan hero, is referred to as "tamer of horses." Zeus, the father-god, is sometimes "Father of the blinding bolt." Each character has more than one stock epithet. Homer probably chose the epithet according to the context. He chose it according to his metrical needs. The stock epithet had other uses. It reminded the audience of a character's traits. It helped them follow the action. It may have lessened demands on Homer's memory. The epithets were drawn from a memory pool and not created each time.

NAME ______________________ CLASS ______________________ DATE __________ SCORE ________

LYRIC POEMS

Sappho

translated by Mary Barnard

(Textbook page 281)

REVIEWING THE SELECTIONS

1. In "You Are the Herdsman of Evening," Sappho finds a quiet beauty in the way many things scatter during the day and then return again at evening. List three things that the evening star, Hesperus, "herds homeward."

   a. ______________________ b. ______________________ c. ______________________

2. "Sleep, Darling" and "We Drink Your Health" both describe people who are loved by others.

   a. Who is the loved one described as a "golden flower" in "Sleep, Darling"? ______________

   b. Who is the loved one whose soft eyes are likened to honey in "We Drink Your Health"?

   ____

3. Draw a line to match each character in the first column with the best description in the second column.

a. The speaker in "To an Army Wife, in Sardis"	was dark-haired and wore an embroidered headband.
b. Someone in bed alone	says that whatever one loves is the best sight on earth.
c. The speaker in "Don't Ask Me What to Wear"	watches the moon and stars set and feels time passing.

4. What color is Cleis's hair? What does the speaker think Cleis should wear in her hair?

   ____

Reader's Response

In Sappho's poem "You May Forget But," the speaker says that someone in the future will "think of us." Which events that you have participated in this year would you most like to be remembered for? Fill out a chart like the one below.

Event	Your Role	Reason You Hope It's Remembered
1.		
2.		
3.		

NAME ______________________ CLASS ______________ DATE ________ SCORE ______

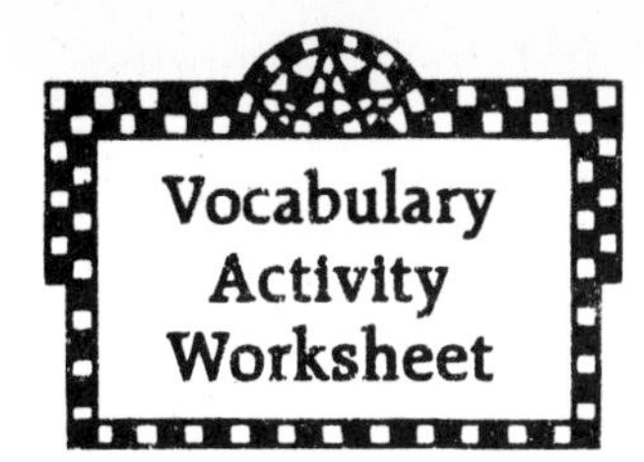

FUNERAL SPEECH OF PERICLES *from* HISTORY OF THE PELOPONNESIAN WAR

Thucydides

translated by Benjamin Jowett (Textbook page 286)

DEVELOPING VOCABULARY

Directions: Read carefully the explanation of each word. Then write a sentence of your own using that word. In your sentence, include clues to the word's meaning.

obscurity (əb·skyoor'ə·tē) ***n.*** Inconspicuousness; lack of fame. ▶ A Latin word that means "to conceal" is the source of *obscurity.* ▪ Despite years of fame and riches, the movie star died in obscurity. **Page 287**

ORIGINAL SENTENCE ______________________________

____

reprobation (rep'rə·bā'shən) ***n.*** Disapproval, condemnation; rejection. ▶ This is a very strong word, signifying emphatic rejection or condemnation. ▪ The judge's loud reprobation of the prisoner's disrespectful attitude was heard throughout the courthouse. **Page 287**

ORIGINAL SENTENCE ______________________________

____

adversary (ad'vər·ser'ē) ***n.*** An opponent; enemy. ▶ The *Adversary* is a title sometimes used in literature to refer to the devil. ▪ The cross-town high school was the football team's biggest adversary. **Page 287**

ORIGINAL SENTENCE ______________________________

____

impediment (im·ped'ə·mənt) ***n.*** Hindrance. ▶ The verb form is *impede,* which means "to hinder." ▪ Terra's new boots proved to be an impediment on the hike as they pinched her feet. **Page 288**

ORIGINAL SENTENCE ______________________________

____

(continued)

requite (ri·kwīt′) ***v.*** To repay or reward. ▶ The root word *quite* means "to pay." ▪ Morgan wanted to requite the favor so that she wouldn't feel indebted to her friend. **Page 288**

ORIGINAL SENTENCE ______________________________

____

sepulcher (sep′əl·kər) ***n.*** A vault, chamber, or grave for the dead. ▶ This word derives from a Latin word meaning "to bury." ▪ The bereaved widow visited her dead husband's sepulcher every day. **Page 290**

ORIGINAL SENTENCE ______________________________

____

commiserate (kə·miz′ər·āt) ***v.*** To feel pity or sympathy for. ▶ This verb is often used with the word *over* or *with.* ▪ She was able to commiserate with her friend's grief because she had suffered the same loss. **Page 291**

ORIGINAL SENTENCE ______________________________

____

vicissitude (vi·sis′ə·tood′) ***n.*** Unpredictable and irregular change in fortune, life, and so on; ups and downs. ▶ This word is usually used in its plural form, *vicissitudes.* ▪ The vicissitudes of the stock market cause some people to earn and then lose large sums of money. **Page 291**

ORIGINAL SENTENCE ______________________________

____

emulate (em′yoo·lāt′) ***v.*** To imitate in order to equal or surpass. ▶ A synonym for this word is "rival." ▪ Santiago's success at painting looked so easy, but David found it hard to emulate. **Page 291**

ORIGINAL SENTENCE ______________________________

____

arduous (är′joo·əs) ***adj.*** That which requires great care or effort. ▶ The Latin word on which this word is based also means "steep" or "high." ▪ He found the workout so arduous that he could barely walk afterwards. **Page 291**

ORIGINAL SENTENCE ______________________________

____

NAME ____________ CLASS ____________ DATE ________ SCORE ________

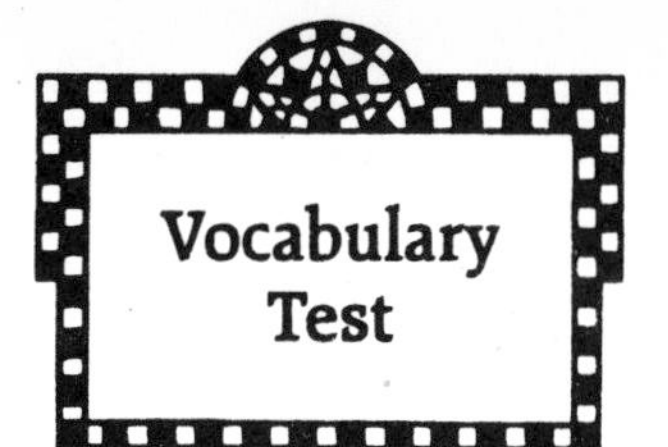

FUNERAL SPEECH OF PERICLES *from* HISTORY OF THE PELOPONNESIAN WAR

Thucydides

translated by Benjamin Jowett (Textbook page 286)

VOCABULARY TEST

Directions: Match each word in column I with the correct definition in column II. Place the letter of the definition you choose in the space provided. *(10 points each)*

I	II
______ 1. commiserate	a. requiring great care or effort
______ 2. sepulcher	b. disapproval
______ 3. impediment	c. a vault, chamber, or grave
______ 4. adversary	d. an opponent
______ 5. obscurity	e. to repay or reward
______ 6. requite	f. lack of fame
______ 7. vicissitude	g. to feel pity for
______ 8. arduous	h. to imitate
______ 9. emulate	i. unpredictable change in fortune
______ 10. reprobation	j. hindrance

NAME ______________________ CLASS ____________________ DATE __________ SCORE ________

FUNERAL SPEECH OF PERICLES *from* HISTORY OF THE PELOPONNESIAN WAR

Thucydides

translated by Benjamin Jowett (Textbook page 286)

REVIEWING THE SELECTION

1. Pericles speaks at a ceremony held to honor fallen members of Athens' armed services. List two reasons he says the ceremony would be better without speeches.

   a. ____

   b. ____

2. Pericles begins by praising Athens. Circle the adjectives that best apply to the people of Athens, as Pericles describes them.

democratic	exclusive	suspicious	adaptable	respectful
cheerful	tolerant	tricky	courageous	simple

3. According to Pericles, the heroes who died were fighting because they could not bear the thought that ____.

4. Pericles says that the fallen heroes were afraid not of death but of ______________________, and that their memorials are engraved not on stone but in ______________________________

Reader's Response

Write a sentence explaining which of Pericles' words to the families of the fallen heroes might, in your opinion, have offered most (or least) comfort to them. Then write a second sentence explaining why you think as you do.

1. ____

   ____

2. ____

   ____

NAME ______________________ CLASS ______________ DATE ________ SCORE ______

FUNERAL SPEECH OF PERICLES *from* HISTORY OF THE PELOPONNESIAN WAR

Thucydides

translated by Benjamin Jowett (Textbook page 286)

REPETITION AND WORDINESS

Good writers love words, but they are careful not to waste them. They know unnecessary words only make their writing seem dull or lifeless. Revise repetitious and wordy sentences by eliminating or replacing unnecessary words.

WORDY She kept looking at her reflection in the mirror and wondering who she really was as a person.

REVISED She saw herself in the mirror and wondered who she was.

WORDY He was hopeful that it would not be too long before he would be able to find some employment.

REVISED He hoped he would soon find a job.

Everyday expressions like the following ones are repetitive. Learn to replace them with simpler words or phrases.

Expression	Replacement
advance forward	advance
at that point in time	then
at this point in time	now
call your attention to the fact that	remind you
owing to the fact that	since/because
past history	history/the past
the fact that he or she did not succeed	his or her failure
the question as to whether	whether
and the reason why is that	because
there is no doubt but that	no doubt/doubtless

Exercise 1. Identifying Repetition and Wordiness

Details about Athens in the following sentences are based on the *Funeral Speech of Pericles.* In each sentence, underline words that should be omitted because they add nothing to content or meaning.

EXAMPLE Athens is a city whose citizens should be proud of its heritage.

1. Athens does not copy its neighbors, but is an example to them in the various and different areas of government, military, and daily life.

2. The form of government used by the people in Athens is democracy.

(continued)

3. The military training by which the city trains its soldiers in Athens is excellent.
4. The Athenians enjoy relaxing from their work and the jobs they do all day long.
5. Athens is very proud of its military and soldiers and fighting ships that protect the city.
6. The Athenian people are very brave and have great courage in battle.
7. All in all, considering the entire picture, the people of Athens pride themselves on thinking before they act.
8. Pericles praises the attitude, and bravery, and courage of the men who died fighting for the city of Athens.
9. Pericles comforts the parents of the dead soldiers who died on the battlefield while fighting for Athens by reminding them of the honor of a soldier's death.
10. Pericles emphasizes and focuses his speech on the rewards of virtue that the people of Athens should seek.

Exercise 2. Correcting Repetition and Wordiness

Each of the following sentences about the *Funeral Speech of Pericles* is wordy and/or repetitious. On the blanks provided, rewrite each of the sentences, correcting the problem by removing unnecessary words. You may also change or move words and phrases.

EXAMPLE The occasion at which Pericles gave his funeral speech was the annual public funeral held once a year for the soldiers who had died while fighting for Athens in a war.

Pericles gave his speech for the annual public funeral for the Athenian war dead.

1. Pericles begins his speech by telling his listeners how difficult and hard his job as a speaker who must present a funeral speech really is.

____

____

2. At that point in time, Pericles goes on to explain to the people listening to his speech that it is hard to satisfy the families of the dead with words and phrases that fairly and accurately describe and tell to their families' satisfaction the virtues of the soldiers who have died.

____

____

3. Pericles decides in his speech that the first thing to do is to pay a tribute and praise Athens' ancestors because it makes sense to do that first in a funeral oration.

____

____

(continued)

4. Continuing on with the same idea, Pericles goes on to explain that it makes sense to praise first the ancestors due to the fact that their hard work and sacrifices and dedication made the city of Athens a really strong and great city.

____

____

5. So all in all, the speech of Pericles that he gives to give honor to the soldiers who died while fighting for the city of Athens really spends a great deal of time praising and giving honor to the work and deeds of the ancestors who came before the soldiers.

____

____

Exercise 3. Revising a Paragraph

The following paragraph explains why Thucydides presents history through the speeches of famous men such as Pericles. Revise the paragraph by crossing out or replacing unnecessary words and phrases. You may change words, move words around, and combine sentences that belong together. The first two sentences have been revised for you as an example.

Thucydides was a great historian who wrote about ~~the history and what happened in~~ Athens. One way that he presented the history of Athens that he was writing was through the famous and well-known speeches of famous people. The speeches that these famous people gave show the attitudes and values and ideas of the people they are addressing in the speech they are giving. For example, the funeral speech given by Pericles is very patriotic and supportive in a positive way about the city of Athens. Thucydides believed, which was really right, that Pericles's speech really represented the viewpoint of the people of the city of Athens. By writing history through the famous speeches of these well-known people and figures, Thucydides was able to show the values and attitudes of the people as well as the events that were taking place.

NAME ______________________ CLASS ____________________ DATE ________ SCORE ______

FUNERAL SPEECH OF PERICLES *from* HISTORY OF THE PELOPONNESIAN WAR

Thucydides

translated by Benjamin Jowett (Textbook page 286)

READING COMPREHENSION

Directions: In the space provided, write the letter of the best answer to each question. *(10 points each)*

1. Why did Thucydides include a speech by Pericles as part of this history of the Peloponnesian War?
   a. Ancient historians often gave speeches to teach moral lessons.
   b. Pericles' speech embodies the views of patriotic Athens.
   c. both of the above
   d. none of the above 1. ______

2. Whom does the funeral oration honor?
   a. Pericles
   b. Thucydides
   c. Athenian soldiers who died in battle
   d. Athenian poets 2. ______

3. Why does Pericles first praise Athens' ancestors?
   a. Their valor helped make Athens great.
   b. They started the war.
   c. They ended the war.
   d. It was traditional to start a speech that way. 3. ______

4. How does Pericles describe Athenian government?
   a. as a copy of Sparta's government
   b. as an example to their neighbors
   c. as one governed by a few in power
   d. as a dictatorship 4. ______

5. Which characteristic best describes Athenians?
   a. They have little respect for authority.
   b. They work hard but enjoy relaxing.
   c. They act before thinking.
   d. They take no interest in public affairs. 5. ______

(continued)

6. How does Pericles describe the military training of Athens?
   a. as a harsh physical program
   b. as a program that needs improving
   c. as a program that relies on law to enlist soldiers
   d. as a program that relies on the natural honor of its citizens — 6.______

7. Which topic does Pericles discuss in describing Athens and its citizens?
   a. the attitude toward wealth
   b. the bravery of the people
   c. the beauty of the landscape
   d. the love of knowledge — 7.______

8. Why does Pericles dwell on the greatness of Athens?
   a. to convince Athens' enemies
   b. to prove the greatness of those who died for the city
   c. to win support for the election
   d. to show his love for the city — 8.______

9. What was the general attitudes of those soldiers who died for Athens?
   a. They did not seek death, but resolved to show bravery in the noble cause of fighting.
   b. They did not even consider the possibility of death.
   c. They were eager to die for Athens.
   d. They were terrified to die and resisted fighting. — 9.______

10. What advice does Pericles give to the parents of the dead?
    a. to take comfort in the glory of the noble deaths
    b. to ask the Athenian government for payments for their losses
    c. to protest against more wars
    d. to hate the enemies who killed their sons — 10.______

NAME ______________________ CLASS ______________________ DATE __________ SCORE ________

from the APOLOGY

Plato

translated by Benjamin Jowett

(Textbook page 295)

DEVELOPING VOCABULARY

Directions: Read carefully the explanation of each word. Then write a sentence of your own using that word. In your sentence, include clues to the word's meaning.

procure (prō·kyo͞or′) ***v.*** To obtain or make happen by an effort; secure. ▶ The root word comes from the Latin for "care." ▪ After searching the woods for hours, the botanist was finally able to procure the rare plant specimen. **Page 296**

ORIGINAL SENTENCE ____

____

acquit (ə·kwit′) ***v.*** To clear someone of a charge or accusation. —**acquittal** ***n.*** ▶ This word derives from the Latin, meaning "to set free." ▪ It took only an hour for the jury to acquit the innocent woman of all charges. **Page 296**

ORIGINAL SENTENCE ____

____

censure (sen′shər) ***v.*** To condemn severely. ▶ A person who censures may be known as a *censor.* ▪ The ethics committee voted to censure the representative for misusing campaign funds. **Page 296**

ORIGINAL SENTENCE ____

____

intimation (in′tə·mā′shən) ***n.*** A hint; subtle implication. ▶ The verb form is *intimate,* which means "to hint or imply subtly." It is pronounced in′tə-māt. ▪ The smirk on his face gave me an intimation that he was joking. **Page 297**

ORIGINAL SENTENCE ____

____

reprove (ri·pro͞ov′) ***v.*** To scold or censure. ▶ This word derives from the Latin root *probare,* meaning "to test or prove." ▪ Jared's father often had to reprove his son for his bad manners. **Page 299**

ORIGINAL SENTENCE ____

____

NAME ______________ CLASS ______________ DATE ________ SCORE ______

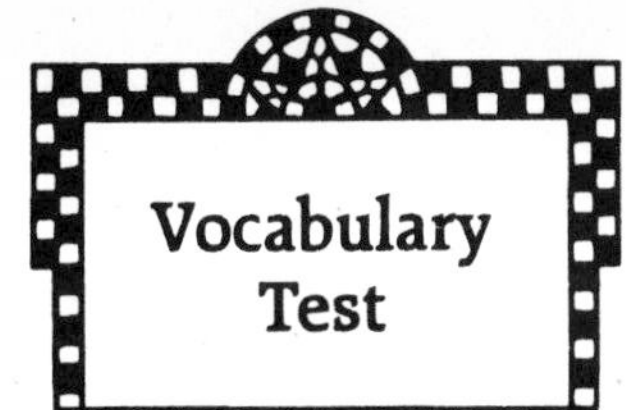

from the APOLOGY

Plato

translated by Benjamin Jowett

(Textbook page 295)

VOCABULARY TEST

A. In the space provided, write the letter of the word or phrase closest in meaning to the word in italics. *(10 points each)*

1. *acquit:* a. to stop suddenly b. to clear a person of wrongdoing c. to criticize d. to tell a lie 1.______

2. *censure:* a. to condemn severely b. to count c. to plead d. to concentrate 2.______

3. *intimation:* a. affection b. criticism c. an original creation d. a hint 3.______

4. *procure:* a. to make happen by effort b. to steal c. to lay blame upon d. to show support 4.______

5. *reprove:* a. to show proof again b. to go back on a promise c. to scold or express disapproval d. to deceive 5.______

B. From the words listed below, choose the word that best completes the sentence. Write the word. *(10 points each)*

censure procure acquit reprove intimation

6. In all the sifting and searching of evidence, the detective found not even a(n) ______________ of a clue.

7. Dismayed by the rowdy behavior of the courtroom spectators, the judge had to ______________ them.

8. After much research, the attorney was able to ______________ the information necessary for the trial to continue.

9. With the evidence that now showed a clear motive, she knew that there was no chance a jury would ______________ the suspect.

10. When it became clear that the witness was lying about his whereabouts, the judge did not hesitate to ______________ him.

NAME ______________________ CLASS ________________ DATE ________ SCORE ______

from the APOLOGY

Plato
translated by Benjamin Jowett (Textbook page 295)

REVIEWING THE SELECTION

1. Socrates says that he decided at the outset not to plead for his life. Circle the letter of the sentence that best explains the reason he gives.
   a. He knows that his death will show his opponents that they are wrong.
   b. He does not want to compromise his principles just to avoid danger.
   c. He is old and tired, and he feels ready to die.

2. Socrates thinks that death is a good thing because his (internal oracle / guilty conscience), which always has let him know when he is making a mistake, does not oppose him now. (Underline the correct phrase.)

3. An advantage of death, Socrates says, is that in the afterlife he will be able to
   a. talk to the great figures of history
   b. reunite with his wife
   c. become reincarnated

4. At the end of his monologue, Socrates asks that the judges punish his sons if they (steal from the rich / care more about riches than virture) or (pretend they are more than they really are / pretend to be judges); and as a result he and his sons will receive (peace of mind / justice). (Underline the correct phrases.)

Reader's Response

Socrates says that no evil can be done to a good person. What do you think he means by a "good" person? Do you agree with Socrates' statement? Write several sentences explaining your answers.

____

____

____

____

____

____

NAME ______________________ CLASS ________________ DATE ________ SCORE ______

from the APOLOGY

Plato

translated by Benjamin Jowett

(Textbook page 295)

NOUN CLAUSES

A **noun clause** is a subordinate clause used as a noun. Like a noun, a noun clause may function as the subject of a verb, as a predicate nominative, as a direct or indirect object, as the object of a preposition, or as an appositive.

EXAMPLES *Whoever sees Jorge coming* should warn the others. (subject)
A party is *what Jorge least expects.* (predicate nominative)
His belief, *that he is going to a party,* came from Maria. (appositive)
He always believes *what she tells him.* (direct object)
Maria can take a picture from *where she is standing.* (object of preposition)

A noun clause usually begins with one of the following introductory words. Notice that many of these words can also be used to introduce adjective or adverb clauses.

that	who	whomever	whose	where	however
what	whoever	which	when	wherever	
whatever	whom	whichever	whenever	how	

The introductory word *that* is sometimes omitted from the noun clause.

EXAMPLE Luisa knew [that] she had won first place.

Exercise 1. Identifying Noun Clauses

Underline the noun clauses in the following sentences about Plato's *Apology.* Some sentences have more than one noun clause. (Remember that a noun clause, like other clauses, must have a subject and a verb.)

EXAMPLE In his *Apology,* Plato describes what Socrates stands for.

1. Socrates is convicted by a jury for what he teaches to young minds.

2. The jury's expectation, that Socrates will apologize, is wrong.

3. He does not tell the jury what they expect.

4. His words are not what a man facing death might be expected to say.

5. He explains that he will not resort to wailing and lamenting.

(continued)

6. Socrates tells whoever will listen that he prefers death to unrighteousness.

7. He believes that trying to escape death by lying is wrong.

8. He calls whoever would condemn him a murderer.

9. From what Socrates says, the jury learns that he is not afraid to die.

10. What appeals to him about death is talking to history's great figures.

Exercise 2. Writing with Noun Clauses

Combine each of the following pairs of sentences about Socrates by changing the italicized sentence into a noun clause. Begin the noun clause with the word given in parentheses. Omit or change words as needed. Write your new sentence in the blanks provided. (Hint: Your new sentences should not have the word *something* in them.)

EXAMPLE Socrates' oracle tells him something. *He should not compromise his ideals.* (that)

Socrates' oracle tells him that he should not compromise his ideals.

1. Socrates explains something. *He sees death as a good.* (that)

____

____

2. *Death is like a journey.* Socrates believes something. (that)

____

____

3. Socrates wants to continue his search for something. *His search is for the truth.* (what)

____

____

4. Socrates realizes something. *His oracle, his inner guide, does not oppose him.* (that)

____

____

(continued)

5. Socrates requests something. *He wants the judges to punish his sons if they care too little about virtue.* (that)

___

___

Exercise 3. Revising a Paragraph

Revise the following paragraph about Plato and Socrates by using noun clauses in place of italicized groups of words. Change or omit words as needed. Not every sentence needs revising. One sentence has been revised for you as an example. (Hint: The word *something* or *someone* should not appear in your revised paragraph.)

What we know about Socrates

Plato wrote about Socrates, who was Plato's beloved teacher. ~~We know something about Socrates. It~~ comes mostly from Plato's writings. Socrates did not record something. *It is the nature of his personal philosophy.* He spent most of his time teaching someone. *He or she had to be eager to pursue the truth.* Plato describes the teaching method Socrates used. Instead of preaching or offering his own solutions, Socrates insisted something. *Students question all ideas.* This method of questioning is known as the Socratic method. Plato tried to capture something by writing the *Dialogues. It is the person Socrates was.*

NAME ______________________ CLASS ______________________ DATE __________ SCORE __________

from the APOLOGY

Plato

translated by Benjamin Jowett

(Textbook page 295)

READING COMPREHENSION

Directions: In the space provided, write the letter of the best answer to each question. *(10 points each)*

1. What is the occasion for Socrates' monologue?
   a. He is giving a speech to his students.
   b. He is apologizing for hurting Plato's reputation.
   c. He is speaking against the war with Sparta.
   d. He is defending his philosophy and way of life at his trial. 1. ______

2. What does Socrates say led to his first conviction?
   a. He irritated his accusers by telling them the truth.
   b. He bewildered his accusers by remaining silent.
   c. He wept and wailed in front of the court.
   d. He was caught trying to escape from Athens. 2. ______

3. Why doesn't Socrates try to avoid his conviction?
   a. He doesn't want to compromise his virtue and principles.
   b. He believes it is useless to try.
   c. He has already taken poison.
   d. He plans to escape. 3. ______

4. What does Socrates say all men should try to avoid?
   a. death
   b. unjust imprisonment
   c. displeasing the court
   d. unrighteousness 4. ______

5. What does Socrates prophesy will happen to his accusers?
   a. They will die.
   b. The citizens of Athens will applaud them.
   c. Younger men will criticize their decision.
   d. They will be imprisoned. 5. ______

6. What happens to Socrates' oracle at the time of his trial?
   a. It abandons him.
   b. It prophesies the future.
   c. It speaks to him loudly.
   d. It is silent. 6. ______

(continued)

7. Why does Socrates think the oracle has not stopped him from fighting his conviction?
   a. The oracle is dead.
   b. The oracle knows the situation is hopeless.
   c. Socrates had not been faithful to the oracle in the past.
   d. It's a sign that death is a good, not an evil. 7.______

8. Which of the following reasons does Socrates give to explain how death might be good?
   a. Death will allow him to catch up on his sleep.
   b. In death, there is no sickness.
   c. Death delivers him to the true judges in the other world.
   d. Death will allow him to talk with dead members of his family. 8.______

9. What does Socrates *most* look forward to about death?
   a. continuing his search into true and false knowledge with other immortals
   b. not having a physical body anymore
   c. not having to think anymore
   d. having the power to haunt the evil people who convicted him 9.______

10. What last favor does Socrates ask of his judges?
    a. to work toward clearing his name
    b. to overthrow his condemners
    c. to guide his sons toward virtue
    d. to take care of his wife 10.______

NAME ______________________ CLASS ______________________ DATE __________ SCORE ________

OEDIPUS REX

Sophocles
translated by Dudley Fitts and Robert Fitzgerald

(Textbook page 307)

DEVELOPING VOCABULARY

Directions: Read carefully the explanation of each word. Then write a sentence of your own using that word. In your sentence, include clues to the word's meaning.

supplication (sup'lə·kā'shən) ***n.*** A humble prayer or request to a deity or superior. ▶ This word derives from a Latin word meaning "to kneel down or beg humbly." ▪ With a look of supplication, the dog sat on its hind legs and begged for food. **Page 308**

ORIGINAL SENTENCE ____

____

compunction (kəm·pungk'shən) ***n.*** Remorse; feeling of guilty uneasiness. ▶ This word derives from a Latin word meaning "to prick hard" or "to sting." ▪ Because they felt compunction for the damage they had done, the vandals offered to make the repairs. **Page 312**

ORIGINAL SENTENCE ____

____

expedient (ek·spē'dē·ənt) ***n.*** A thing useful to achieve an end. ▶ The verb form of this word is *expedite*, which means "to speed up the process of." ▪ To be successful, the lawyer saw building her political connections as a necessary expedient. **Page 317**

ORIGINAL SENTENCE ____

____

decrepit (dē·krep'it) ***adj.*** Weak or worn out by old age or long use. ▶ This word derives from a Latin word meaning "cracked." ▪ The decrepit bicycle had a rusted frame and worn, patched tires. **Page 321**

ORIGINAL SENTENCE ____

____

(continued)

incarnate (in·kär′nit; -nāt′) ***adj.*** Appearing as a recognizable, living example; personified. ▶ *Incarnation* is the noun form of this word. ▪ Mother Teresa's love and care for the poor have made her seem like goodness incarnate. **Page 330**

ORIGINAL SENTENCE ____

____

disdain (dis·dān′) ***n.*** Scorn felt for someone considered inferior. ▶ This word can also be used as a verb. ▪ In the fairy tale *The White Snake*, a princess feels disdain for the love of a commoner until he proves his worth to her. **Page 339**

ORIGINAL SENTENCE ____

____

void ***n.*** That which is empty; vacuum. ***adj.*** Containing nothing; empty. ▶ This versatile word can also be used as a verb, meaning "to invalidate." ▪ His heart was void of any compassion; he had no feelings for anyone. **Page 355**

ORIGINAL SENTENCE ____

____

venerate (ven′ər·āt′) ***v.*** To look upon with reverence. ▶ The Latin root word here stems from the name Venus, which means "love." ▪ Fans sometimes venerate celebrities, even modeling their own lives on those of their idols. **Page 356**

ORIGINAL SENTENCE ____

____

primal (prī′məl) ***adj.*** 1. Original. 2. Of chief importance. ▶ This word derives from a Latin word meaning "first." ▪ According to Greek mythology, the primal, or first, parents were heaven and earth. **Page 361**

ORIGINAL SENTENCE ____

____

engender (en·jen′dər) ***v.*** To cause to be; produce. ▶ The Latin verb on which this word is based means "to generate." ▪ With his conciliatory words, the diplomat was able to engender peace between the warring countries. **Page 365**

ORIGINAL SENTENCE ____

____

NAME ______________________ CLASS ______________________ DATE ________ SCORE ________

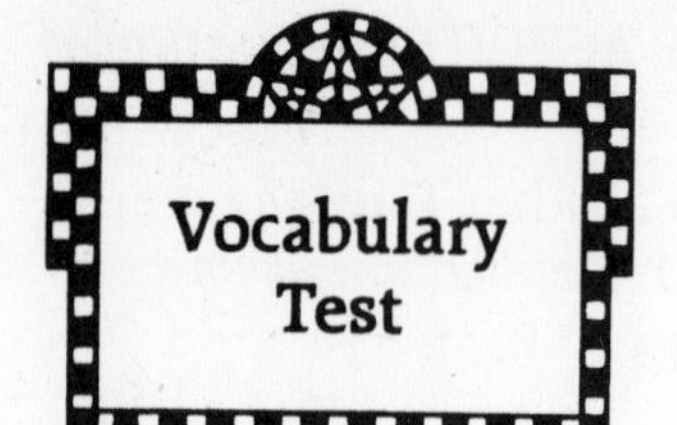

OEDIPUS REX

Sophocles

translated by Dudley Fitts and Robert Fitzgerald

(Textbook page 307)

VOCABULARY TEST

In the space provided, write the letter of the word or phrase closest in meaning to the word in italics. *(10 points each)*

1. *engender:* a. to cause to be b. to silence c. to wish d. to heal — 1. ______
2. *void:* a. despair b. abundance c. empty space d. weeds — 2. ______
3. *decrepit:* a. strong b. weak c. greedy d. forgetful — 3. ______
4. *incarnate:* a. appearing as a living example b. meat-eating c. without restraint d. expressing contempt — 4. ______
5. *primal:* a. refined b. original c. fearful d. inconvenient — 5. ______
6. *compunction:* a. great pride b. relief c. remorse d. late — 6. ______
7. *venerate:* a. to annoy b. to prolong c. to divide d. to revere — 7. ______
8. *supplication:* a. prophecy b. prayer or request c. demand d. balm — 8. ______
9. *disdain:* a. scorn b. cooperation c. great success d. decision — 9. ______
10. *expedient:* a. a soldier's protective shoes b. a former king or ruler c. a thing useful to achieve an end d. a humble servant — 10. ______

NAME ______________________ CLASS ______________ DATE ________ SCORE ______

OEDIPUS REX, PART 1

Sophocles

translated by Dudley Fitts and Robert Fitzgerald

(Textbook page 307)

REVIEWING THE SELECTION

In items 1–3 below, underline the correct word or phrase in each given pair.

1. As the play opens, the city of Thebes is in the grip of a plague. The king tells the townspeople that he has sent someone to ask the god (Zeus/Apollo) what should be done.

2. a. According to the god, what must be done before the plague can end? (King Laius's murderer must be found./Offerings must be made to the gods.)

   b. What does Oedipus promise? (that he will avenge the death of Laius/that he will find a cure for the plague)

3. Oedipus thinks that (Creon/Teiresias), the seer, must be plotting with the queen's brother, (Creon/Jocasta), to overthrow him, because the seer says that (Oedipus is the murderer/Creon is a god).

4. Draw a line connecting the name of each character in the first column with the best description of that person.

a. Queen Jocasta	is the only witness to the killing of Laius.
b. The shepherd	once said that Oedipus was not his father's son.
c. A drunken man in Corinth	tells Oedipus to ignore seers and prophecies.
d. Oedipus	once killed someone who forced him off the road.

Reader's Response

Tragic heroes, such as Oedipus, are brought to their downfalls through a weakness in their characters. At this point in the play, have you seen any weakness in Oedipus? Write two or three sentences explaining your answer.

____

____

____

____

____

NAME ______________________ CLASS ______________________ DATE __________ SCORE ________

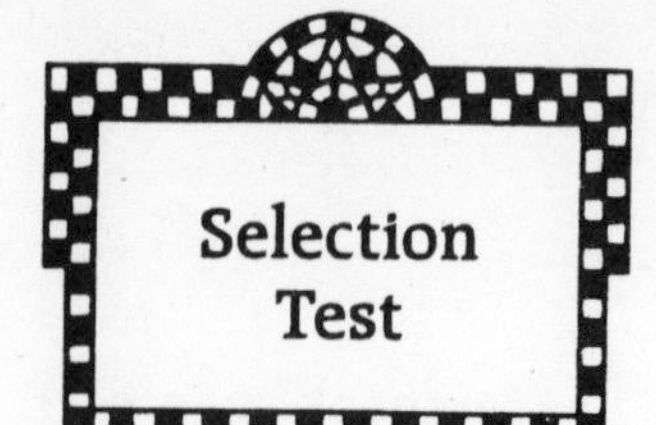

OEDIPUS REX, PART 1

Sophocles

translated by Dudley Fitts and Robert Fitzgerald

(Textbook page 307)

READING COMPREHENSION

Directions: In the space provided, write the letter of the best answer to each question. *(10 points each)*

1. Why are the people of Thebes in despair at the beginning of the play?
   a. The king is dead.
   b. A plague is killing the city's people and livestock.
   c. Their beloved Queen Jocasta lies on her deathbed.
   d. Their army has just been defeated by Corinth.

   1. ______

2. How does Oedipus find out what is causing the city's problems?
   a. from the oracle at Delphi
   b. from the queen
   c. from a messenger from Corinth
   d. from the leader of his army

   2. ______

3. What is the cause of the city's problems?
   a. The people have worshiped the wrong gods.
   b. The queen has been plotting to murder the king.
   c. Oedipus refuses to follow the will of the gods.
   d. The city is harboring the murderer of King Laius.

   3. ______

4. What does Oedipus vow to do to remedy the situation?
   a. to pray to the gods and beg their forgiveness
   b. to discover the murderer and exile him from Thebes
   c. to exile the queen
   d. to build a new temple to appease the gods

   4. ______

5. Who is Teiresias?
   a. the queen's brother
   b. the real father of Oedipus
   c. a holy prophet who knows the truth
   d. the leader of the Theban army

   5. ______

6. Who is Creon?
   a. the queen's first husband
   b. the real father of Oedipus
   c. a holy prophet who knows the truth
   d. the queen's brother

   6. ______

(continued)

7. How does Teiresias anger Oedipus?
   a. He accuses Oedipus of being the murderer.
   b. He accuses Queen Jocasta of being the murderer.
   c. He refuses to fight Corinth.
   d. He tries to sneak out of the city. 7. ______

8. With whom does Oedipus think Teiresias is conspiring?
   a. Queen Jocasta
   b. the king of Corinth
   c. his army generals
   d. Creon 8. ______

9. Creon claims
   a. that Teiresias is the one plotting against Oedipus
   b. to be a god
   c. that he wants to be king
   d. that he is innocent of Oedipus's charges 9. ______

10. At the end of Scene 2, Oedipus
    a. believes Creon
    b. wants to kill Creon
    c. wants to divorce Jocasta
    d. wants to resign as king 10. ______

NAME ______________________ CLASS ______________ DATE ________ SCORE ______

OEDIPUS REX, PART 2

Sophocles
translated by Dudley Fitts and Robert Fitzgerald

(Textbook page 342)

REVIEWING THE SELECTION

In items 1–3 below, underline the correct word or phrase in each given pair.

1. A messenger from Corinth brings the news that King Polybus, whom Oedipus considers his father, is dead. Ironically, this messenger was once a shepherd who brought the baby (Oedipus/Creon) from a Theban shepherd to the king and queen of (Thebes/Corinth).

2. The Theban shepherd is summoned. After much hesitation, he says that he got the baby from (a priest of the god Apollo/Queen Jocasta).

3. Queen Jocasta goes into the palace. There, according to a second messenger, she (hangs herself/blinds herself). When Oedipus finds Jocasta, he (blinds himself/saves her).

4. List two favors that Oedipus begs of Creon as the play ends.

   a. ______________________________

   b. ______________________________

Reader's Response

As the play closes, Creon advises Oedipus to think about how he brought about his own destruction. Do you think that Oedipus is responsible for his own destruction? Write a sentence stating your opinion. Then write two or three sentences explaining why you think as you do.

Your Opinion: ______________________________

____

Your Reasons: ______________________________

____

____

NAME ______________________ CLASS ______________________ DATE __________ SCORE __________

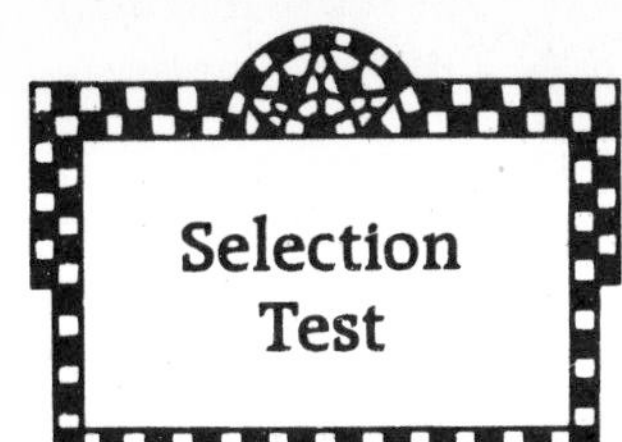

OEDIPUS REX, PART 2

Sophocles
translated by Dudley Fitts and
Robert Fitzgerald

(Textbook page 342)

READING COMPREHENSION

Directions: In the space provided, write the letter of the best answer to each question. *(10 points each)*

1. What news does the messenger of Corinth bring to Oedipus?
   a. His army is defeated.
   b. The people of Corinth want Oedipus to be their king.
   c. His mother is dead.
   d. His father is displeased with him. 1. ______

2. How does Jocasta respond to this news?
   a. She says it proves the prophecies are wrong.
   b. She says it proves the prophecies are true.
   c. She believes that the plague will now end.
   d. She believes Oedipus will surrender to Corinth. 2. ______

3. What does Oedipus still fear after hearing the news?
   a. that he might kill his mother
   b. that he might marry his mother
   c. that Creon will kill him
   d. that Corinth's army will kill him 3. ______

4. What shocking news does the messenger give to Oedipus to relieve his fears?
   a. that his brothers are all dead
   b. that his real mother is dead
   c. that Polybus and Merope are not his real father and mother
   d. that Corinth wants to make peace with Thebes 4. ______

5. How does the messenger know these things about Oedipus?
   a. Apollo told him the truth.
   b. Oedipus's brothers confessed to him.
   c. Another shepherd found Oedipus as a baby and gave him to Polybus.
   d. The messenger is a prophet. 5. ______

6. What is Jocasta's reaction to the messenger's revelations?
   a. She tells Oedipus to question the messenger more closely.
   b. She begs Oedipus not to ask any more questions.
   c. She rushes off to the palace.
   d. She refuses to believe the messenger. 6. ______

(continued)

7. Who comes to verify the messenger's story?
   a. Oedipus's mother
   b. a shepherd of King Laius
   c. Creon
   d. Apollo

   7. ______

8. What terrible truth does Oedipus learn when the messenger's story is finally verified?
   a. Oedipus must die.
   b. King Laius and Queen Jocasta are his real parents.
   c. Creon has tricked him.
   d. His real father was a slave.

   8. ______

9. What happens to Queen Jocasta?
   a. She hangs herself.
   b. Oedipus kills her.
   c. Creon rescues her.
   d. She is sent to prison.

   9. ______

10. What does Oedipus do in his sorrow and shame?
   a. He hangs himself.
   b. He blinds himself.
   c. He kills his children.
   d. He poisons himself.

   10. ______

NAME ______________________ CLASS ________________ DATE ______ SCORE ______

OEDIPUS REX

Sophocles

translated by Dudley Fitts and Robert Fitzgerald

(Textbook page 307)

DANGLING AND MISPLACED MODIFIERS

Modifiers are words and phrases that describe or limit the meaning of other words or phrases. Modifiers can be single words, or they can be phrases or clauses. When a modifying phrase or clause does not clearly modify a word in the sentence, the result is a **dangling modifier.** You can correct dangling modifiers by adding the missing word or phrase to the sentence. Or you can change the phrase to an adverb clause.

DANGLING *Swimming in the ocean*, sand got in her eyes.

CORRECTED *Swimming in the ocean*, she got sand in her eyes.

CORRECTED *While she was swimming in the ocean*, she got sand in her eyes.

When a modifying phrase or clause is too far from the word or phrase it modifies, the result is a **misplaced modifier**. Correct the sentence by moving the modifier as close as possible to the word it modifies. Misplaced modifiers are usually prepositional or verbal phrases or adjective clauses.

MISPLACED She could see her friends playing volleyball *from her window.* (prepositional phrase)

CORRECTED *From her window*, she could see her friends playing volleyball.

MISPLACED She met a friend on the boardwalk *that had a bad sunburn.* (adjective clause)

CORRECTED She met a friend *that had a bad sunburn* on the boardwalk.

Exercise 1. Identifying Dangling and Misplaced Modifiers

Each of the following sentences about *Oedipus Rex* contains an italicized phrase or clause. In the blank before each sentence, write *D* if the phrase or clause is a dangling modifier. Write *M* if it is a misplaced modifier. Write *C* if the modifying phrase or clause is correctly placed.

EXAMPLE __D__ *Standing in the courtroom*, the verdict is announced.

______ 1. *Worrying about the plague*, a trip to Delphi is arranged.

______ 2. The plague is hurting the whole city, *which has killed many people.*

______ 3. *Arriving from Delphi*, Creon announces the reason for the plague.

______ 4. *After learning the reason*, a promise is made.

______ 5. The truth is known by Teiresias, *of the king's murderer.*

______ 6. *Forcing Teiresias to speak*, the truth is revealed.

(continued)

______ 7. Queen Jocasta begs Oedipus not to ask more questions *out of concern.*

______ 8. The messenger *from Corinth* brings the news of King Polybus's death.

______ 9. The news relieves Oedipus *of King Polybus's death.*

______ 10. *Not realizing the truth,* Oedipus thinks the prophecy about killing his father is not true.

Exercise 2. Correcting Dangling and Misplaced Modifiers

Each of the following sentences about *Oedipus Rex* has a dangling or a misplaced modifier. In the blanks provided, rewrite each of the sentences, correcting the dangling or misplaced modifiers. Change, move, or add words as necessary.

EXAMPLE The clock is my mother's treasured antique that you hear chiming. (misplaced modifier)

The clock that you hear chiming is my mother's treasured antique.

1. Oedipus learns that King Polybus is not his real father from the messenger. (misplaced modifier)

____

____

2. When he was a baby, the messenger made a rescue. (dangling modifier)

____

____

3. His ankles tied together, the messenger had cut the bonds from the baby. (misplaced modifier)

____

____

4. The messenger gave the baby to King Polybus that he rescued. (misplaced modifier)

____

____

(continued)

5. Deeply anguished by the truth, blindness was the result. (dangling modifier)

____

____

Exercise 3. Revising a Paragraph

Revise the following paragraph about *Oedipus Rex* by correcting dangling and misplaced modifiers. You may add, change, or move words as necessary. The first misplaced modifier has been corrected for you as an example. Not every sentence needs a correction; you may even find that a sentence is unnecessary and should be deleted.

About King Oedipus and his family, Sophocles wrote *Oedipus Rex* as part of a trilogy. It is the first play by Sophocles of the trilogy. Much of the play is dialogue. In fact, most of the action takes place offstage that is violent. But the audience still enjoys the rich dialogue. Gradually revealed throughout the play, Oedipus's ignorance of the truth is the central problem. Irony is one of the elements among audiences that makes the play so popular. The audience knows the truth almost from the beginning about Oedipus. Hearing the dramatically ironic words of Oedipus, the enjoyment of the play increases.

NAME ______________________ CLASS ______________________ DATE ________ SCORE ________

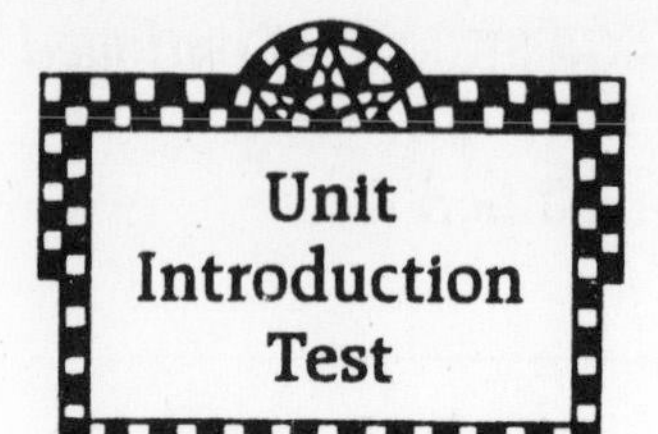

UNIT 4: GREEK AND ROMAN LITERATURES

(Textbook pages 372–378)

INTRODUCTION/Roman Literature

Directions. In the space provided, write the letter of the best answer to each question. *(10 points each)*

1. Who, according to Rome's great epic, the *Aeneid*, is the father of Rome?
   a. Aeneas
   b. Virgil
   c. Achilles
   d. Athena

   1.______

2. Until Julius Caesar, the primary form of Roman government was a(n)
   a. dictatorship
   b. republic
   c. anarchy
   d. monarchy

   2.______

3. Julius Caesar died when
   a. senators assassinated him
   b. he led his army into a battle
   c. he was stricken by the plague
   d. he hanged himself

   3.______

4. The earliest Roman gods and goddesses were associated with
   a. city life
   b. farming
   c. beauty
   d. love

   4.______

5. During his reign as emperor, Augustus is credited with
   a. rebuilding Rome
   b. establishing a state religion
   c. destroying Rome
   d. building a large navy

   5.______

6. Under the reign of Augustus, Roman poets, historians, and writers
   a. worked in secrecy
   b. were highly critical of the emperor
   c. were encouraged and supported by the emperor's court
   d. focused on Greek civilization

   6.______

(continued)

7. The Roman empire began to crumble because
   a. it was small and weak
   b. the people revolted
   c. the emperor died
   d. it was too large and unwieldy 7.______

8. To stop the disintegration of the empire, Diocletian
   a. gathered a huge army to defeat his enemies
   b. conquered new lands for the empire
   c. imposed harsh taxes on the people
   d. divided the empire into eastern and western units 8.______

9. The emperor Constantine had a significant impact on world history because
   a. he killed Diocletian
   b. he declared the Roman empire dead
   c. he gave Christians freedom to worship
   d. he stopped an invasion by the Germans 9.______

10. Besides Rome, another important city in the empire was
    a. Constantinople
    b. Athens
    c. Florence
    d. Venice 10.______

NAME ______________________ CLASS ________________ DATE ________ SCORE ______

from the AENEID, *from* BOOK 2: THE FALL OF TROY

Virgil

translated by Robert Fitzgerald

(Textbook page 383)

DEVELOPING VOCABULARY

Directions: Read carefully the explanation of each word. Then write a sentence of your own using that word. In your sentence, include clues to the word's meaning.

undulate (un′dyo͞o·lāt) ***v.*** To move in a wavelike manner. ▶ This word derives from a Latin word meaning "small wave." ▪ "The wave" is a popular cheer that undulates around the stadium. **Page 386**

ORIGINAL SENTENCE ____

____

impel (im·pel′) ***v.*** To propel; drive forward. ▶ A synonym for this word is *force.* ▪ Her conscience impelled her to speak out against injustices. **Page 391**

ORIGINAL SENTENCE ____

____

predatory (pred′ ə·tôr′ē) ***adj.*** Living by hunting and feeding on other animals. ▶ The noun form of this word is *predator.* ▪ The predatory nature of ordinary cats is evident in the way they prowl at night and stalk small animals. **Page 392**

ORIGINAL SENTENCE ____

____

respite (res′pit) ***n.*** A temporary period of rest or relief. ▶ The pronunciation of this word derives from the Middle English spelling, *respit.* ▪ After a tiring first half, the team was glad for the respite at halftime. **Page 394**

ORIGINAL SENTENCE ____

____

futile (fyo͞ot′′ l) ***adj.*** Useless; hopeless. ▶ The noun form of this word is *futility,* which means "uselessness." ▪ When her mother would not change her mind, Tamala realized that her pleas for a later curfew were futile. **Page 394**

ORIGINAL SENTENCE ____

____

(continued)

consecrate (kän′si·krāt) *v.* To set apart as holy and sacred. ▶ The Latin root of this word means "sacred." ▪ The ground had to be consecrated before the cathedral could be built. **Page 396**

ORIGINAL SENTENCE ____________________

goad (gōd) *v.* To urge into action. ▶ To *goad* implies a negative or irritating urging, as with an insult or challenge. ▪ The coach sometimes likes to goad the players to practice harder by calling them lazy. **Page 400**

ORIGINAL SENTENCE ____________________

undermine (un′der·mīn′) *v.* 1. To wear away the foundations of. 2. To cause to weaken by craft or stealth. ▶ The prefix *under-* here implies secrecy or treachery. ▪ The opponents took every opportunity to undermine each other's defenses. **Page 401**

ORIGINAL SENTENCE ____________________

omnipotent (äm·nip′ə·tənt) *adj.* All-powerful. ▶ The Latin word *omni* means "all," and *potent* means "powerful." ▪ Small children see their parents as omnipotent people who can do anything. **Page 402**

ORIGINAL SENTENCE ____________________

tenuous (ten′yo͞o·əs) *adj.* 1. Not dense, as the atmosphere at a high altitude. 2. Insubstantial; fragile; inadequate. ▶ This word comes from a Latin word meaning "thin" or "slight." ▪ The cloud coverage was tenuous at the mountaintop and so did not obscure the magnificent view. **Page 406**

ORIGINAL SENTENCE ____________________

NAME ______________________ CLASS ______________________ DATE __________ SCORE __________

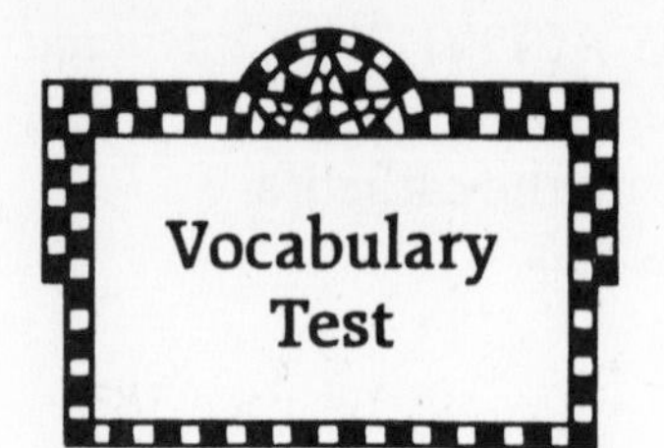

from the AENEID, *from* BOOK 2: THE FALL OF TROY

Virgil

translated by Robert Fitzgerald

(Textbook page 383)

VOCABULARY TEST

In the space provided, write the letter of the word or phrase closest in meaning to the word in italics. *(10 points each)*

1. *respite:* a. heavy rain b. temporary relief c. showing esteem d. to say something in return 1. ______

2. *impel:* a. to propel or drive forward b. to hover c. to strike forcefully d. to hold back 2. ______

3. *goad:* a. a deity b. to curse c. to urge into action d. a heavy burden 3. ______

4. *tenuous:* a. strong b. boundless or unending c. fragile or insubstantial d. arranged in threes 4. ______

5. *consecrate:* a. to force b. to engage or occupy c. to come to agreement d. to set apart as holy and sacred 5. ______

6. *undermine:* a. to wear away the foundations of b. to submit to c. to fall short of d. to grasp the meaning of 6. ______

7. *futile:* a. successful b. productive c. useless d. gentle 7. ______

8. *undulate:* a. to move in jerky motions b. to move in a wavelike manner c. to unclench d. to beat rhythmically 8. ______

9. *predatory:* a. living by feeding on other animals b. living by feeding on plants c. showing prejudice d. unselfish 9. ______

10. *omnipotent:* a. not showing favoritism b. all-powerful c. having great riches d. lacking strength 10. ______

NAME ______________________ CLASS ________________ DATE ________ SCORE ______

from the AENEID, *from* BOOK 2: THE FALL OF TROY

Virgil

translated by Robert Fitzgerald (Textbook page 383)

REVIEWING THE SELECTION

1. After the Trojan War has raged for many years, the Greeks pretend to give up and go home. They hide on an offshore island and leave behind a (wooden horse/treasure chest) filled with (Greek soldiers/precious jewels). (Underline the correct answer.)

2. What strange event happens when the Trojan priest Laocoon is about to sacrifice a bull?

____

____

3. The Greek troops triumph, and Aeneas sees (Priam/Hector) killed as Troy burns around him. (Underline the correct answer.)

4. Draw a line from each name in the first column to the phrase that best describes that person.

a. Cassandra	prevents Aeneas from killing Helen.
b. Aeneas's mother	is killed but appears in a vision to say good-bye.
c. Aeneas	warns against bringing the wooden horse into the city of Troy.
d. Creusa	becomes the leader of a group of refugees.

Reader's Response

The Trojans ignore clues to the Greeks' plot and are taken by surprise. Write two or three sentences about a time when you missed clues and received a surprise, either negative or positive.

____

____

____

____

____

____

NAME ______________________ CLASS ______________ DATE ________ SCORE ______

from the AENEID, *from* BOOK 2: THE FALL OF TROY

Virgil
translated by Robert Fitzgerald (Textbook page 383)

PARALLEL STRUCTURE

Parallel structure means using similar grammatical forms to express ideas of equal importance. When you do not use similar forms, the result is a faulty sentence.

FAULTY *To imagine* is *creating.* (infinitive paired with a gerund)

PARALLEL *To imagine* is *to create.* (two infinitives)

PARALLEL *Imagining* is *creating.* (two gerunds)

FAULTY Helena likes *learning new routines* and *to practice at the barre in dance class.* (gerund phrase and infinitive phrase)

PARALLEL Helena likes *to learn new routines* and *to practice at the barre in dance class.* (two infinitive phrases)

The **correlative construction** is a parallel structure that uses paired **correlative conjunctions** such as *both/and, either/or, neither/nor, not only/but also,* and *whether/or.* Correlative conjunctions should come immediately before each part of a parallel construction or before each repeated preposition.

FAULTY He knows both *about cooking* and *that he can find good takeout food.* (phrase paired with a clause)

PARALLEL He knows both *about cooking* and *about finding good takeout food.* (two phrases)

Exercise 1. Identifying Faulty Parallelism

Some of the following sentences about the *Aeneid* contain faulty parallelism. If the sentence has faulty parallelism, write *F* in the blank before the sentence. If the sentence is correct, write *C* in the blank.

EXAMPLE __F__ The *Aeneid* reveals how cunning the Greeks were and that they had brutal ways of fighting.

______ 1. Aeneas begins his story and remembers that terrible night.

______ 2. The Trojans think that the Greeks have left the wooden horse either as a gift or it is a trick.

______ 3. Some of the Trojans advise burning the horse or to cut it open.

______ 4. But the people are both frightened and fascinated by the giant horse.

______ 5. They finally drag the giant horse to shore and then are pulling it inside the city walls.

______ 6. The Trojans are tricked not only by the Greeks but also by their own ignorance.

(continued)

______ 7. They ignore the advice of the wiser men, and what the obvious clues about the horse are.

______ 8. While both the people sleep and it is dark, the hidden Greeks attack Troy.

______ 9. Aeneas immediately goes to fight, worrying neither about dying nor about fighting a huge army.

______ 10. While rushing to King Priam's palace, Aeneas sees dead bodies on the streets, in homes, and lying across porches.

Exercise 2. Correcting Faulty Parallelism

Each of the following sentences about the *Aeneid* has faulty parallelism. On the blanks provided, write a new, correct sentence for each faulty sentence. Change words as necessary to correct faulty parallel structure.

EXAMPLE Aeneas helps to defend the royal palace, and he is protecting King Priam.
Aeneas helps to defend the royal palace and to protect King Priam.

1. To stop the attacking Greeks, the Trojans hurl down rooftiles and beams and are also using precious ornaments as missiles.

____

____

2. The small band of Trojan soldiers both fights bravely and it acts skillfully in a hopeless situation.

____

____

3. Queen Hecuba begs King Priam to take off his weapons and that he should join her at the altar for protection.

____

____

4. Aeneas blames Helen both for the fall of Troy and murdering King Priam.

____

5. His mother tells Aeneas not to kill Helen out of revenge and about going home to check on his family.

____

____

(continued)

3. Revising Paragraphs

Revise the following paragraph by making parallel ideas parallel in structure. Change words as necessary to improve the paragraph. Not every sentence needs correcting. The first correction has been made for you.

Virgil's *Aeneid* is an epic poem with all the makings of a smash movie hit. It has great characters, action, suspense, and ~~includes~~ special effects. Aeneas would make a great movie superstar. He is a man who loves both action and is a loving family man. He fights both the forces of evil outside and inside himself. He tricks the Greeks by disguising himself, slays Greek soldiers by the dozen, and struggling to keep his own thirst for revenge in control. He's a hero who has not only courage but also wants to follow his conscience.

The *Aeneid*'s action begins with the discovery of a huge wooden horse and ending with the tragic death of the hero's wife. There are snake bites, surprise attacks, men battle each other to the death, and tearful farewells. The action is full of suspense because the many battles either mean life or death for the people of Troy. The reader might know from the beginning that Troy is eventually destroyed. But he or she doesn't know if the men in Aeneas's small band all live, Helen will survive, or if Aeneas can protect his family. The poem even has special effects. The wooden horse clangs mysteriously, snakes suddenly bite the priest, and a fire is raging in the dark night. The *Aeneid* may be almost two thousand years old, but with some polish and if we buff it, it could be a great hit.

NAME ______________________ CLASS ____________________ DATE ________ SCORE ______

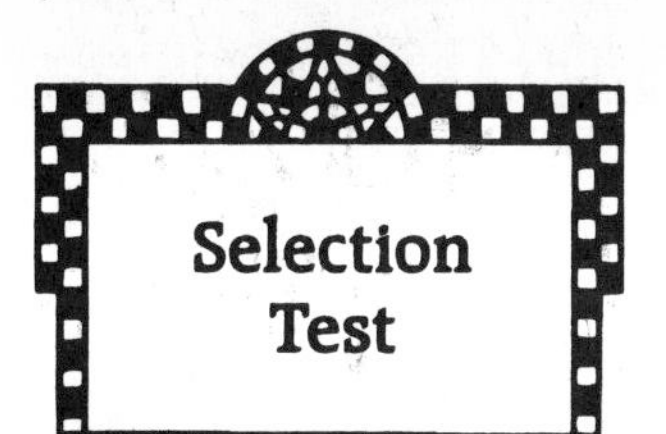

from the AENEID, *from* BOOK 2: THE FALL OF TROY

Virgil

translated by Robert Fitzgerald

(Textbook page 383)

READING COMPREHENSION

Directions: In the space provided, write the letter of the best answer to each question. *(10 points each)*

1. Virgil's epic poem, the *Aeneid,* was a conscious imitation of the epics of
   a. Plato
   b. Homer
   c. Sophocles
   d. Ovid

   1. ______

2. Who narrates this selection from the *Aeneid*?
   a. Helen
   b. Hector
   c. Aeneas
   d. Priam

   2. ______

3. What is the main subject of the excerpt from Book 2?
   a. the fall of Troy
   b. the marriage of Aeneas
   c. the kidnapping of Helen
   d. the death of Aeneas

   3. ______

4. What is hidden in the giant wooden horse?
   a. poisonous snakes
   b. Greek soldiers
   c. Trojan soldiers
   d. golden treasure

   4. ______

5. Why do the Trojans accept the wooden horse?
   a. It is a Trojan custom to accept all offered gifts.
   b. They are impressed by its craftsmanship.
   c. They believe the Greeks have fled and left it.
   d. The horse is important to their religion.

   5. ______

6. What happens while Aeneas sleeps?
   a. The Greeks quietly leave Troy.
   b. Hector appears in Aeneas's dreams and assures him of peace.
   c. The Greek soldiers come out of the wooden horse and attack Troy.
   d. Twin snakes come out of the sea and attack Laocoon and his sons.

   6. ______

(continued)

7. When Aeneas wakes, what is his first impulse?
   a. to save his family and flee Troy
   b. to seek shelter in the temple of Minerva
   c. to save Cassandra's life
   d. to fight the Greeks to the death

   7. ______

8. Whom does Aeneas see being killed?
   a. Achilles
   b. Priam
   c. Helen
   d. his mother

   8. ______

9. How does Aeneas's father escape the burning city of Troy?
   a. He rides on a horse.
   b. He runs very quickly.
   c. Aeneas carries him.
   d. He steals a chariot.

   9. ______

10. What does the ghost of Aeneas's wife tell him?
    a. to leave Troy and not to grieve her death
    b. to fight the Greeks to the death
    c. to save Helen
    d. that he is responsible for her death

    10. ______

NAME ______________________ CLASS ______________ DATE ________ SCORE ______

LYRIC POEMS

Catullus

translated by Reney Myers, Robert J. Ormsby, and Peter Whigham (Textbook page 411)

REVIEWING THE SELECTIONS

1. In "Wretched Catullus, Leave off Playing the Fool," the speaker remembers how happy he was when things went well with the woman he loved. List two of the things he vows to do now, beginning at line 12.

   a. ______________________________

   b. ______________________________

2. In "Lesbia Says She'ld Rather Marry Me," the narrator says that the words of women in love are as unreliable as if they were written on (paper/air) ______________ or (ice/running water) ______________.

3. How does Catullus explain his contradictory feelings in the lyric poem "I Hate and I Love"?

   ____

4. What happy event does the narrator describe in "If Ever Anyone Anywhere"?

   ____

Reader's Response

In the space provided, write one or two lines from a modern love song that you find meaningful. Or, if you do not know a song, create two lines of your own. Then write one or two sentences about your response to the lines.

Lines of the song: ______________________________

____

____

Your response: ______________________________

____

____

NAME ______________________ CLASS ______________________ DATE __________ SCORE __________

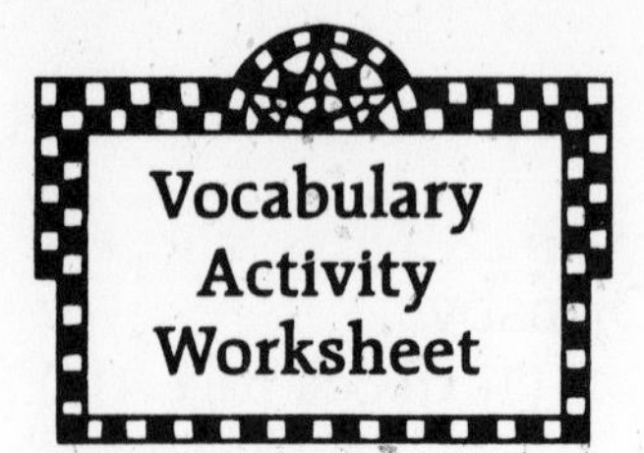

THE GOLDEN MEAN *and* CARPE DIEM Horace

translated by William Cowper and Thomas Hawkins

(Textbook page 416)

DEVELOPING VOCABULARY

Directions: Read carefully the explanation of each word. Then write a sentence of your own using that word. In your sentence, include clues to the word's meaning.

adverse (ad·vurs′) ***adj.*** Unfavorable; harmful. ► This word derives from a Latin word meaning "to turn toward (with hostility)." ▪ Adverse winds make it difficult for sailboats, which need the wind behind them. **Page 416**

ORIGINAL SENTENCE ____

____

timorous (tim′ ər·es) ***adj.*** Fearful; timid. —**timorously** ***adv.*** ► The Latin noun for this word is *timor*, meaning "fear." ▪ The first clap of thunder turned her old dog into a timorous puppy who immediately hid under the bed. **Page 416**

ORIGINAL SENTENCE ____

____

eminence (em′i·nəns) ***n.*** 1. An elevated thing or place, as a mountain. 2. Greatness. ► This word is also used as a title of respect, as in "Your Eminence." ▪ The mountain climbers saw the eminence towering above them as a challenge. **Page 416**

ORIGINAL SENTENCE ____

____

magnanimous (mag·nan′ ə·məs) ***adj.*** Noble-spirited; generous.—**magnanimity** ***n.*** ► This word derives from two Latin words: *magnus*, meaning "great," and *animus*, meaning "soul." ▪ The scholarship that Mrs. Wu provided was a magnanimous gesture that benefited many students. **Page 417**

ORIGINAL SENTENCE ____

____

protract (prō·trakt′) ***v.*** To prolong; lengthen. ► The prefix *pro-* here means, "out," and the Latin root word *tractus* means "to draw out." ▪ Because he didn't want to say goodbye, he tried to protract their conversation. **Page 417**

ORIGINAL SENTENCE ____

____

NAME ______________________ CLASS ______________________ DATE ________ SCORE ______

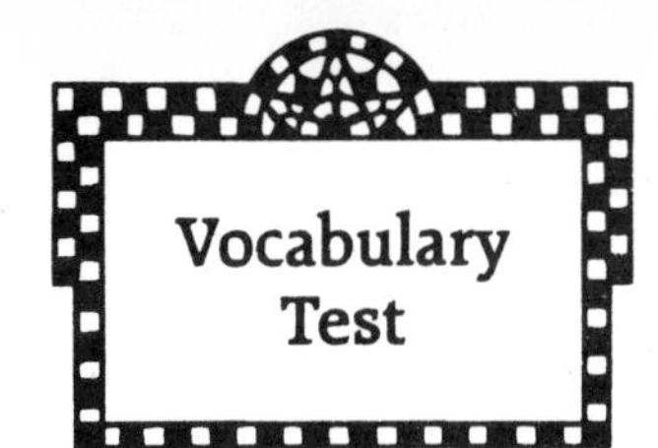

THE GOLDEN MEAN *and* CARPE DIEM Horace

translated by William Cowper
and Thomas Hawkins

(Textbook page 416)

VOCABULARY TEST

A. Match each word in column I with the correct definition in column II. Place the letter of the definition you choose in the space provided. *(10 points each)*

I	II
______ 1. eminence	a. to prolong; lengthen
______ 2. timorous	b. an elevated thing or place
______ 3. adverse	c. moving or working in an opposite direction
______ 4. magnanimous	d. noble-spirited; generous
______ 5. protract	e. fearful; timid

B. Complete each sentence below with a word from column I above. Write the appropriate word in the blank provided. *(10 points each)*

6. Jorge was very ______________________ about climbing up the mountain cliff; it was a long drop down.

7. To delay the climb, he tried to ______________________ the preparations as long as possible.

8. Secretly, he hoped that if he waited long enough ______________________ weather might prevent the climb.

9. The guide knew from experience that the ______________________ of the cliffs towering above them could easily frighten a new climber.

10. The guide saw that Jorge was nervous about the climb, and at the end of the day was ______________________ in praising his climbing skills.

NAME ______________________ CLASS ______________________ DATE __________ SCORE ________

THE GOLDEN MEAN *and* CARPE DIEM Horace

translated by William Cowper
and Thomas Hawkins

(Textbook page 416)

REVIEWING THE SELECTIONS

1. In the third stanza of "The Golden Mean," the speaker uses examples to show why people should not reach too high or try to become too great. What happens to each of these examples?

   a. the tallest pines ____

   b. the highest tower ____

   c. the cloud-capped mountaintop ______________________________________

2. In the last stanza of "The Golden Mean," the speaker tells what people should do when "hindrances" make it hard for them to reach their goals. What should they do?

   ____

   ____

3. According to the speaker of "The Golden Mean," what should people do if favorable winds fill their sails? (This is when they have achieved far more than they expected.)

   ____

   ____

4. The speaker in "Carpe Diem" tells a friend, Leuconoe, that one thing is Leuconoe's own. What is that thing?

   ____

   ____

Reader's Response

Do you agree with the speaker of "The Golden Mean" that people should not reach too high or strive too much for greatness? Can you think of times today when this effort might be harmful for people? When it might be helpful? Write two or three sentences explaining your answer.

____

____

NAME ______________________ CLASS ________________ DATE ________ SCORE ______

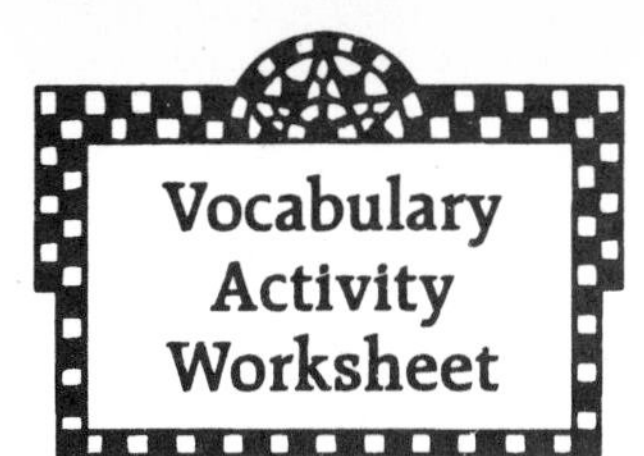

from METAMORPHOSES

Ovid

translated by Rolfe Humphries (Textbook page 422)

DEVELOPING VOCABULARY

Directions: Read carefully the explanation of each word. Then write a sentence of your own using that word. In your sentence, include clues to the word's meaning.

inert (in·urt') ***adj.*** Characterized by mental or physical inactivity or slowness. ▶ The noun form of this word, *inertia*, means "resistance to motion or change." ■ The dangerous chemical was in its safest form when solid and inert. **Page 422**

ORIGINAL SENTENCE ____

____

discordant (dis·kôrd''nt) ***adj.*** Not in agreement; conflicting. ▶ The Latin root for this word means "strife." ■ My mother always complains that the jazz I listen to is too discordant for her to enjoy. **Page 422**

ORIGINAL SENTENCE ____

____

bid ***v.*** To command. ▶ Both *bid* and *bade* are correct forms for the past tense. ■ Not liking ceremony, the general bid the soldiers not to salute. **Page 423**

ORIGINAL SENTENCE ____

____

torrid (tôr'id) ***adj.*** 1. Very hot, especially in reference to climate. 2. Extremely passionate. ▶ The Latin verb for "to parch or burn" gives this adjective its meaning. ■ The torrid desert sun was hotter than the tourists ever imagined. **Page 424**

ORIGINAL SENTENCE ____

____

sage ***n.*** A person greatly respected for wisdom and judgment. ▶ As an adjective, this word means "wise." ■ The sage offered his young disciples words of wisdom and advice, which proved very useful. **Page 424**

ORIGINAL SENTENCE ____

____

(continued)

fallow (fal′ ō) ***adj.*** Plowed but not cultivated or planted. ▶ Soil is left fallow for a period of time so that it remains fertile and is not overused. ▪ The fallow fields looked bare compared to the wheat-covered fields around them. **Page 425**

ORIGINAL SENTENCE ____

____

revel (rev′əl) ***v.*** To be festive in a noisy manner. ▶ This verb is used with the preposition *in.* ▪ The cast party allowed the actors to revel in the success of their production. **Page 426**

ORIGINAL SENTENCE ____

____

brandish (bran′dish) ***v.*** To wield in an exultant manner. ▶ This word derives from an Old French word meaning "sword or blade." ▪ After slaying the dragon, the knight brandished his sword in victory. **Page 426**

ORIGINAL SENTENCE ____

____

dire (dīr) ***adj.*** Dreadful; awful. ▶ This word comes from a Latin word meaning "fearful or ill-omened." ▪ The sudden, unexpected flooding created dire circumstances for the people who lived by the river. **Page 426**

ORIGINAL SENTENCE ____

____

piety (pī′ ə·tē) ***n.*** Loyalty (to God, parents, or country, for example). ▶ The Latin stem of this word comes from the word meaning "pious." ▪ My great aunt lives a life of simple piety, walking to church each day. **Page 426**

ORIGINAL SENTENCE ____

____

NAME ______________________ CLASS ______________________ DATE ________ SCORE ________

from METAMORPHOSES

Ovid

translated by Rolfe Humphries (Textbook page 422)

VOCABULARY TEST

Match each word in column I with the correct definition in column II. Place the letter of the definition you choose in the space provided. *(10 points each)*

	I	II
______	1. fallow	a. a person respected for wisdom and judgment
		b. to be festive and noisy
______	2. bid	c. loyalty or devotion
		d. very hot
______	3. torrid	e. dreadful; awful
		f. to command
______	4. brandish	g. plowed but not cultivated or planted
		h. to wield in an exultant manner
______	5. discordant	i. conflicting; not in agreement
		j. characterized by mental or physical inactivity
______	6. dire	
______	7. piety	
______	8. revel	
______	9. inert	
______	10. sage	

NAME ______________________ CLASS ____________________ DATE __________ SCORE ______

from METAMORPHOSES

Ovid

translated by Rolfe Humphries (Textbook page 422)

REVIEWING THE SELECTION

1. Ovid describes the state of the universe before creation as (chaos/torment). (Underline the correct word).

2. According to Ovid, why were God's other creations, such as plants and animals, not sufficient?

____

____

3. List three things that people did not do during the Golden Age.

   a. ____

   b. ____

   c. ____

4. During the Iron Age, what, according to Ovid, was "the root of evil"?

____

____

Reader's Response

Ovid describes a golden age, a silver age, a bronze age, and an iron age. Newscasters today refer to the space age and the age of technology; social observers refer to the "roaring" 1920s and the "swinging" 1960s. On the lines below, write the term that you think best describes the 1990s. Then explain why you find the term appropriate.

Term: ____

Reasons: ____

____

____

____

NAME ______________________ CLASS ________________ DATE ________ SCORE ______

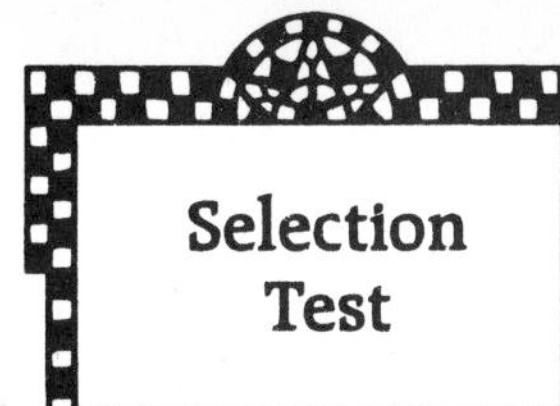

from METAMORPHOSES

Ovid

translated by Rolfe Humphries (Textbook page 422)

READING COMPREHENSION

Directions: In the space provided, write the letter of the best answer to each question. *(10 points each)*

1. Ovid's poem begins with
   a. the Golden Age
   b. the end of time
   c. the creation of the world
   d. his birth 1. ______

2. Which word best describes the world in the very beginning?
   a. chaos
   b. wet
   c. hot
   d. weightless 2. ______

3. What does Ovid see as the main work of God during creation?
   a. creating beauty
   b. bringing order to the universe
   c. letting nature take its course
   d. creating fire 3. ______

4. Humankind is formed by God, according to Ovid, because
   a. God was bored and wanted someone to talk to
   b. God needed someone to plow the fields
   c. God wanted to rule humans as his subjects
   d. God decided the world needed a more thoughtful and capable creature 4. ______

5. The Golden Age is best described as a time
   a. of famine and hunger
   b. of great peace and abundance
   c. of fear and strife
   d. of great productivity 5. ______

6. Which of the following is true of the Golden Age?
   a. Winters were mild.
   b. Law was easily enforced.
   c. Abundant crops were planted and harvested.
   d. People were unhurried and happy. 6. ______

(continued)

7. Which of the following is a significant change in the Age of Silver?
   a. the changing of the seasons
   b. people began exploring new territories
   c. wars began
   d. nectar dripped from oak trees
   7. ______

8. Which Age followed the Age of Silver?
   a. Bronze
   b. Iron
   c. Copper
   d. Brass
   8. ______

9. Ovid describes the Iron Age as
   a. good
   b. indifferent
   c. hot
   d. evil
   9. ______

10. Which of the following is true in the Iron Age?
    a. People care for one another in times of need.
    b. Warfare is fought for any reason.
    c. The earth is valued as a precious resource.
    d. Family life is respected and virtuous.
    10. ______

NAME ______________________ CLASS ____________________ DATE ________ SCORE ______

THE BURNING OF ROME *from* THE ANNALS

Tacitus

translated by George Gilbert Ramsay (Textbook page 430)

DEVELOPING VOCABULARY

Directions: Read carefully the explanation of each word. Then write a sentence of your own using that word. In your sentence, include clues to the word's meaning.

calamitous (kə·lam′ə·təs) ***adj.*** Causing an extreme misfortune; disastrous. ▶ The noun form of this word is *calamity*, meaning "a disaster." ▪ The terrible storm brought calamitous winds to the tiny island. **Page 430**

ORIGINAL SENTENCE ____

____

tortuous (tôr′chōō·əs) ***adj.*** Winding; crooked; not straight. ▶ Do not confuse this word with *torturous*, which means "pertaining to torture." ▪ Drivers had to be especially careful on the tortuous mountain road. **Page 430**

ORIGINAL SENTENCE ____

____

inextricable (in·eks′tri·kə·bəl) ***adj.*** Incapable of being set free or disentangled from. ▶ A related definition is "too intricate or complicated to solve." ▪ After lying to several people about where he had been, he found himself in an inextricable web of deceit. **Page 431**

ORIGINAL SENTENCE ____

____

conducive (kən·dōōs′iv) ***adj.*** That contributes. ▶ This adjective is followed by the word *to*. ▪ Most people find that loud music is not conducive to effective studying. **Page 433**

ORIGINAL SENTENCE ____

____

(continued)

propitiate (prō·pish′ē·āt′) ***v.*** To appease or pacify. ▶ This verb connotes pacifying a higher power, such as a king or god that has been offended. ▪ After the failed revolution, the rebels who could not propitiate the king fled for their lives. **Page 433**

ORIGINAL SENTENCE ______________________________

____

bounty (boun′tē) ***n.*** 1. Reward. 2. Generosity. ▶ This word derives from the Latin word *bonus,* meaning "good." ▪ When they learned of the large bounty for the outlaws, the ranchers decided to track them down. **Page 434**

ORIGINAL SENTENCE ______________________________

____

avowal (ə·vou′əl) ***n.*** An open acknowledgment or admission. ▶ This word is the noun form of *avow,* which means "to acknowledge openly." ▪ A marriage ceremony is an avowal of mutual commitment. **Page 434**

ORIGINAL SENTENCE ______________________________

____

iniquity (i·nik′wi·tē) ***n.*** Wickedness; sinfulness; wrongdoing. ▶ This is a strong word that denotes a grossly immoral act or sin. ▪ Dante's *Inferno* describes his vision of the price sinners pay for their iniquity. **Page 434**

ORIGINAL SENTENCE ______________________________

____

atone (ə·tōn′) ***v.*** To make amends for. ▶ This verb is followed by the preposition *for.* ▪ He did extra chores for a week to atone for his reckless behavior. **Page 434**

ORIGINAL SENTENCE ______________________________

____

slake (slāk) ***v.*** 1. To satisfy; quench. 2. To cause a fire to die out. ▶ This word derives from the Middle English word meaning "to lessen." ▪ The ice water was just the thing to slake the runner's thirst. **Page 434**

ORIGINAL SENTENCE ______________________________

____

NAME ____________ CLASS ____________ DATE ________ SCORE ________

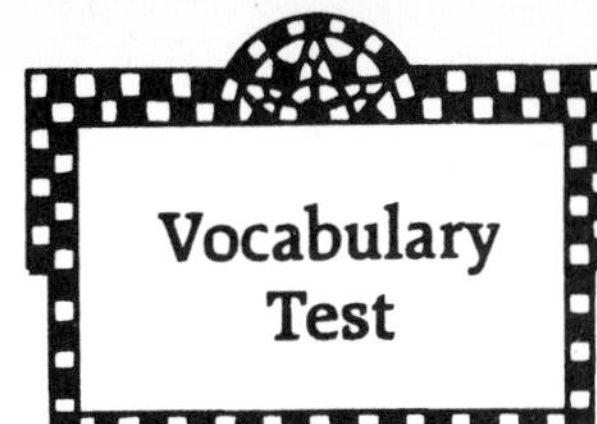

The Burning of Rome
from The Annals

Tacitus
translated by George Gilbert Ramsay (Textbook page 430)

VOCABULARY TEST

In the space provided, write the letter of the word or phrase closest in meaning to the word in italics. *(10 points each)*

1. *iniquity*: a. request for information b. clattering noise c. sinfulness; wrongdoing d. showing mercy — 1. ______
2. *conducive*: a. that contributes b. made firm c. highly pleasing d. very skillful — 2. ______
3. *slake*: a. to withhold b. to desire c. to satisfy d. to imagine — 3. ______
4. *inextricable*: a. lacking culture or refinement b. easily angered c. without caution d. incapable of being disentangled — 4. ______
5. *propitiate*: a. to triumph b. to appease or pacify c. to make believe d. to wipe or smear — 5. ______
6. *atone*: a. to make amends for b. to kneel c. to struggle towards a goal d. to boast — 6. ______
7. *tortuous*: a. smooth b. shiny c. winding d. painful — 7. ______
8. *avowal*: a. a secret b. an open acknowledgment c. a denial d. a diplomatic mission — 8. ______
9. *bounty*: a. punishment b. the sturdiest part of something c. a large cup d. reward — 9. ______
10. *calamitous*: a. bringing great joy b. loose or puffed out c. charming d. causing extreme misfortune — 10. ______

NAME ______________________ CLASS ______________ DATE ________ SCORE ______

THE BURNING OF ROME *from* THE ANNALS

Tacitus

translated by George Gilbert Ramsay (Textbook page 430)

REVIEWING THE SELECTION

1. At first, Tacitus says that no one is sure what caused the terrible fire that swept Rome. It may have been accidental, or (Greek soldiers/Emperor Nero) may have had it set. (Underline the correct answer.)

2. Emperor Nero returns to the city when the palace is burning. According to rumor, what does he do at the moment when the entire city is in flames?

____

____

3. How does Nero profit from the terrible fire?

____

____

4. Whom does Nero blame for the fire? What does he do to these people?

____

____

Reader's Response

On the lines below, write a dialogue in which Tacitus confronts Nero with his suspicion that Nero may have started the fire. How might the emperor defend himself? Continue your dialogue on a separate sheet of paper if necessary.

Tacitus: _______________________________________

____

Nero: ____

____

Tacitus: _______________________________________

____

NAME ______________________ CLASS ____________________ DATE ________ SCORE ________

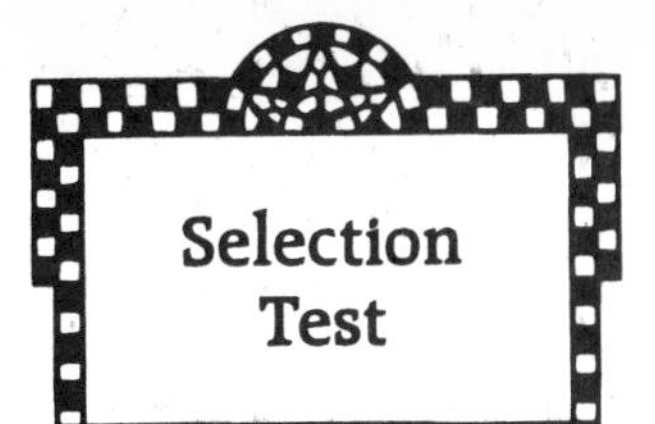

THE BURNING OF ROME
from THE ANNALS

Tacitus

translated by George Gilbert Ramsay (Textbook page 430)

READING COMPREHENSION

Directions: In the space provided, write the letter of the best answer to each question. *(10 points each)*

1. As a historian, Tacitus believed that
   a. he should weave his opinions into his accounts
   b. historical accounts should be purely objective
   c. only wars and great acts of destruction should be recorded
   d. Roman emperors were ruled by godly wisdom 1. ______

2. According to Tacitus, many of Rome's citizens lost their lives in the fire because
   a. Romans believed the fire was destined by the gods
   b. Nero ordered that the fires be allowed to burn
   c. the city's narrow streets caused the fire to rage freely, at the same time inhibiting people's escape
   d. people did not believe the fire was out of control 2. ______

3. What was Nero's initial response to the fire?
   a. He sang and danced in his royal gardens.
   b. He set up shelters, made provisions available, and lowered the price of grain.
   c. He fled the city for his country estate.
   d. He requested aid from neighboring countries. 3. ______

4. What rumor got started about where Nero was during the fire?
   a. Nero was in the first line of firefighters.
   b. Nero was hiding in the basement of the palace.
   c. Nero was out of the country.
   d. Nero was singing on the stage in his house. 4. ______

5. What was the general belief among the people when the fire broke out again in the open parts of the city?
   a. that Nero deliberately set the fire in order to build a new city
   b. that the gods were very angry with Nero
   c. that the gods were very angry with the Roman people
   d. that even the gods were powerless to control such a fierce fire 5. ______

(continued)

6. Which of the following was a result of the fire?
   a. the lingering death of Emperor Nero
   b. the violent uprising of the Roman people against Nero
   c. the fall of Troy
   d. the destruction of ancient monuments of Rome

6. ______

7. Why was Tacitus upset about Nero's new palace?
   a. It was much less grand than the old palace.
   b. Nero built it on the site of a former temple.
   c. Nero tried to create canals and landscapes that were wasteful and impractical.
   d. Many slaves died during its construction.

7. ______

8. The new city had
   a. carefully planned blocks and buildings
   b. narrow streets
   c. irregular blocks
   d. many new trees planted

8. ______

9. What did Nero do to the Christians?
   a. He exiled them from Rome.
   b. He gave them special places of honor in his court.
   c. He tortured and sacrificed them for entertainment.
   d. He made them bow down to him.

9. ______

10. What was Tacitus' attitude toward Nero's treatment of the Christians?
    a. He agreed with Nero's treatment.
    b. While he disapproved of Christians, he felt their deaths served no purpose.
    c. He thought Nero was too kind to the Christians.
    d. He was sympathetic, as he was a Christian himself.

10. ______

NAME ______________________ CLASS ____________________ DATE ________ SCORE ______

UNIT 4: GREEK AND ROMAN LITERATURES

WORD ANALOGIES/Extending Vocabulary

Directions: In the space provided, write the letter of the pair of words with the relationship that is closest to that of the capitalized words. *(10 points each)*

1. TIMOROUS : AFRAID ::
   a. powerful : meek
   b. shy : timid
   c. brave : cautious
   d. terror : horrible
   1. ______

2. ACQUITTAL : LIBERATE ::
   a. conviction : imprison
   b. innocence : defend
   c. guilt : pardon
   d. criminal : punish
   2. ______

3. LOATH : WILLING ::
   a. anxious : ready
   b. idle : lazy
   c. agreeable : conditional
   d. reluctant : eager
   3. ______

4. RELENT : YIELD ::
   a. surrender : oppose
   b. regret : enjoy
   c. resist : defy
   d. destroy : create
   4. ______

5. DECREPIT : VIGOROUS ::
   a. young : energetic
   b. tame : domestic
   c. wasteful : useful
   d. weak : strong
   5. ______

6. GOAD : DISCOURAGE ::
   a. urge on : warn against
   b. convince : confuse
   c. push away : force to
   d. prevent : stop
   6. ______

7. OBSCURITY : UNKNOWN ::
   a. esteem : weak
   b. prestige : famous
   c. isolation : friendly
   d. deception : honest
   7. ______

8. INIQUITY : WICKED ::
   a. truth : dishonest
   b. purity : virtuous
   c. good : evil
   d. justice : legal
   8. ______

9. SAGE : WISDOM ::
   a. doctor : illness
   b. poet : fame
   c. athlete : team
   d. warrior : courage
   9. ______

10. DESTITUTE : POVERTY ::
    a. opulent : beggar
    b. rich : poor
    c. wealthy : prosperity
    d. penniless : money
    10. ______

NAME ______________________ CLASS ______________________ DATE __________ SCORE __________

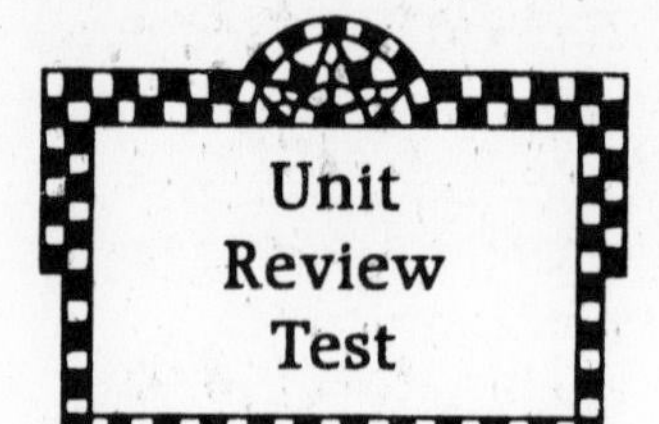

UNIT 4: GREEK AND ROMAN LITERATURES

UNIT REVIEW TEST/Applying Skills I

A. Reading Comprehension. In the space provided, write the letter of the best answer to each question. *(8 points each)*

1. In the *Iliad*, by Homer, which of the following best describes the relationship between Achilles and Agamemnon?
   a. long-time enemies
   b. brothers fighting an enemy attack
   c. father and son
   d. military co-leaders who get into a fight

   1. ______

2. In Book 22 of the *Iliad*, Hector fights Achilles
   a. on the battlefield with the Trojan army
   b. all alone outside the city walls
   c. on the high seas
   d. in their chariots on the battlefield

   2. ______

3. What terrible secret does Oedipus learn in the play *Oedipus Rex* by Sophocles?
   a. His wife murdered his brother.
   b. His son has planned to kill him and overtake the throne.
   c. He has murdered his father and married his mother.
   d. The plague has killed his parents.

   3. ______

4. Where does Socrates give the monologue described by Plato in the *Apology*?
   a. in the streets of Athens
   b. in his home
   c. in a courtroom
   d. in a classroom in his school

   4. ______

5. In the *Aeneid* by Virgil, the Trojans are
   a. surprised by Greeks who invade Troy inside a wooden horse
   b. happy over their defeat of the Greek army
   c. preparing to sail for Greece
   d. upset about King Priam's marriage

   5. ______

6. In *The Burning of Rome*, whom does Tacitus blame for the fire?
   a. careless soldiers
   b. Emperor Nero
   c. the Christians
   d. the Greeks

   6. ______

(continued)

B. Identifying Characters. Each description below refers to a main character or speaker in one of the selections you have just read. Identify the character or speaker by choosing the letter of the best answer. Write the letter in the space provided. *(8 points each)*

7. He searches the city for his lost wife, calling her name in the darkness, until her ghost appears to him and urges him not to grieve.

   a. Aeneas in the *Aeneid* c. Oedipus in *Oedipus Rex*
   b. Socrates in the *Apology* d. Hector in the *Iliad* 7.______

8. He wants to know about his birth and his family, no matter how unpleasant the knowledge might be.

   a. Achilles in the *Iliad* c. Oedipus in *Oedipus Rex*
   b. King Priam in the *Aeneid* d. Hector in the *Iliad* 8.______

9. This poet says goodbye to a former love, vows to stop praising her, and wants to stop playing the fool.

   a. Virgil in the *Aeneid*
   b. Catullus in his lyric poems
   c. Creon in *Oedipus Rex*
   d. Horace in his odes 9.______

10. He feels that the whole earth is a monument to dead heroes, for they live in the hearts and memories of all people, and he feels that praise of Athens is praise of its dead heroes.

   a. Pericles in the *Funeral Speech of Pericles*
   b. Agamemnon in the *Iliad*
   c. King Priam in the *Aeneid*
   d. Socrates in the *Apology* 10.______

C. Composition. Choose *one* of these topics and write a brief essay on a separate sheet of paper. *(20 points)*

1. Compare and contrast the battle between Achilles and Hector in the *Iliad* and the battle between Aeneas and the Greek invaders in the *Aeneid.* Consider the causes, events, and results of the two battles.

2. Oedipus in *Oedipus Rex* and the Trojan people in the *Aeneid* both pay a huge price for ignoring reason and pursuing reckless actions. Describe their actions and the dire consequences that result. Explain how and why Oedipus and the Trojans missed clues that might have enabled them to avert the tragedies suffered by those involved.

NAME ______________________ CLASS ______________________ DATE __________ SCORE __________

UNIT 4: GREEK AND ROMAN LITERATURES

CRITICAL THINKING AND WRITING/Applying Skills II

A. Reading a Dialogue Excerpt. Read the excerpt carefully. Then answer the questions that follow.

from the PHAEDO

Plato

translated by

BENJAMIN JOWETT

The dialogue* Phaedo, *from Plato's* Dialogues, *records a conversation between Socrates and his disciples just before Socrates' death. In this excerpt, Socrates continues a discussion about the soul's immortality and the afterlife. Simmias, Cebes, and Crito are disciples of Socrates.

"Wherefore, Simmias, seeing all these things, what ought not we to do that we may obtain virtue and wisdom in this life? Fair is the prize, and the hope great!

"A man of sense ought not to say, nor will I be very confident, that the description which I have given of the soul and her mansions is exactly true. But I do say that, inasmuch as the soul is shown to be immortal, he may venture to think, not improperly or unworthily, that something of the kind is true. The venture is a glorious one, and he ought to comfort himself with words like these, which is the reason why I lengthen out the tale. Wherefore, I say, let a man be of good cheer about his soul, who having cast away the pleasures and ornaments of the body as alien to him and working harm rather than good, has sought after the pleasure of knowledge; and has arrayed the soul, not in some foreign attire, but in her own proper jewels, temperance, and justice, and courage, and nobility, and truth—in these adorned she is ready to go on her journey to the world below, when her hour comes. You, Simmias and Cebes, and all other men will depart at some time or other. Me already, as a tragic poet would say, the voice of fate calls. Soon I must drink the poison; and I think that I had better repair to the bath first, in order that the women may not have the trouble of washing my body after I am dead."

When he had done speaking, Crito said: "And have you any commands for us, Socrates—anything to say about your children, or any other matter in which we can serve you?"

"Nothing particular, Crito," he replied; "only, as I have always told you, take care of yourselves; that is a service which you may be ever rendering to me and mine and to all of us, whether you promise to do so or not. But if you have no

(continued)

thought for yourselves and care not to walk according to the rule which I have prescribed for you, not now for the first time, however much you may profess or promise at the moment, it will be of no avail."

"We will do our best," said Crito, "And in what way shall we bury you?"

"In any way that you like; but you must get hold of me and take care that I do not run away from you."

Then he turned to us and added with a smile: "I cannot make Crito believe that I am the same Socrates who has been talking and conducting the argument; he fancies that I am the other Socrates whom he will soon see, a dead body—and he asks, How shall he bury me? And though I have spoken many words in the endeavor to show that when I have drunk the poison I shall leave you and go to the joys of the blessed—these words of mine, with which I was comforting you and myself, have had, as I perceive, no effect upon Crito. And therefore I want you to be surety for me to him now, as at the trial he was surety to the judges for me; but let the promise be of another sort; for he was surety for me to the judges that I would remain, and you must be my surety to him that I shall not remain, but go away and depart; and then he will suffer less at my death and not be grieved when he sees my body being burned or buried. I would not have him sorrow at my hard lot or say at the burial, 'Thus we lay out Socrates,' or, 'Thus we follow him to the grave or bury him'; for false words are not only evil in themselves, but they infect the soul with evil. Be of good cheer then, my dear Crito, and say that you are burying my body only, and do with that whatever is usual, and what you think best."

B. Analyzing a Dialogue Excerpt. In the space provided, write the letter of the best answer to each question. *(6 points each)*

1. What is Socrates' attitude toward his own death?
   a. He fears it.
   b. He wants to avoid it.
   c. He sees it as a journey for the soul and does not fear it.
   d. He regrets that he must die because his work on earth is unfinished. 1. ______

2. Socrates' attitude toward his disciples and others is one of
   a. impatience
   b. consideration
   c. anger
   d. indifference 2. ______

3. What does Socrates say the soul should be dressed in?
   a. temperance, justice, and courage
   b. the pride of a person's achievements
   c. the jewels of pleasure and indulgence
   d. patience, caution, and foresight 3. ______

(continued)

4. To what does the "voice of fate" call Socrates?
   a. a bath
   b. poison
   c. an escape from prison
   d. a reunion with his family
   4. ______

5. What is Socrates' attitude about funeral preparations?
   a. They should be made well in advance.
   b. Cremation is preferable to burial.
   c. A tomb should be prepared for the soul's comfort in the afterlife.
   d. He is indifferent to funeral preparations because death means a separation of the body and the soul.
   5. ______

6. What words best describe the **tone**, or feeling, behind Socrates' conversation?
   a. serious and morbid
   b. sad and mournful
   c. philosophical but playful
   d. angry but resigned
   6. ______

7. Socrates demonstrates his **verbal irony** by saying something that is very different from what might be expected. Why is his comment about bathing before dying ironic?
   a. He makes a joke during a very serious moment.
   b. He does not like to take baths.
   c. His students, not the women, will give him a bath.
   d. It is not customary for Greeks to wash dead bodies.
   7. ______

8. Which of these items best describes the attitude of Socrates' disciple Crito?
   a. Crito is angry at Socrates' comments.
   b. Crito is relieved at not having to serve Socrates further.
   c. Crito is comforted by Socrates' comments.
   d. Crito deeply grieves at the thought of Socrates' death.
   8. ______

9. The ancient Greeks enjoyed tragedies. Although these events in Socrates' life were real, how might they be viewed as a tragedy?
   a. Socrates does not try to prevent his own death.
   b. Even a good and noble person like Socrates can suffer at the hands of fate.
   c. No one tries to talk Socrates into defending himself.
   d. Socrates takes his own life by drinking the poison.
   9. ______

10. What do you think was Plato's main purpose in writing this dialogue describing the last moments of Socrates' life?
    a. to portray Socrates' weakness in not trying to prevent his own death
    b. to show the judicious character of the people who condemned him to death
    c. to show that Socrates died as he lived—searching for and teaching about truth
    d. to show that his students do not really understand Socrates
    10. ______

(continued)

C. Writing About a Dialogue Excerpt

Socrates was Plato's teacher and mentor. In a sense, Socrates was a hero to Plato, and Plato's *Dialogues* is a portrait of this hero. How does the *Phaedo* show Socrates' heroism? What traits of Socrates does Plato portray that qualify Socrates as a hero? Write one paragraph describing Socrates' heroic traits as Plato reveals them in the *Phaedo*. Use examples from the excerpt to support your answer. *(40 points)*

Unit 4: Greek and Roman Literatures

UNIT INTRODUCTION TEST/Greek Literature
(Textbook pages 214–223)

1. c
2. b
3. a
4. b
5. b
6. b
7. a
8. c
9. c
10. d

from the Iliad, *from* Book 1

Homer
translated by Robert Fitzgerald
(Textbook page 229)

VOCABULARY ACTIVITY WORKSHEET

Developing Vocabulary
Responses will vary.

VOCABULARY TEST

1. b
2. a
3. c
4. c
5. a
6. b
7. d
8. c
9. a
10. d

REVIEW AND RESPONSE WORKSHEET

Reviewing the Selection

1. Agamemnon (called the Lord Marshal) is the leader of the Greek forces. Achilles (called a prince) is the greatest Greek warrior.
2. The entire book is based on a quarrel between Agamemnon and Achilles that begins when Agamemnon takes Briseis away from Achilles, gravely offending the latter's honor.
3. He hands her over because Athena has advised him to and has promised him rich rewards in the future.
4. a

Reader's Response
Answers will vary. Some students may imagine that Briseis, a captive, resents or fears Achilles as much as Agamemnon. Others may imagine that she prefers Achilles' slightly more reasonable personality to Agamemnon's overbearing ways.

SELECTION TEST

Reading Comprehension

1. b
2. b
3. c
4. d
5. a
6. d
7. b
8. a
9. c
10. a

from the Iliad, *from* Books 22 *and* 24

Homer
translated by Robert Fitzgerald
(Textbook page 246)

VOCABULARY ACTIVITY WORKSHEET

Develping Vocabulary
Responses will vary.

VOCABULARY TEST

1. ponderous
2. flouted
3. defiling
4. bereaved
5. allay
6. implacable
7. Resolute
8. deft
9. felicity
10. shrouded

REVIEW AND RESPONSE WORKSHEET

Reviewing the Selection

1. He is ashamed, feeling responsible for the heavy losses the Trojans have suffered be-

(continued)

cause in his pride he refused to allow them to retreat from Achilles sooner. Even now, he is too proud to back down from what he feels is his duty, however futile.

2. b
3. In his great anger, Achilles says that dogs and birds will eat Hector's body before Hector has a proper funeral.
4. a. Priam pleads on his knees for the return of Hector's body.
   b. Patroclus is eventually buried by the Greeks with proper rites.
   c. Hermes helps Hector's father to enter the Greek camp.
   d. Achilles weeps with Hector's father.

Reader's Response

Responses will vary. Students may draw examples from personal experience (for example, a time when an angry outburst cost a friendship) or from political or historical events (for example, wars or massacres).

SELECTION TEST

Reading Comprehension

1. d	5. d	8. b
2. b	6. b	9. d
3. c	7. b	10. c
4. a		

LANGUAGE SKILLS WORKSHEET

Transitional Expressions
Exercise 1

1. Although, still	6. moreover, too
2. and	7. As a result
3. so	8. provided that
4. In spite of, so	9. Of course
5. Since	10. Furthermore

Exercise 2

Responses may vary. Sample sentences:

1. The invocation that begins the poem is a formal plea to the Muse for help and states the poem's theme.
2. Homer uses *in medias res;* therefore, the poem starts in the middle of the action.
3. Since *in medias res* means the reader might not know what happened previously, Homer uses flashbacks to show previous actions.
4. Although there were poets before Homer who created poems in the oral traditions, Homer is among the first poets whose work was recorded in writing.
5. Certain features of Homer's epic poems were widely imitated; for example, Virgil used these features in the *Aeneid* and Milton used these features in *Paradise Lost.*

Exercise 3

Students' paragraphs will vary. Sample paragraph:

Because the *Iliad* is an extremely long poem and was recited orally, it was probably difficult to maintain the poem's metrical structure. For this reason, Homer uses devices such as the *stock epithet.* The stock epithet is a word or phrase that is repeatedly used to describe a character. For example, Hector, the Trojan hero, is referred to as "tamer of horses," and Zeus, the father-god, is sometimes "Father of the blinding bolt." Each character has more than one stock epithet. Homer probably chose the epithet according to the context and his metrical needs. The stock epithet had other uses, also. It reminded the audience of a character's traits and helped them follow the action. It may also have lessened demands on Homer's memory, since the epithets were drawn from a memory pool and not created each time.

(continued)

Lyric Poems

Sappho
translated by Mary Barnard
(Textbook page 281)

REVIEW AND RESPONSE WORKSHEET

Reviewing the Selections

1. a. sheep b. goats c. children
2. Cleis (the speaker's daughter); the bride
3. a. The speaker in "To an Army Wife, in Sardis" says that whatever one loves is the best sight on earth.
   b. Someone in bed alone watches the moon and stars set and feels time passing.
   c. The speaker in "Don't Ask Me What to Wear" was dark-haired and wore an embroidered headband.
4. golden, fresh flowers

Reader's Response

Responses will vary. Students may list public events like sports competitions, debates, charity work, and so forth, or more personal events, such as helping friends through difficult times or achieving personal goals.

Funeral Speech of Pericles *from* History of the Peloponnesian War

Thucydides
translated by Benjamin Jowett
(Textbook page 286)

VOCABULARY ACTIVITY WORKSHEET

Developing Vocabulary

Responses will vary.

VOCABULARY TEST

1. g
2. c
3. j
4. d
5. f
6. e
7. i
8. a
9. h
10. b

REVIEW AND RESPONSE WORKSHEET

Reviewing the Selection

1. Students might list any of the following reasons: The reputations of many should not rest on the eloquence of one; it is difficult to avoid exaggeration or understatement; it is difficult to satisfy everyone in the audience; those who knew the dead are likely to think the speaker says too little, while those who did not know the dead are likely to feel envious; listeners may not believe the speaker.
2. democratic, adaptable, respectful, cheerful, tolerant, courageous, simple
3. Athens might be taken from them.
4. dishonor, people's hearts (the hearts of men)

Reader's Response

Responses will vary. Students should note that Pericles urges the parents of the fallen heroes to have more children if they can, and to take pleasure in their memories and in the honor the heroes have earned. He exhorts siblings to try to live up to the heroes' examples and acknowledges that it will be difficult. He also reminds bereaved family members that the heroes' children will be supported by the government. His admonition to women—that they not show more than their "natural" weakness nor be the object of gossip—may alienate some students.

LANGUAGE SKILLS WORKSHEET

Repetition and Wordiness

Exercise 1

1. Athens does not copy its neighbors, but is an example to them in the various and different areas of government, military, and daily life.
2. The form of government used by the people in Athens is democracy.
3. The military training by which the city trains its soldiers in Athens is excellent.

(continued)

4. The Athenians enjoy relaxing from their work and the jobs they do all day long.
5. Athens is very proud of its military and soldiers and fighting ships that protect the city.
6. The Athenian people are very brave and have great courage in battle.
7. All in all, considering the entire picture, the people of Athens pride themselves on thinking before they act.
8. Pericles praises the attitude, and bravery and courage of the men who died fighting for the city of Athens.
9. Pericles comforts the parents of the dead soldiers who died on the battlefield while fighting for Athens by reminding them of the honor of a soldier's death.
10. Pericles emphasizes and focuses his speech on the rewards of virtue that the people of Athens should seek.

Exercise 2

Sentences may vary. Sample sentences:

1. Pericles begins his speech by telling his listeners how difficult giving a funeral speech is.
2. Pericles then explains that it is hard to satisfy the family and friends of the dead with words that accurately describe the dead soldiers' virtues.
3. Pericles decides that the first thing to do in a funeral oration is to praise Athens's ancestors.
4. Next, Pericles explains that it makes sense to praise first the ancestors, because their hard work and sacrifices made Athens great.
5. The funeral speech that Pericles gives to honor the dead soldiers actually spends a great deal of time honoring Athens's ancestors.

Exercise 3

Students' revised paragraphs will vary. Sample paragraph:

Thucydides was a great historian who wrote about Athens. One way that he presented Athenian history was through the speeches of famous people. These speeches show the values of the people being addressed. For example, Pericles' funeral speech is very patriotic. Thucydides believed that the speech represented the viewpoint of the Athenians. By writing history through famous speeches, Thucydides was able to show the values of the people as well as events.

SELECTION TEST

Reading Comprehension

1. b
2. c
3. a
4. b
5. b
6. d
7. b
8. b
9. a
10. a

from the APOLOGY

Plato

translated by Benjamin Jowett

(Textbook page 295)

VOCABULARY ACTIVITY WORKSHEET

Developing Vocabulary

Responses will vary.

VOCABULARY TEST

A. 1. b
2. a
3. d
4. a
5. c

B. 6. intimation
7. reprove
8. procure
9. acquit
10. censure

(continued)

REVIEW AND RESPONSE WORKSHEET
Reviewing the Selection
1. b
2. internal oracle
3. a
4. care more about riches than about virtue; pretend they are more than they really are; justice

Reader's Response
Responses will vary. Students might use ideas expressed in the selection: that things that seem bad may actually be good; that events, good and bad, do not happen by chance, for fate has purposes that mortals cannot see; that the gods do not neglect the good people; that virtue ("righteousness") is its own reward.

LANGUAGE SKILLS WORKSHEET

Noun Clauses

Exercise 1
Students should underline the following groups of words:
1. what he teaches to young minds
2. that Socrates will apologize
3. what they expect
4. what a man facing death might be expected to say
5. that he will not resort to wailing and lamenting
6. whoever will listen/that he prefers death to unrighteousness
7. that trying to escape death by lying is wrong
8. whoever would condemn him
9. what Socrates says/that he is not afraid to die
10. What appeals to him about death

Exercise 2
Answers will vary. Sample sentences:
1. Socrates explains that he sees death as a good.
2. That death is like a journey is Socrates' belief.
3. Socrates wants to continue his search for what is true.
4. Socrates realizes that his oracle, his inner guide, does not oppose him.
5. Socrates requests that the judges punish his sons if they care too little about virtue.

Exercise 3
Students' revised paragraphs will vary. Sample revision:

Plato wrote about Socrates, who was Plato's beloved teacher. What we know about Socrates comes mostly from Plato's writings. Socrates did not record what the nature of his personal philosophy was. He spent most of his time teaching whoever was eager to pursue the truth. Plato describes the teaching method Socrates used. Instead of preaching or offering his own solutions, Socrates insisted that students question all ideas. This method of questioning is known as the Socratic method. Plato tried to capture who Socrates was by writing the *Dialogues.*

SELECTION TEST

Reading Comprehension
1. d
2. a
3. a
4. d
5. c
6. d
7. d
8. c
9. a
10. c

(continued)

OEDIPUS REX

Sophocles
translated by Dudley Fitts and
Robert Fitzgerald
(Textbook page 307)

VOCABULARY ACTIVITY WORKSHEET

Developing Vocabulary

Responses will vary.

VOCABULARY TEST

1. a	5. b	8. b
2. c	6. c	9. a
3. b	7. d	10. c
4. a		

OEDIPUS REX, PART 1

REVIEW AND RESPONSE WORKSHEET

Reviewing the Selection

1. Apollo
2. a. King Laius's murderer must be found.
   b. that he will avenge the death of Laius
3. Teiresias; Creon; Oedipus is the murderer
4. a. Queen Jocasta tells Oedipus to ignore seers and prophecies.
   b. The shepherd is the only witness to the killing of Laius.
   c. A drunken man in Corinth once said that Oedipus was not his father's son.
   d. Oedipus once killed someone who forced him off the road.

Reader's Response

Responses will vary. Students may mention Oedipus's refusal to see the clues that point to his own guilt as the murderer of King Laius. Oedipus's most obvious weakness, though, is his pride, which prevents him from making peace with Creon, from leaving Thebes once he suspects his guilt, and from listening to Teiresias' and Jocasta's warnings. His pride also urges him to summon the shepherd.

SELECTION TEST

Reading Comprehension

1. b	5. c	8. d
2. a	6. d	9. d
3. d	7. a	10. b
4. b		

OEDIPUS REX, PART 2

REVIEW AND RESPONSE WORKSHEET

Reviewing the Selection

1. Oedipus; Corinth
2. Queen Jocasta
3. hangs herself; blinds himself
4. Responses will vary. Students might mention any two of the following items: to drive Oedipus into exile; to protect Oedipus's two daughters; to let Oedipus talk with his daughters once more; to let Oedipus go to the mountains where he was abandoned as a baby; not to take his daughters away from him.

Reader's Response

Responses will vary. Some students may feel that Oedipus was an innocent victim of circumstance and that he made a greater attempt than most people do to live virtuously. Others may feel that Oedipus deserved to suffer for the arrogance he showed, both as a young prince who murdered five people just because he was run off the road, and as a king who, instead of admitting his own ignorance, threatened and condemned an honorable prophet and a loyal brother-in-law.

(continued)

SELECTION TEST

Reading Comprehension

1. b
2. a
3. b
4. c
5. c
6. b
7. b
8. b
9. a
10. b

LANGUAGE SKILLS WORKSHEET

Dangling and Misplaced Modifiers

Exercise 1

1. D
2. M
3. C
4. D
5. M
6. D
7. M
8. C
9. M
10. C

Exercise 2

Responses will vary. Possible sentences:

1. Oedipus learns from the messenger that King Polybus is not his real father.
2. When he was a baby, Oedipus was rescued by the messenger.
3. The messenger had cut the bonds that tied the baby's ankles together.
4. The messenger gave the baby that he rescued to King Polybus.
5. Deeply anguished by the truth, Oedipus blinded himself.

Exercise 3

Students' revised paragraphs may vary. Sample paragraph:

Sophocles wrote *Oedipus Rex* as part of a trilogy about King Oedipus and his family. It is the first play of the trilogy. Much of the play is dialogue. In fact, most of the action that is violent takes place offstage. Oedipus's ignorance of the truth, which is gradually revealed throughout the play, is the central problem. Irony is one of the elements that makes the play so popular among audiences. The audience knows the truth about Oedipus almost from the beginning. Hearing the dramatically ironic words of Oedipus increases the enjoyment of the play.

UNIT INTRODUCTION TEST/Roman Literature
(Textbook pages 372–378)

1. a
2. b
3. a
4. b
5. a
6. c
7. d
8. d
9. c
10. a

from the AENEID, *from* BOOK 2

Virgil
translated by Robert Fitzgerald
(Textbook page 383)

VOCABULARY ACTIVITY WORKSHEET

Developing Vocabulary

Responses will vary.

VOCABULARY TEST

1. b
2. a
3. c
4. c
5. d
6. a
7. c
8. b
9. a
10. b

REVIEW AND RESPONSE WORKSHEET

Reviewing the Selection

1. wooden horse, Greek soldiers
2. Twin snakes come from the water and wrap themselves around Laocoon and his two sons.
3. Priam
4. a. Cassandra warns against bringing the wooden horse into the city of Troy.
   b. Aeneas's mother prevents Aeneas from killing Helen.
   c. Aeneas becomes the leader of a group of refugees.
   d. Creusa is killed but appears in a vision to say goodbye.

Reader's Response

Responses will vary. Students may recount events ranging from surprise parties to failing a class or losing an athletic competition.

(continued)

They may find parallels between their reasons for missing the clues and the Trojans' reasons for missing the clues related to the wooden horse left by the Greeks.

LANGUAGE SKILLS WORKSHEET

Parallel Structure

Exercise 1

1. C	5. F	8. F
2. F	6. C	9. C
3. F	7. F	10. F
4. C		

Exercise 2

Students' sentences may vary somewhat. Sample sentences:

1. To stop the attacking Greeks, the Trojans hurl down rooftiles, beams, and precious ornaments as missiles.
2. The small band of Trojan soldiers fights both bravely and skillfully in a hopeless situation.
3. Queen Hecuba begs King Priam to take off his weapons and to join her at the altar for protection.
4. Aeneas blames Helen both for the fall of Troy and for the murder of King Priam.
5. His mother tells Aeneas not to kill Helen out of revenge and to go home to check on his family.

Exercise 3

Students' revisions will vary. Sample paragraphs:

Virgil's *Aeneid* is an epic poem with all the makings of a smash movie hit. It has great characters, action, suspense, and special effects. Aeneas would make a great movie superstar. He is a man who loves both action and his family. He fights the forces of evil both outside and inside himself. He tricks the Greeks by disguising himself, slays Greek soldiers by the dozen, and struggles to keep his own thirst for revenge in control. He's a hero who has not only courage, but also a conscience.

The *Aeneid's* action begins with the discovery of a huge wooden horse and ends with the tragic death of the hero's wife. There are snake bites, surprise attacks, life-and-death battles, and tearful farewells. The action is full of suspense because the many battles mean either life or death for the people of Troy. The reader might know from the beginning that Troy is eventually destroyed. But he or she doesn't know if the men in Aeneas's small band all live, if Helen survives, or if Aeneas protects his family. The poem even has special effects. The wooden horse clangs mysteriously, snakes suddenly bite the priest, and a fire rages furiously in the dark night. The *Aeneid* may be almost two thousand years old, but with some polish and a little buffing, it could be a great hit.

SELECTION TEST

Reading Comprehension

1. b	5. c	8. b
2. c	6. c	9. c
3. a	7. d	10. a
4. b		

LYRIC POEMS

Catullus

translated by Reney Myers, Robert J. Ormsby, and Peter Whigham
(Textbook page 411)

REVIEW AND RESPONSE WORKSHEET

Reviewing the Selections

1. Responses will vary. Students might mention any two of the following items: He will pass her up; won't need her; won't think of her; will not try to spend time with her; won't invite her anywhere; won't praise her; won't try to make her happy when she's sad; won't love her; won't kiss her; will abstain.

(continued)

2. air, running water
3. He says that, indeed, he *cannot* explain them.
4. Lesbia's unexpected return to him after he thought the relationship was over

Reader's Response

Responses will vary. Students may quote lines or phrases from popular songs or create lines of their own and may either explain how the lyrics relate to their experiences or describe the feelings or thoughts the lyrics evoke in them.

THE GOLDEN MEAN *and* CARPE DIEM

Horace
translated by William Cowper and Thomas Hawkins
(Textbook page 416)

VOCABULARY ACTIVITY WORKSHEET

Developing Vocabulary

Responses will vary.

VOCABULARY TEST

A. 1. b
2. e
3. c
4. d
5. a

B. 6. timorous
7. protract
8. adverse
9. eminence
10. magnanimous

REVIEW AND RESPONSE WORKSHEET

Reviewing the Selections

1. a. are blasted most strongly by the wind
   b. falls down hardest
   c. is struck by lightning
2. show their strength and generosity
3. take in half their canvas (or, roll up half their sail; or, slow down; or, try not to achieve too much)
4. this day

Reader's Response

Responses will vary. Students may comment on the price of too much stress and too much work. People who work very hard so that they can have nice things often don't have time to enjoy them. On the other hand, not striving at all might be considered lazy or selfish, and might eventually become boring.

from METAMORPHOSES

Ovid
translated by Rolfe Humphries
(Textbook page 422)

VOCABULARY ACTIVITY WORKSHEET

Developing Vocabulary

Responses will vary.

VOCABULARY TEST

1. g
2. f
3. d
4. h
5. i
6. e
7. c
8. b
9. j
10. a

REVIEW AND RESPONSE WORKSHEET

Reviewing the Selection

1. chaos
2. A being with a more capable mind, a ruler, was needed.
3. Responses will vary. Students might list any of the following items: people had no laws; needed no judges; did not make boats; did not have towns; did not have weapons or wars; did not farm.
4. underground metals, specifically gold and iron

(continued)

Reader's Response

Responses will vary. Students may suggest either direct or metaphorical terms reflecting social, political, or environmental issues.

SELECTION TEST

Reading Comprehension

1. c	5. b	8. a
2. a	6. d	9. d
3. b	7. a	10. b
4. d		

THE BURNING OF ROME

Tacitus

translated by George Gilbert Ramsay

(Textbook page 430)

VOCABULARY ACTIVITY WORKSHEET

Developing Vocabulary

Responses will vary.

VOCABULARY TEST

1. c	5. b	8. b
2. a	6. a	9. d
3. c	7. c	10. d
4. d		

REVIEW AND RESPONSE WORKSHEET

Reviewing the Selection

1. Emperor Nero
2. He mounts a stage and sings of the siege of Troy.
3. Nero profits by building himself a new palace with marvelously landscaped grounds: the rebuilt town has more regular blocks, broader streets, and lower houses; houses have more fire safety features, and water availability is improved.
4. Christians. He tortures them cruelly by having them torn to pieces by dogs, crucified, burned, and so on.

Reader's Response

Responses will vary, but students should show an awareness of Tacitus's deep mistrust of the emperor and enmity toward him. They may also note that Nero's grandiose plans are out of touch with the concerns of the everyday citizen.

SELECTION TEST

Reading Comprehension

1. a	5. a	8. a
2. c	6. d	9. c
3. b	7. c	10. b
4. d		

WORD ANALOGIES/Extending Vocabulary

1. b (timorous : afraid : : shy : timid)
   Relationship : synonyms
   Timorous, and *afraid* are synonyms sharing the meaning "fearful." *Shy* and *timid* are synonyms sharing that same meaning. The analogy is strengthened by the fact that the four words are all synonyms of each other.
2. a (acquittal : liberate : : conviction : imprison)
   Relationship : cause and effect
   One is *liberated* as the result of an *acquittal*, that is, "the clearing of charges." One is *imprisoned* as the result of a *conviction*. The analogy is strengthened by the fact that *acquittal* and *conviction* are opposites, as are *liberate* and *imprison*.
3. d (loath : willing : : reluctant : eager)
   Relationship: antonyms
   Loath, "unwilling," is an antonym of *willing*. *Reluctant* and *eager* are also antonyms. The analogy is strengthened by the fact that *loath* and *reluctant* are synonyms of each other, as are *willing* and *eager*.

(continued)

4. c (relent : yield : : resist : defy)
Relationship : synonyms
Relent and *yield* are synonyms sharing the meaning "to give up." *Resist* and *defy* are synonyms sharing the meaning "not to give up." The analogy is strengthened by the fact that *relent* and *resist* are antonyms of each other, as are *yield* and *defy.*
5. d (decrepit : vigorous : : weak : strong)
Relationship : antonyms
Decrepit, "weak or worn out," is an antonym of *vigorous. Weak* is an antonym of *strong.* The analogy is strengthened by the fact that *decrepit* and *weak* are synonyms, as are *vigorous* and *strong.*
6. a (goad : discourage : : urge on : warn against)
Relationship: antonyms
Goad, "to spur into action," is an antonym of *discourage. Urge on* is the opposite of *warn against.* The analogy is strengthened by the fact that *goad* and *urge on* have the same meaning, as do *discourage* and *warn against.*
7. b (obscurity : unknown : : prestige : famous)
Relationship : object (condition) to characteristic
Someone who lives in *obscurity,* "lack of fame," has the characteristic of being *unknown.* Someone of *prestige* has the characteristic of being *famous.*
8. b (iniquity : wicked : : purity: virtuous)
Relationship: object (quality) to characteristic
Iniquity, "sinfulness," has the characteristic of being *wicked. Purity* has the characteristic of being *virtuous.* The analogy is strengthened by the fact that *iniquity* and *purity* are opposites, as are *wicked* and *virtuous.*
9. d (sage : wisdom : : warrior : courage)
Relationship: person to quality
A *sage* is known for the quality of *wisdom.* A *warrior* is known for the quality of *courage.*
10. c (destitute : poverty : : wealthy : prosperity)
Relationship : object (condition) to characteristic
Poverty is a characteristic of the *destitute. Prosperity* is a characteristic of the *wealthy.* The analogy is strengthened by the fact that *destitute* and *wealthy* are opposites, as are *poverty* and *prosperity.*

UNIT REVIEW TEST/Applying Skills I

A. Reading Comprehension

1. d	4. c
2. b	5. a
3. c	6. b

B. Identifying Characters

7. a	9. b
8. c	10. a

C. Composition

Responses will vary. Important points to cover are included below.

1. Differences:

- The battle between Hector and Achilles is one-on-one, while Aeneas and his band are greatly outnumbered.
- The battle between Hector and Achilles is described briefly, as Homer pays more attention to the thoughts and words of the two men as they prepare to fight; although Virgil also focuses on Aeneas's thoughts and feelings, he describes a lengthy and violent battle between the Greeks and Aeneas's band of fighters.
- The outcome: the Greek Achilles humiliates the fallen Trojan Hector in front of his family by dragging his body around the city walls; the Trojan Aeneas fights bravely and survives to escape with his father and son.
- The story of the *Iliad* is told by a third per-

(continued)

son narrator, while Aeneas tells the story of the fall of Troy in the first person.

Similarities:

- The goddess Athena intervenes between Hector and Achilles; during the fall of Troy Aeneas is visited by his mother, the goddess Venus.
- In both cases, the battles are between Greeks and Trojans, and the main characters fight for their own honor as well as for their people.
- The heroes in both battles are depicted as bold and brave, but with some capacity for sympathy, fear, and regret.
- Both battles illustrate the terrible price of conflict.

2. Reckless actions despite obvious clues include:

Oedipus's determination to find the murderer of King Laius despite warnings from the prophet Teiresias and Oedipus's wife, Queen Jocasta. When it becomes clear that by murdering King Laius, Oedipus had fulfilled the first part of the prophecy that he would someday murder his own father, Oedipus still insists on knowing the secret of his birth. The discovery, despite repeated warnings, that he has married his own mother, leads to Jocasta's death and Oedipus's blindness and exile. Oedipus might have avoided his tragedy by heeding the various warnings, yet the plague on Thebes would have continued.

The Trojans' decision to accept the wooden horse into the city despite the better judgment of their wise men. The Trojans are initially suspicious of the wooden horse, but allow the spy Sinon and the fate of Laocoon and his sons to sway them. When they begin hauling the horse into the city, they stop four times and hear the clanging of Greek weapons inside it but ignore the noise. Rather than heed their own suspicions or investigate the obvious noise, the Trojans invite their own destruction.

CRITICAL THINKING AND WRITING/Applying Skills II

B. Analyzing a Dialogue Excerpt

1. c
2. b
3. a
4. b
5. d
6. c
7. a
8. d
9. b
10. c

C. Writing About a Dialogue Excerpt

Paragraphs will vary. Students might assert that Socrates was a hero because he lived—and died—for his beliefs. Even at the cost of his life, Socrates was not willing to compromise his values. He believed strongly in seeking "the pleasures of knowledge" and in living a life of "virtue and wisdom." In these beliefs he did not waver, even as he faced an unjust death. Instead, he met death bravely. Socrates' concern for his students and friends at the moment of his death was also heroic. He tried to calm their fears, not his own. He even made jokes about bathing and about Crito's holding onto his dead body in order to lighten the somber mood of the group. He was a hero who refused to be beaten even by death.

NAME ______________________ CLASS ______________ DATE ________ SCORE ________

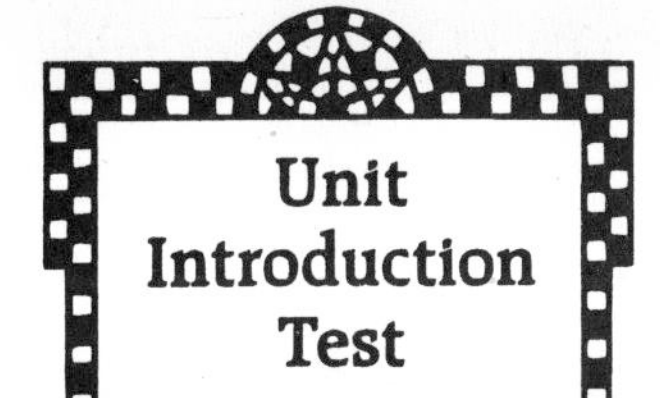

UNIT 5: INDIAN LITERATURE

(Textbook pages 446–453)

INTRODUCTION/Indian Literature

Directions: In the space provided, write the letter of the best answer to each question. *(10 points each)*

1. The Aryans were
   a. great epics of Indian literature
   b. members of Hindu caste
   c. migrants who came to India from central Asia around 1500 B.C.
   d. founders of the Indus Valley civilization
   1. ______

2. The earliest known forms of Indian literature are known as the
   a. Ramayana
   b. Vedas
   c. Hindus
   d. Guptas
   2. ______

3. The Vedas
   a. contain animal stories
   b. are a collection of sacred Indian hymns
   c. are a collection of epics
   d. were written down during the Vedic period
   3. ______

4. The Hindu belief in reincarnation
   a. promises physical rebirth into another life
   b. depends only on one's status in this life
   c. is limited to members of the Brahman class
   d. means a higher form or social position in the next life
   4. ______

5. A major influence on Indian literature and culture is the religion of Buddhism, which was founded in India by
   a. the god Krishna
   b. Brahma the Creator
   c. Ashoka
   d. Siddharta Gautama
   5. ______

6. Buddhism
   a. emphasizes meditation and nonviolence
   b. continues to be the dominant religion in India
   c. divides Indians into classes, or castes
   d. stresses action over contemplation
   6. ______

(continued)

7. A major problem that the epic hero of Indian literature, as well as the modern Hindu, faces in respect to his or her dharma or religious duty has been
   a. acting in a nonviolent manner
   b. identifying one's dharma
   c. converting others to one's dharma
   d. conducting one's dharma even when it appears destructive to do so — 7. ______

8. Sanskrit, the language of classic Indian literature, is highly regarded for its
   a. ever-changing nature
   b. modernity
   c. beauty and subtlety
   d. colloquial, or everyday, feel — 8. ______

9. The two great epics of Indian literature are
   a. the *Mahabharata* and the *Rig Veda*
   b. the *Mahabharata* and the *Ramayana*
   c. the *Bhagavad-Gita* and the *Rig Veda*
   d. the *Panchatantra* and the *Upanishads* — 9. ______

10. One of the major struggles for Indian culture, reflected in Indian literature, is to achieve
    a. separation between church and state
    b. adoption of universal vegetarianism
    c. unity in the face of diversity
    d. conformity in literary form — 10. ______

NAME ______________________ CLASS ________________ DATE ______ SCORE ______

NIGHT, *from the* RIG VEDA

translated by
Wendy Doniger O'Flaherty

(Textbook page 456)

REVIEWING THE SELECTION

In the hymn "Night," the night is personified as a goddess. Complete each of the following sentences by describing what the goddess Night does.

1. She draws ______________________
2. She looks ______________________
3. She puts ______________________
4. She fills ______________________
5. She stems ______________________
6. She pushes ______________________
7. She wards off ______________________
8. She is full of ______________________

Reader's Response

The personification of night makes night seem alive. On the blanks below, complete the following sentences about day so that the daytime is personified and made to seem alive.

1. She brings ______________________.
2. She looks ______________________.
3. She speaks ______________________.
4. She rushes ______________________.
5. She withdraws ______________________.

NAME ______________________ CLASS ____________________ DATE _________ SCORE _______

Hundred Questions *from the* Mahabharata

translated by R.K. Narayan (Textbook page 461)

DEVELOPING VOCABULARY

Directions: Read carefully the explanation of each word. Then write a sentence of your own using that word. In your sentence, include clues to the word's meaning.

pilgrimage (pil'grim·ij) ***n.*** **1.** Trip undertaken by a pilgrim, especially to a holy place. **2.** A long journey. ▶ The suffix *-age* is a noun-forming suffix meaning "belonging to" or "related to." ▪ Despite the hardships of the journey, many Indians make a yearly pilgrimage to the holy waters of the Ganges River. **Page 461**

ORIGINAL SENTENCE ____

____

inordinate (in·ôr'də·nit) ***adj.*** Lacking restraint; excessive. ▶ This word comes from the Latin verb *ordinare*, "to arrange." ▪ Some students spend such inordinate amounts of time on video games that they have no time for studies. **Page 463**

ORIGINAL SENTENCE ____

____

sanction (sank'shən) ***n.*** Official approval given for an action. ▶ Also used as a verb, to *sanction* something means "to give it approval." ▪ Although members of the city council at first refused to approve the new park, they finally gave sanction for its construction. **Page 464**

ORIGINAL SENTENCE ____

____

fatuous (fach'o͞o·əs) ***adj.*** Contentedly stupid; foolish. ▶ Use the suffix *-ness* to create the noun form of this word: *fatuousness.* ▪ He thought his fatuous behavior was funny, but everyone else thought that he was just foolish. **Page 464**

ORIGINAL SENTENCE ____

____

judicious (jo͞o·dish'əs) ***adj.*** Showing good judgment; wise and cautious. —**judiciousness** ***n.*** ▶ This word is derived from the Latin source words *judicare*, meaning "judge," and *judicium*, meaning "judgment." ▪ Well known for her judicious mind, the judge seldom made an error in her rulings. **Page 465**

ORIGINAL SENTENCE ____

____

NAME ______________ CLASS ______________ DATE ________ SCORE ________

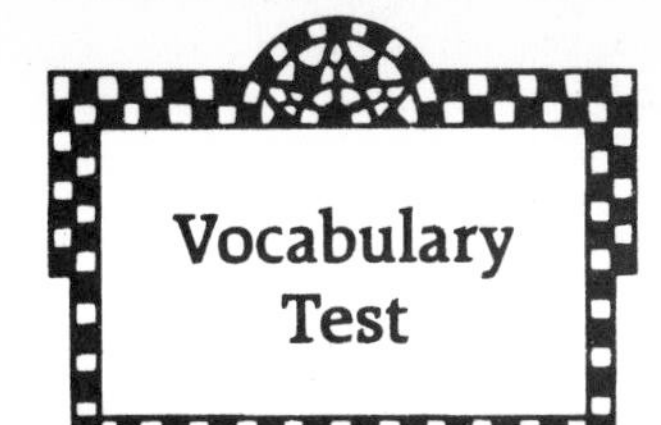

HUNDRED QUESTIONS *from the* MAHABHARATA

translated by R. K. Narayan (Textbook page 461)

VOCABULARY TEST

A. Match each word in column I with the correct definition in column II. Place the letter of the definition you choose in the space provided. *(10 points each)*

	I	II
______	1. fatuous	a. excessive
______	2. inordinate	b. a trip, especially to a holy place
______	3. judicious	c. stupid or foolish
______	4. pilgrimage	d. showing good judgment
______	5. sanction	e. official approval

B. Read each sentence carefully. Decide if the word in italics is used correctly. If it is, write *C.* If it is used incorrectly, write *I.* *(10 points each)*

______ 6. A lifelong fan of baseball, Mr. Robinson made a *pilgrimage* to the Hall of Fame in Cooperstown each year.

______ 7. All of the parts were *inordinate,* placed in the exact order for replacing them on the machine.

______ 8. Although Delbert's friends seemed to appreciate his *fatuous* antics, his teachers did not.

______ 9. Ellen's *judicious* use of resources was credited with saving the company thousands of dollars.

______ 10. The *sanction* of the stock market caused many investors to become nervous, fearful that they would lose their money.

NAME ______________ CLASS ______________ DATE ________ SCORE ________

HUNDRED QUESTIONS *from the* MAHABHARATA

translated by R. K. Narayan (Textbook page 461)

REVIEWING THE SELECTION

1. Why do the five Pandava brothers chase the deer into the forest?

____

2. What happens to the first four Pandava brothers when they ignore the warning about drinking water from the pond?

____

3. Who is the yaksha?

____

4. Why does the yaksha ask Yudhistira the hundred questions?

____

Reader's Response

Below are three of the questions that the yaksha asks Yudhistira. Write your answers to these questions.

1. What is ignorance?

____

____

2. What makes a person happy?

____

____

3. What is the definition of *mercy*?

____

____

NAME ______________________ CLASS ______________________ DATE __________ SCORE __________

HUNDRED QUESTIONS *from the* MAHABHARATA

translated by R. K. Narayan (Textbook page 461)

READING COMPREHENSION

Directions: In the space provided, write the letter of the best answer to each question. *(10 points each)*

1. What is the central story of the *Mahabharata?*
   a. a rivalry between families descended from King Bharata
   b. a complete history of India in poetic form
   c. the beginning of the world
   d. the conflict between Great Britain and India 1. ______

2. Who is Yudhistira?
   a. the sage who compiled the *Mahabharata*
   b. a brahman, a member of the priestly caste
   c. a forest god
   d. the oldest of the Pandava brothers 2. ______

3. At the beginning of *Hundred Questions,* what happens to disturb the tranquility of the Pandava brothers?
   a. The jealous cousin, Duryodhana, appears.
   b. Yudhistira is killed.
   c. The Pandava brothers break their sacred vows.
   d. A brahman asks Yudhistira for help. 3. ______

4. What causes the four brothers to fall as if dead?
   a. failing to answer questions correctly
   b. Yama's arrows
   c. refusing to answer questions before drinking water
   d. fighting the forest god 4. ______

5. What does Yudhistira conclude when he sees his dead brothers?
   a. He thinks they were killed by a mortal enemy.
   b. He realizes that no mortal could have killed them.
   c. He thinks they are not really dead.
   d. He immediately remembers the brahman who asked him for help. 5. ______

6. Which of these statements describes the questions that the yaksha asks?
   a. They are all profound questions.
   b. Few of them are very important.
   c. They cover a wide range.
   d. They are all about knowledge and happiness. 6. ______

(continued)

7. When the yaksha allows him to choose one brother to return to life, who does Yudhistira choose?
   a. his step-brother Nakula
   b. his younger brother Bhima
   c. his younger brother Arjuna
   d. his step-brother Sahadeva

   7. ______

8. Why does the yaksha make Yudhistira answer the hundred questions?
   a. to drink more water
   b. to end the twelve-year exile
   c. to test his strength of mind
   d. to free his wife

   8. ______

9. Who is the yaksha?
   a. Yama, the god of justice
   b. Brahma, a Hindu creator god
   c. Father, the sky-god
   d. Duryodhana's evil agent

   9. ______

10. What is the ultimate boon granted to Yudhistira for answering the hundred questions?
    a. the end to all conditions of the exile
    b. the ability to go unrecognized for a year
    c. the power to kill his cousin Duryodhana
    d. the opportunity to be reborn as a Brahman

    10. ______

NAME ______________________ CLASS ________________ DATE ________ SCORE ______

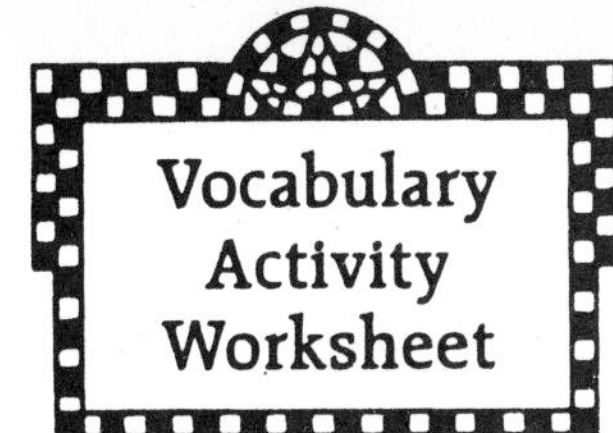

PHILOSOPHY AND SPIRITUAL DISCIPLINE *from the* BHAGAVAD-GITA

translated by Barbara Stoler Miller (Textbook page 469)

DEVELOPING VOCABULARY

Directions: Read carefully the explanation of each word. Then write a sentence of your own using that word. In your sentence, include clues to the word's meaning.

primordial (prī·môr'dē·əl) *adj.* Existing or occurring from the world's beginning. ▶ The origin of this word is Latin, from *primus*, "first," and *ordiri*, "to begin." ▪ The ancient-looking fish was such a primitive type that we believed it to be a primordial species. **Page 471**

ORIGINAL SENTENCE ____

____

pervade (pər·vād') *v.* To exist widely. —**pervasive** ***adj.*** ▶ This word and the word *evade*, "to escape," share the same Latin root: *vadere*, meaning "to go." ▪ The odor of the paper mill pervaded the entire town. **Page 471**

ORIGINAL SENTENCE ____

____

manifest (man'ə·fest') *adj.* Evident, especially to the sense of sight; clear. ▶ The word's antonym, or opposite, can be formed by adding the prefix *un-*: *unmanifest.* ▪ The new computer's advantages were manifest: it had a wider screen and a user-friendly keyboard. **Page 472**

ORIGINAL SENTENCE ____

____

immutable (im·myo͞ot'ə·bəl) *adj.* Unchangeable. ▶ The literal meaning of this word is "not subject to change." ▪ Generations passed, buildings were erected and torn down, trees grew and were harvested, but beyond it all was the reassuring backdrop of the Rocky Mountains, immutable and constant. **Page 471**

ORIGINAL SENTENCE ____

____

(continued)

impartial (im·pär′shəl) ***adj.*** Unbiased; not favoring either side in a dispute or contest. ▶ The prefix *im-* means "no" or "not." ■ The mediator brought in to settle the dispute had a reputation for being fair and impartial. **Page 472**

ORIGINAL SENTENCE ____

____

diffuse (di·fyo͞os′) ***adj.*** Spread out. ▶ *Diffuse* can also mean "wordy." ■ After three days, the fog finally became diffuse enough that the airport could be reopened. **Page 472**

ORIGINAL SENTENCE ____

____

mundane (mun′dān′) ***adj.*** Of the world; ordinary; day-to-day. ▶ This word usually describes the concerns of day-to-day living. ■ The dancers dedicated themselves to their art, not worrying about the mundane matters of life. **Page 473**

ORIGINAL SENTENCE ____

____

lucid (lo͞o′sid) ***adj.*** Easily understood. ▶ This word is often used to describe writing that is especially clear and easy to understand. ■ Her translation from Latin to English was so lucid that we readily understood the story. **Page 473**

ORIGINAL SENTENCE ____

____

equanimity (ek′wə·nim′ə·tē) ***n.*** The ability to maintain composure and calmness. ▶ This word is derived from the Latin *aequus,* meaning "even," and *animus,* meaning "the mind." ■ Despite the danger to herself, she maintained a quiet equanimity during the earthquake that helped others to calm down. **Page 473**

ORIGINAL SENTENCE ____

____

sensuous (sen′sho͞o·əs) ***adj.*** Perceived by the senses, especially with pleasure or enjoyment. ▶ The suffix *-ous* indicates the word is an adjective. ■ The balmy ocean breeze, the warm sun, and the crisp, sweet taste of the fresh coconut added up to a day of sensuous enjoyment. **Page 474**

ORIGINAL SENTENCE ____

____

NAME ______________________ CLASS ______________________ DATE __________ SCORE __________

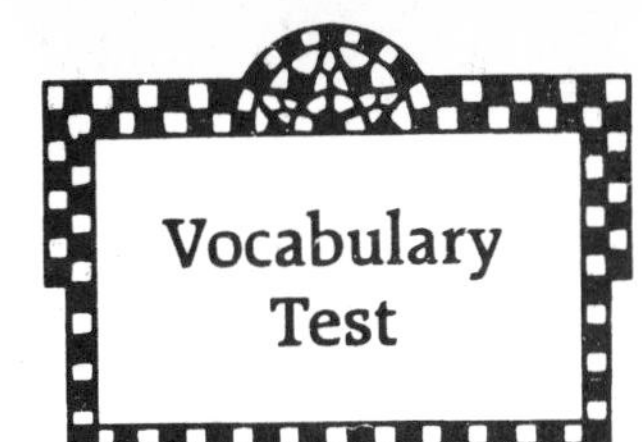

PHILOSOPHY AND SPIRITUAL DISCIPLINE *from the* BHAGAVAD-GITA

translated by Barbara Stoler Miller (Textbook page 469)

VOCABULARY TEST

A. Match each word in column I with the correct definition in column II. Write the letter of the definition you choose in the space provided. *(7 points each)*

I	II
______ 1. diffuse	a. evident, visible
______ 2. equanimity	b. to exist widely
______ 3. immutable	c. of the world; ordinary
______ 4. impartial	d. perceived by the senses, especially with pleasure
______ 5. lucid	e. existing at or from the beginning
______ 6. manifest	f. spread out
______ 7. mundane	g. the ability to remain calm; evenness of mind
______ 8. pervade	h. unchangeable
______ 9. primordial	i. favoring no one side
______ 10. sensuous	j. easily understood

B. From the words listed below, choose the word that best completes the sentence. Write the word in the space provided. *(6 points each)*

diffuse immutable impartial lucid mundane

11. The law of gravity is ______________________, that is, not subject to change.

12. The smoke of the forest fire finally became so ______________________ that we could begin to see the extent of the damage.

13. The monks at the monastery were not concerned about ______________________ matters, but spent their lives in heavenly pursuits.

14. The proposals for solving the pollution problem were so ______________________ that they required no further explanation.

15. One of our constitutional guarantees is the right to a fair trial by an ______________________ jury of our peers.

NAME ______________________ CLASS ______________________ DATE __________ SCORE __________

PHILOSOPHY AND SPIRITUAL DISCIPLINE *from the* BHAGAVAD-GITA

translated by Barbara Stoler Miller (Textbook page 469)

REVIEWING THE SELECTION

1. At the beginning of the selection, why is Arjuna feeling sad?

____

____

2. What does Krishna tell Arjuna about the "embodied self" that helps Arjuna?

____

____

3. Krishna tells Arjuna how people can find inner peace. Circle the letters of the items that people must give up to find this peace.
   a. military duties
   b. the mind's desires
   c. craving for pleasures
   d. thoughts of immortality

4. According to Krishna, what is a sage?

____

____

Reader's Response

According to Krishna, everyone has a *dharma*, a sacred duty. What sacred duties do twentieth-century Americans have? Do they have sacred duties toward their country? Their families? Religious groups? Write several sentences explaining your answer.

____

____

____

____

NAME ______________________ CLASS ____________________ DATE ________ SCORE ______

PHILOSOPHY AND SPIRITUAL DISCIPLINE *from the* BHAGAVAD-GITA

translated by Barbara Stoler Miller (Textbook page 469)

SUBJECT-VERB AGREEMENT

The **subject** of a sentence is the person, place, or thing the sentence is about. The **verb** expresses the action of the subject or helps to make a statement about it. In standard English, the subject and verb must agree in number. A singular subject requires a singular verb.

EXAMPLES *Arjuna* (s) *is* (v) unhappy.

He (s) *asks* (v) Krishna many questions.

A plural subject requires a plural verb.

EXAMPLES The Pandava *brothers* (s) *are* (v) home from exile.

They (s) *want* (v) their share of the kingdom.

In some special cases, subject-verb agreement becomes more difficult. Use the following rules to help you.

1. Use a plural verb for subjects joined by *and*, even if both subjects are singular. Use a singular verb for subjects joined by *or* or *nor* if both subjects are singular. If a singular subject and a plural subject are joined by *or* or *nor*, the verb agrees with the closer subject.

EXAMPLES *Arjuna* (s) and *Krishna* (s) *prepare* (v) for battle. (subjects joined by *and* take plural verb form)

Neither *pleasure* (s) nor *pain* (s) *is* (v) important to the faithful Hindu. (singular subjects joined by *or* or *nor* take singular verb form)

Arjuna (s) or other *warriors* (s) *fight* (v) a battle today. (singular and plural subjects joined by *or* take plural verb form because plural subject is closer to verb)

2. An indefinite pronoun may also be the subject of a sentence. Some indefinite pronouns are always plural and take a plural verb; others are always singular and take a singular verb. A few indefinite pronouns may be either singular or plural, depending on the meaning of the sentence.

Singular	each, either, neither, one, no one, anyone, everyone, someone, anybody, somebody, everybody, nobody
Plural	several, few, both, many
Singular or plural	some, any, none, all, most

(continued)

EXAMPLES *Everybody* [s] *respects* [v] him. (singular indefinite pronoun with singular verb)

Many [s] *die* [v] on the battlefield. (plural indefinite pronoun with plural verb)

All [s] *are* [v] concepts important to Hinduism. (*all* used as plural subject with plural verb)

3. Phrases coming between the subject and verb do not affect agreement.

EXAMPLES The *actions* [s] of sacred duty *are* [v] justified.

The embodied *self* [s] of all creatures *exists* [v] forever.

The indefinite pronouns *some, any, none, most,* and *all* are an exception to this rule. An intervening phrase may help you to decide whether the pronoun is singular or plural.

EXAMPLES *All* of Krishna's arguments *are* important.
All of the spirit *endures* after death.

Exercise 1. Identifying Correct Subject-Verb Agreement

Details in the following sentences are about the *Mahabharata.* If the subject-verb agreement in each sentence is correct, write *C* on the blank provided. If it is incorrect, write *I* on the blank.

EXAMPLE __C__ The concept of *dharma* is important in Hinduism.

______ 1. The Pandavas and Kauravas are cousins.

______ 2. The rivalry between the families causes a war.

______ 3. According to Arjuna, each of the brothers deserve his respect.

______ 4. Everyone expect the war to be terrible.

______ 5. The dharma of warriors is to fight.

______ 6. Many of the warriors are killed.

______ 7. Arjuna, the third of the Pandava brothers, is sad at the thought of killing his relatives.

______ 8. Arjuna and Krishna engages in a dialogue about duty.

______ 9. The logic or the power of the arguments cause Arjuna to accept his duty.

______ 10. Some of the concepts of Hinduism is strange to westerners.

Exercise 2. Using Correct Subject-Verb Agreement

The infinitive form of the verb appears in parentheses in each of the following sentences about the *Mahabharata.* For each sentence, write the correct form of the verb on the blank provided.

(continued)

(Hint: Use the present tense form of the verb.)

EXAMPLE The *Bhagavad-Gita* (to be) __*is*__ the most sacred part of the *Mahabharata.*

1. The father of the Kauravas (to be) ________________ Dhritarashtra.

2. Yudhistira, the oldest of the Pandava brothers, is tricked and (to lose) ________________ the family fortune.

3. For this reason, all of the Pandavas (to go) ________________ into exile for twelve years.

4. When they return, each of the Pandavas (to want) ________________ his proper share of the kingdom.

5. Each of the armies (to prepare) ________________ for battle.

6. Some of us (to have) ________________ doubts from time to time.

7. Some of the dialogue between Arjuna and Krishna (to concern) ________________ the embodied self.

8. Krishna (to address) ________________ many of Arjuna's concerns.

9. Krishna argues that, by doing one's duty, one (to avoid) ________________ shame.

10. This selection from one of India's oldest texts (to be) ________________ still widely read today.

Exercise 3. Proofreading a Paragraph

Details in the following paragraph are about the concepts of *dharma* and the "embodied self." Proofread the paragraph by correcting subject-verb agreement errors. The first error is corrected for you. There are eight additional errors for you to correct. (Hint: Some of the verbs in the paragraph are used correctly.)

Krishna argue^s that it are the warrior's dharma to fight. Shame and cowardice awaits the warrior who will not fight. A warrior who fight in the battles have no reason to be sad about killing his enemies. Although their bodies is killed, their embodied selves endure forever. The embodied self leave the dead body and take on a new one. If the warrior is killed in battle while doing his sacred duty, he win heaven.

NAME ______________________ CLASS ______________________ DATE ________ SCORE ________

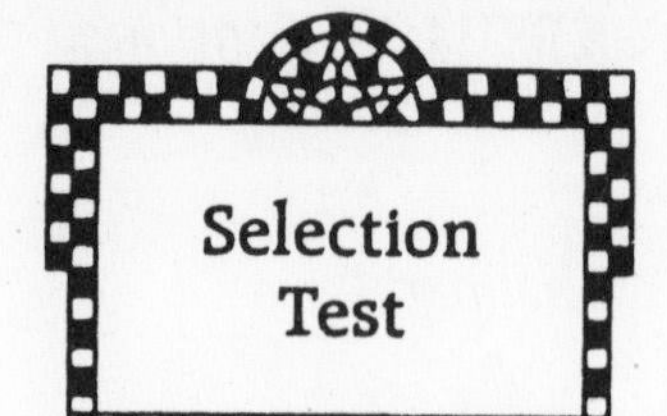

PHILOSOPHY AND SPIRITUAL DISCIPLINE *from the* BHAGAVAD-GITA

translated by Barbara Stoler Miller (Textbook page 469)

READING COMPREHENSION

Directions: In the space provided, write the letter of the best answer to each question. *(10 points each)*

1. What is the source of the *Bhagavad-Gita*?
   a. the *Rig Veda*
   b. the *Mahabharata*
   c. the *Panchatantra*
   d. the *Ramayana*

   1. ______

2. Who are the main participants in the dialogue in this episode from the *Bhagavad-Gita*?
   a. Arjuna and his oldest brother, Yudhistira
   b. Arjuna and his enemy-cousin, Duryodhana
   c. Arjuna and his charioteer, Krishna
   d. Arjuna and his mother, Kunthi

   2. ______

3. What feelings paralyze Arjuna at the beginning of the passage?
   a. pity and grief
   b. envy and anger
   c. greed and lust
   d. overconfidence and pride

   3. ______

4. What is Arjuna's concern?
   a. He may be killed.
   b. He may kill his elders.
   c. His family may lose the battle.
   d. He is unworthy of the honor of battle.

   4. ______

5. What is the basis of the argument Krishna uses to justify killing in battle?
   a. that everyone has to go to war at one time or another
   b. that the true self is not born and does not die
   c. that the gods do not like cowardly men
   d. that the Kauravas deserve to be slain in battle

   5. ______

(continued)

6. How does Krishna describe shame for a man of honor?
   a. It is preferable to death.
   b. It is akin to vanity and should be ignored.
   c. It is the inevitable result of making war on one's fellow humans.
   d. It is worse than death. 6. ______

7. According to Krishna, how will people regard Arjuna if he does not fulfill his duty as a warrior?
   a. revere him as a peacemaker
   b. honor him for his courage
   c. despise him as a coward
   d. forget him 7. ______

8. According to Krishna, what is better for a warrior than a battle of sacred duty?
   a. nothing
   b. peace
   c. dialogue
   d. death 8. ______

9. To what does Krishna compare the embodied self as it discards worn-out bodies?
   a. a rainbow forming at the end of a storm
   b. a man moving from one caste to another
   c. a man losing a battle
   d. a man changing clothes 9. ______

10. Krishna says that a man deep in contemplation with sure insight and thought is one
    a. who gives up desires
    b. who refuses to fight
    c. who pays attention to his senses
    d. who prefers fortune to misfortune 10. ______

NAME ______________________________ CLASS ______________________ DATE __________ SCORE ________

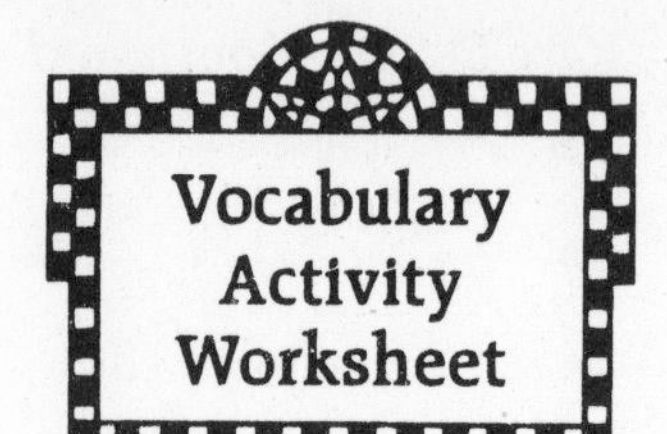

RIGHT-MIND AND WRONG-MIND *from the* PANCHATANTRA

translated by Arthur William Ryder (Textbook page 480)

DEVELOPING VOCABULARY

Directions: Read carefully the explanation of each word. Then write a sentence of your own using that word. In your sentence, include clues to the word's meaning.

residue (rez'ə·do͞o') ***n.*** Leftover portion; remainder. ▶ The origin of this word is the Latin *residuus*, which means "remaining." ▪ Tons of garbage were left as the residue of the city's annual food festival in the park. **Page 480**

ORIGINAL SENTENCE ____

____

vulnerable (vul'nər·ə·bəl) ***adj.*** Easily attacked, tempted, or damaged. ▶ An early Latin source word for *vulnerable* is *vulnus*, which means "a wound." ▪ The Greek hero Achilles was killed by an arrow in his heel, the only vulnerable spot on his entire body. **Page 480**

ORIGINAL SENTENCE ____

____

dictum (dik'təm) ***n.*** A formal pronouncement or statement. ▶ This word comes from the Latin *dicere*, meaning "to speak." ▪ The restaurant manager's dictum requiring shoes and a shirt was often ignored. **Page 481**

ORIGINAL SENTENCE ____

____

reflect (ri·flekt') ***v.*** To contemplate seriously; ponder.—**reflection *n.*** ▶ This definition of *reflect* implies serious effort to understand or to solve a problem. ▪ The scientist always had to reflect carefully before beginning the experiments. **Page 482**

ORIGINAL SENTENCE ____

____

discern (di·zurn'; -surn') ***v.*** To perceive and recognize differences. ▶ The differences one *discerns* may be concrete, as shapes in the dark, or they may be abstract, as good and evil. ▪ With the sudden appearance of the fog, it was impossible for the sailor to discern the coastline. **Page 483**

ORIGINAL SENTENCE ____

____

NAME ______________________ CLASS ______________ DATE ________ SCORE ________

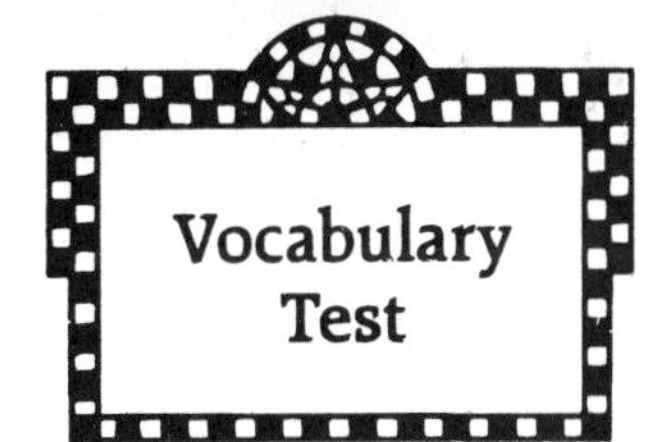

RIGHT-MIND AND WRONG-MIND *from the* PANCHATANTRA

translated by Arthur William Ryder (Textbook page 480)

VOCABULARY TEST

A. Match each word in column I with the correct definition in column II. Place the letter of the definition you choose in the space provided. *(10 points each)*

	I	II
______	1. dictum	a. to contemplate seriously; ponder
______	2. discern	b. to perceive and recognize differences
______	3. residue	c. easily attacked, tempted, or damaged
______	4. reflect	d. a formal pronouncement or statement
______	5. vulnerable	e. leftover portion; remainder

B. In the space provided, write the letter of the word or phrase closest in meaning to the word in italics. *(10 points each)*

______ 6. Their campsite was in a poor location, *vulnerable* to wind, rain, and insects.

a. off-limits b. open c. closed

______ 7. A *residue* of the toxic chemical could still be seen in the bottom of the test tube, but most of it had evaporated.

a. small amount b. large quantity c. solution

______ 8. The federal government issued a *dictum* regulating the nature of advertisements in children's magazines.

a. tax b. survey c. order

______ 9. Frank could not *discern* the difference between a violin and a viola, but he still enjoyed the symphony.

a. perceive b. smell c. endure

______ 10. Cece took a great deal of time to *reflect* before choosing a college.

a. mirror b. consider c. travel

NAME ______________________ CLASS ______________________ DATE __________ SCORE ______

RIGHT-MIND AND WRONG-MIND
from the PANCHATANTRA

translated by Arthur William Ryder (Textbook page 480)

REVIEWING THE SELECTION

1. Wrong-Mind suggests to Right-Mind that the two of them bury most of their treasure. What reason does Wrong-Mind give Right-Mind for doing this?

____

____

2. What happens to the buried treasure?

____

____

3. How does Wrong-Mind's father try to dissuade Wrong-Mind from scheming to have Right-Mind found guilty of stealing the treasure?

____

____

4. How does Right-Mind prove his innocence?

____

____

Reader's Response

Wrong-Mind's father goes along with Wrong-Mind's evil scheme even though the father knows it will not succeed. Why do you think the father does this? What alternate action might Wrong-Mind's father have taken? Write several sentences explaining your answer.

____

____

____

____

____

NAME ____________________ CLASS ____________________ DATE ________ SCORE ______

RIGHT-MIND AND WRONG-MIND *from the* PANCHATANTRA

translated by Arthur William Ryder (Textbook page 480)

PERFECT TENSES

The **perfect tenses**—past, present, and future—are formed with *have, has,* or *had* and the past participial form of the verb. The following rules can help you to use the perfect tenses.

1. Use the **present perfect tense** to express action (or to help make a statement about something) that happened at an indefinite time in the past. Use it also for something that began in the past and continues up to the present. Form the present perfect tense with *have* or *has* plus the past participle.

EXAMPLE Right-Mind and Wrong-Mind *have made* a fortune together.

2. Use the **past perfect tense** to express action (or to help make a statement about something) that was completed in the past before some other past action or event. Form the past perfect tense with *had* plus the past participle.

EXAMPLE After Wrong-Mind and Right-Mind *had buried* the pot of money, they went into the city.

3. Use the **future perfect tense** to express action (or to help make a statement about something) that will be completed in the future before some other future action or event. Form the future perfect tense with *will have* or *shall have* plus the past participle.

EXAMPLE The trial by ordeal *will have ended* before the court identifies the guilty party.

Exercise 1. Identifying the Perfect Tenses

Details in the following sentences are about "Right-Mind and Wrong-Mind." In the blank before each of the sentences, write the letter of the item that identifies the tense of the underlined verb phrase.

a. present perfect b. past perfect c. future perfect

EXAMPLE __a__ Wrong-Mind has decided how to cheat Right-Mind.

______ 1. Right-Mind and Wrong-Mind have lived in the same town for many years.

______ 2. They had lived there for many years before they went out to seek their fortunes.

______ 3. They will have enriched themselves before they return home.

(continued)

______ 4. Wrong-Mind had spent his share of the money before he decided to steal the rest.

______ 5. The name "Wrong-Mind" implies that he has cheated people before.

______ 6. The court had planned to have a trial by ordeal, but later changed its mind.

______ 7. Wrong-Mind's father already had hidden in the tree when the court arrived to hear from the witness.

______ 8. Right-Mind had enjoyed a spotless reputation until Wrong-Mind accused him of theft.

______ 9. The court has found Right-Mind not guilty of the crime.

______ 10. The snake will have eaten the heron's chicks by the time the heron realizes its mistake.

Exercise 2. Using the Perfect Tenses

For each of the following sentences about "Right-Mind and Wrong-Mind," the infinitive form of the main verb appears in parentheses. In the blanks provided, write the correct perfect tense form of each main verb.

EXAMPLE The pot of money that Right-Mind found (to hide) had been hidden by a holy man.

1. It is obvious from the story that Right-Mind (to trust)

   ______________________________ everyone all his life.

2. "By tomorrow evening," said Wrong-Mind, "Right-Mind (to be)

   ______________________________ thrown in jail."

3. Although Right-Mind (to recite) ______________________________ a verse proclaiming his innocence, Wrong-Mind and Right-Mind went to court.

4. Before the king's men hanged Wrong-Mind, they (to plan)

   ______________________________ to punish Right-Mind.

5. Even though Wrong-Mind's father (to try) ______________________________ to convince Wrong-Mind not to carry out his plot, he agrees to participate in it.

(continued)

Exercise 3. Proofreading a Paragraph

The following paragraph is based on the *Panchatantra*, the larger work that contains "Right-Mind and Wrong-Mind." Proofread the paragraph and correct the use of the perfect tenses, which appear in incorrect form in italics. One correction has been made for you as an example. Do not change the underlined verbs. Use them to help you identify the correct form of the perfect tense.

The *Panchatantra had been* [corrected to: has] a source of wisdom in India for centuries; even today, parents in India tell the stories to their children. For in India, as in most parts of the world, storytellers *will have understood* the value of fables as teaching tools for a long time. Even before the *Panchatantra* found a mass audience, however, it *will have been* used to teach the art of governance to young Indian nobles. Although it was written in Sanskrit originally, the *Panchatantra has appeared* in Persian by the sixth century A.D. By the Renaissance, scholars *will have translated* it into Arabic, Greek, Hebrew, Latin, German, and Italian. With a new emphasis on world literature in American schools, thousands of American high school students *had read* excerpts from the *Panchatantra* by the end of this decade!

NAME ______________________ CLASS ____________________ DATE ________ SCORE ______

RIGHT-MIND AND WRONG-MIND *from the* PANCHATANTRA

translated by Arthur William Ryder (Textbook page 480)

READING COMPREHENSION

Directions: In the space provided, write the letter of the best answer to each question. *(10 points each)*

1. How was the *Panchatantra*, a book of fables, first used in ancient India?
   a. as a book of animal stories for children
   b. as a tool for teaching statecraft to princes
   c. as a geographic description of India
   d. as a catalog of the animals of India 1. ______

2. What is the central Hindu concept that the *Panchatantra* teaches?
   a. *niti*; worldly wisdom, turning the tables on evil
   b. reincarnation; the embodied self, being born into another body
   c. dharma; sacred duty, doing what is correct
   d. varna; caste, living a life according to the social position into which one is born 2. ______

3. What is an epigram?
   a. a signature in cursive writing
   b. a letter issued by one noble to another
   c. a brief, clever verse with a moral
   d. a fable 3. ______

4. Who are Right-Mind and Wrong-Mind?
   a. brothers
   b. friends
   c. cousins
   d. princes 4. ______

5. How does Right-Mind respond when Wrong-Mind accuses him of stealing?
   a. He confesses his guilt.
   b. He accuses Wrong-Mind.
   c. He appeals to Wrong-Mind's father for help.
   d. He uses an epigram to proclaim his innocence. 5. ______

6. What crime does Wrong-Mind commit against Right-Mind?
   a. He tricks Right-Mind into stealing the money.
   b. He forces Right-Mind to violate his sacred duty.
   c. He steals the money and blames Right-Mind.
   d. He kills a sacred heron and blames Right-Mind. 6. ______

(continued)

7. What does Wrong-Mind do when the court threatens him with a trial by ordeal?
   a. He confesses his guilt and asks for mercy.
   b. He claims he has a forest goddess as a witness.
   c. He bribes the judges.
   d. He turns into a heron and flies away. 7. ______

8. What does Wrong-Mind's father use in his attempt to persuade his son not to carry out his deception?
   a. a story
   b. a whip
   c. a sonnet
   d. a prayer 8. ______

9. How does Right-Mind expose Wrong-Mind's treachery?
   a. He brings in some gods and goddesses for his defense.
   b. He recites holy chants.
   c. He wins the trial by ordeal.
   d. He smokes out the fake forest goddess. 9. ______

10. What happens to Right-Mind when the court discovers the truth?
    a. He is hanged from a branch of the mimosa tree.
    b. He is serenaded with poetry.
    c. He is rewarded with the king's favor.
    d. He is punished for stealing the money. 10. ______

NAME ______________________ CLASS ______________________ DATE __________ SCORE ______

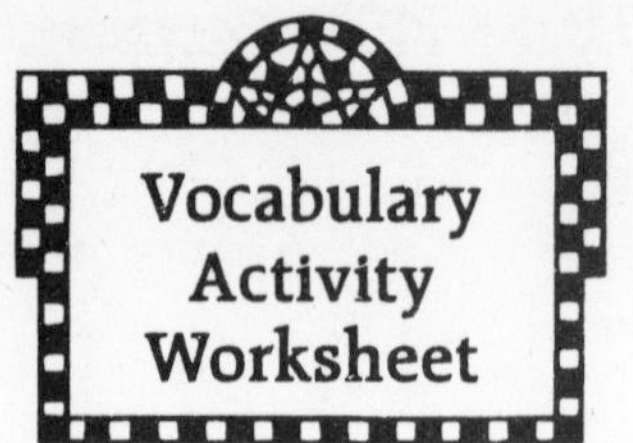

RAMA AND RAVANA IN BATTLE *from the* RAMAYANA

translated by R. K. Narayan (Textbook page 486)

DEVELOPING VOCABULARY

Directions: Read carefully the explanation of each word. Then write a sentence of your own using that word. In your sentence, include clues to the word's meaning.

grapple (grap′əl) ***v.*** To struggle in hand-to-hand combat. ▶ This word is often used in a concrete sense, as in "to *grapple* with an enemy," but it may also be used in an abstract sense, as in "to *grapple* with a problem." ▪ Left with no weapons but their hands, the warriors began to grapple with each other for superiority. **Page 488**

ORIGINAL SENTENCE ____

____

insensible (in·sen′sə·bəl) ***adj.*** Lacking sensation or consciousness; unaware. ▶ Do not confuse this word with the word *insensitive*, which means "not considerate of others." ▪ The football player was not responding to the official, having been left insensible after a hard tackle. **Page 489**

ORIGINAL SENTENCE ____

____

impervious (im·pur′vē·əs) ***adj.*** Incapable of being attacked. ▶ Used in this sense, this word is usually followed by the preposition *to.* ▪ The mayor was impervious to criticism and also unaffected by the daily demonstrations by protesters. **Page 489**

ORIGINAL SENTENCE ____

____

invoke (in·vōk′) ***v.*** To call on God or a god for assistance. ▶ The help called for may be for protection or inspiration. ▪ In the heat of the battle, the soldiers paused to invoke God's help in giving them the courage to fight on. **Page 492**

ORIGINAL SENTENCE ____

____

(continued)

contemptuous (kən·temp′cho͞o·əs) ***adj.*** Regarding another as mean or unworthy; scornful.—**contemptuously** ***adv.*** ▶ The suffix *-ous* means "full of." ▪ The movie star, who regarded her fans as a nuisance, gave them a contemptuous look when they asked for her autograph. **Page 490**

ORIGINAL SENTENCE ________________

dispel (di·spel′) ***v.*** To scatter; disperse. ▶ The history of this word includes the Latin prefix *dis-*, "apart," and the Latin *pellere*, "to drive." ▪ Once they knew the truth, they told everyone in an effort to dispel the false rumor. **Page 487**

ORIGINAL SENTENCE ________________

intermittent (in′tər·mit′ ′nt) ***adj.*** Ending and beginning again at intervals. ▶ This word implies the interruption of something on a regular or measurable basis. ▪ The foghorn blasted out its intermittent warning every five minutes. **Page 490**

ORIGINAL SENTENCE ________________

enterprise (ent′ər·prīz′) ***n.*** An undertaking. ▶ The adjective form of this word, *enterprising*, implies a willingness to undertake projects. ▪ The new job of reorganizing the bank's major accounts was the largest enterprise the new vice-president had yet attempted. **Page 490**

ORIGINAL SENTENCE ________________

vanquish (vang′kwish) ***v.*** To conquer. ▶ This word comes from the Latin word *vincere*, "to conquer." ▪ Ravana used every weapon he could think of in his attempt to vanquish his enemy Rama in battle. **Page 491**

ORIGINAL SENTENCE ________________

pristine (pris′tēn′) ***adj.*** **1.** Original. **2.** Unspoiled. ▶ This word is derived from the Latin *pristinus*, meaning "former." ▪ The caretaker kept the old church in pristine condition, immediately attending to repairs and maintaining the surrounding grounds. **Page 493**

ORIGINAL SENTENCE ________________

NAME ______________________ CLASS ______________________ DATE __________ SCORE __________

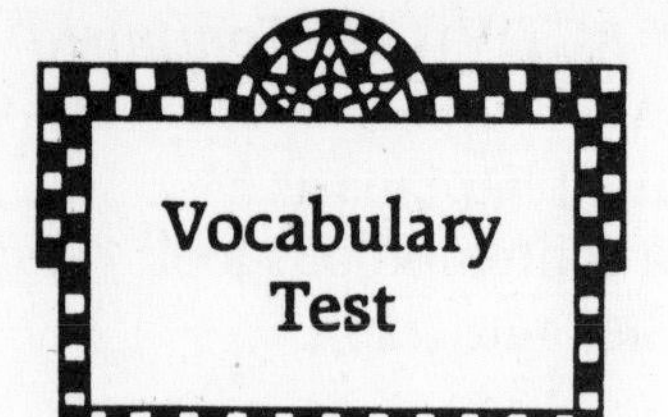

Rama and Ravana in Battle from the Ramayana

translated by R. K. Narayan (Textbook page 486)

VOCABULARY TEST

A. Match each word in column I with the correct definition in column II. Write the letter of the definition you choose in the space provided. *(7 points each)*

I	II
______ 1. contemptuous	a. to call on a god or goddess for assistance
______ 2. dispel	b. regarding someone as unworthy; scornful
______ 3. enterprise	c. to conquer
______ 4. grapple	d. an undertaking
______ 5. impervious	e. to scatter; disperse
______ 6. insensible	f. incapable of being attacked
______ 7. intermittent	g. to struggle in hand-to-hand combat
______ 8. invoke	h. ending and beginning again at regular intervals
______ 9. pristine	i. lacking sensation or consciousness
______ 10. vanquish	j. original; unspoiled

B. Match each word in column I with the correct pair of antonyms in column II. Remember that an antonym is a word opposite in meaning to another word. Write the letter of the set of antonyms that you choose in the space provided. *(6 points each)*

I	II
______ 11. contemptuous	a. lose, suffer defeat
______ 12. insensible	b. contaminated, polluted
______ 13. intermittent	c. conscious, able to feel
______ 14. pristine	d. respectful, gracious
______ 15. vanquish	e. steady, unceasing

NAME ______________________ CLASS ______________________ DATE __________ SCORE ________

RAMA AND RAVANA IN BATTLE
from the RAMAYANA

translated by R. K. Narayan (Textbook page 486)

REVIEWING THE SELECTION

1. Who seems to be winning the battle as the selection begins—Rama or Ravana?

____

____

2. What physical characteristics of Ravana make him a frightening enemy in battle?

____

____

3. What do the gods do to help Rama?

____

____

4. What is special about the weapons called *asthras* that Rama and Ravana use against each other?

____

____

Reader's Response

Ravana is killed by Rama's special asthra because Ravana neglected to strengthen his heart and thus is vulnerable, or weak. In what sense can someone "strengthen" his or her heart? How might not doing so make a person vulnerable in war? in love? Write several sentences explaining your answer.

____

____

____

____

____

NAME ______________________ CLASS ________________ DATE ________ SCORE ______

RAMA AND RAVANA IN BATTLE *from the* RAMAYANA

translated by R. K. Narayan (Textbook page 486)

ESSENTIAL AND NONESSENTIAL CLAUSES

A **subordinate clause** is a group of words that has a subject and a verb but cannot stand alone as a sentence. Subordinate clauses may be either essential or nonessential.

An **essential clause** restricts or limits the meaning of the word it modifies. An essential clause is crucial to the meaning of the sentence. It cannot be omitted without changing that meaning.

EXAMPLE The plan *that Ravana develops* is to use asthras to destroy Rama.

A **nonessential clause** is not essential to the meaning of the sentence. It does not limit the meaning of the word it modifies. Unlike essential clauses, nonessential clauses are set off from the rest of the sentence with commas. Clauses that modify proper nouns are almost always nonessential.

EXAMPLE Rama, *who is married to Sita,* is the incarnation of the god Vishnu.

Note: In standard English, the relative pronoun *that* usually introduces essential clauses. The relative pronoun *which* usually introduces nonessential clauses. *Who, whose,* and *whom* introduce either essential or nonessential clauses.

Exercise 1. Identifying Essential and Nonessential Clauses

Details in the following sentences are from "Rama and Ravana in Battle." In each sentence, underline each essential subordinate clause once. Underline each nonessential subordinate clause twice. The number in parentheses tells you how many clauses you should find.

EXAMPLE "Rama and Ravana in Battle," which is translated by R. K. Narayan, is from the *Ramayana.*

1. The ancient Indian epic, the *Ramayana,* which was written some 2,000 years ago, tells the story of Rama, who is the incarnation of Vishnu. (2)

2. The episode that relates the final battle between Ravana and Rama is titled "Rama and Ravana in Battle." (1)

3. The conflict between Rama and Ravana is caused by the abduction of Sita, who is Rama's wife. (1)

4. Ravana, who has spent his lifetime destroying others, personally joins the battle after hearing reports that his forces are losing. (2)

5. After much bloodshed on both sides, Ravana uses his asthras, which are powerful supernatural weapons. (1)

(continued)

6. Rama uses the asthra that seeks out the enemy's weakness only as a last resort. (1)

7. Heroes whose qualities include strength and courage still appeal to audiences today. (1)

8. Ravana, whom Rama eventually defeats, at first seems to be the stronger of the two enemies whose battle is the subject of this selection. (2)

9. Brahma, who is the creator of the universe, takes the side of Rama and sends him a chariot that enables him to win the battle. (2)

10. The woman who is Rama's faithful wife is rewarded for her virtue by being made a goddess. (1)

Exercise 2. Using Essential and Nonessential Clauses

Combine each of the following sets of sentences about "Rama and Ravana in Battle." Make the second sentence in each set into an essential or nonessential clause as indicated in parentheses. Use the relative pronoun indicated in parentheses to link the sentences. Change, move, or add words as necessary to make the combination. Write your new sentence on the blanks provided.

EXAMPLE The *Ramayana* is a long poem written in couplets. It is an Indian epic. (nonessential: which)
The *Ramayana*, which is an Indian epic, is a long poem written in couplets.

1. The woman is named Sita. Her kidnapping results in the battle. (essential: whose)

____

____

2. Conventional weapons have little effect upon Ravana. He has many heads and arms. (nonessential: who)

____

____

3. Both Ravana and Rama use the supernatural weapons. They are known as *asthras.* (essential: that)

____

____

(continued)

4. Ravana thinks Rama is mortal. Ravana misjudges his enemy. (nonessential: who)

____

____

5. Rama is an honorable person. Indians still consider him a hero. (nonessential: whom)

____

____

Exercise 3. Proofreading a Paragraph

In the following paragraph about "Rama and Ravana in Battle," none of the clauses are set off by commas. Add commas as necessary to set off nonessential clauses. One clause is set off for you as an example.

After his weakness-seeking asthra kills Ravana, Rama approaches Ravana's lifeless body, which is covered with blood from his many wounds. Ravana's faces which have always reflected anger, conceit, and cruelty now reflect serenity and peace. On Ravana's back, Rama is shocked to see a bloodstained scar that seems proof of Ravana's retreating. There is no glory in killing someone who has turned his back. Vibishana who is Ravana's brother steps forward to ease Rama's concern. The scar is the result of a goring from a divine elephant that was protecting itself from an attack by Ravana. The scar appears to be fresh because of the blood that is flowing out of it.

NAME ______________________________ CLASS ______________________ DATE ________ SCORE ________

Rama and Ravana in Battle
from the Ramayana

translated by R. K. Narayan (Textbook page 486)

READING COMPREHENSION

Directions: In the space provided, write the letter of the best answer to each question. *(10 points each)*

1. Rama, the main character in the *Ramayana*, is an incarnation of which Hindu god?
   a. Brahma, the god of creation
   b. Indra, the god of war
   c. Vishnu, the god of preservation
   d. Shiva, the god of destructive forces — 1. ______

2. Which of these statements describes the battle between Rama and Ravana?
   a. Ravana is much more powerful in battle than Rama.
   b. Rama is more powerful in battle than Ravana, but he is afraid of Ravana.
   c. Rama's rage keeps him from being effective in battle.
   d. Rama is a much more powerful enemy than Ravana has expected. — 2. ______

3. What do the gods do to provide special support for Rama?
   a. They send a special chariot for his use.
   b. They cast spells upon Ravana's armies.
   c. They send a divine army for his use.
   d. They do nothing to help either side. — 3. ______

4. What happens to Ravana's assistant, Mahodara?
   a. The monkey-king kills him.
   b. Rama kills him.
   c. The gods trick him into giving himself up.
   d. He is injured but not killed when his chariot collides with Rama's. — 4. ______

5. During the main battle, how does Rama defend himself against the showers of arrows that Ravana shoots at him?
   a. by outdistancing them in his special chariot
   b. by shattering them with his own arrows
   c. by burning them with a wall of flames
   d. by deflecting them with a magic shield — 5. ______

6. When does Ravana begin using asthras, the weapons with supernatural powers?
   a. when the conventional weapons fail to kill Rama
   b. when Ravana realizes that Rama is a god
   c. when instructed to do so by the gods
   d. when he runs out of arrows — 6. ______

(continued)

7. What is unique about Ravana's asthra called "Maya"?
   a. It sets the oceans aflame.
   b. It is a huge bow and arrow.
   c. It circles the earth and attacks Rama from the rear.
   d. It creates illusions and confusion in enemies. 7. ______

8. Despite his awesome powers, Ravana is killed because he has failed to strengthen his
   a. armor
   b. mind
   c. heart
   d. heel 8. ______

9. As a result of all the arrows that Rama uses on Ravana,
   a. Ravana's heads are all permanently cut off
   b. layers of cruelty, conceit, and anger are burned off Ravana
   c. Ravana's armor is melted and his heart is exposed
   d. Ravana's body becomes completely immune to further attack 9. ______

10. Once Rama has killed Ravana, what does he wish for him?
    a. to be buried and forgotten, so that no memory of him will exist
    b. to be honored and cherished, so that his spirit will go to heaven
    c. to be hated and reviled, so that his spirit will go to the underworld
    d. to be hurled into the heavens, so that he will never be seen or thought of again 10. ______

NAME ______________ CLASS ______________ DATE ________ SCORE ________

UNIT 5: INDIAN LITERATURE

WORD ANALOGIES/Extending Vocabulary

Directions: In the space provided, write the letter of the pair of words with the relationship that is closest to that of the capitalized words. *(10 points each)*

1. DISPEL : RUMOR ::
   a. receive : advice
   b. combine : forces
   c. arrest : gossip
   d. dismiss : resident 1. ______

2. INTERMITTENT : CONTINUOUS ::
   a. periodic : steady
   b. permanent : fixed
   c. movable : mobile
   d. constant : frequency 2. ______

3. VANQUISH : ENEMY ::
   a. disappear : criminal
   b. defeat : opponent
   c. guard : imprison
   d. harbor : refuge 3. ______

4. RESIDUE : REMAINDER ::
   a. fossil : skeleton
   b. remnant : leavings
   c. revenue : tax
   d. stock : dividend 4. ______

5. REFLECT : THOUGHT ::
   a. message : repeat
   b. solution : problem
   c. create : imagine
   d. ponder : idea 5. ______

6. PILGRIMAGE : PILGRIM ::
   a. country : immigrant
   b. throne : king
   c. excursion : tourist
   d. isolation : prisoner 6. ______

7. SANCTION : DENIAL ::
   a. permission : refusal
   b. agreement : conflict
   c. support : consent
   d. rejection : request 7. ______

8. IMPARTIAL : JUDGE ::
   a. testify : witness
   b. trial : jury
   c. guilt : defendant
   d. biased : prosecutor 8. ______

9. IMMUTABLE : UNALTERABLE ::
   a. unsure : stubborn
   b. ready : unprepared
   c. movable : stationary
   d. lasting : permanent 9. ______

10. LUCID : STATEMENT ::
   a. diamond : gem
   b. clear : sky
   c. empty : glass
   d. sentence : awkward 10. ______

UNIT 5: INDIAN LITERATURE

UNIT REVIEW TEST/Applying Skills I

A. Reading Comprehension. In the space provided, write the letter of the best answer to each question. *(8 points each)*

1. The *Rig Veda* is an ancient collection of sacred hymns first written down in
   a. Dravidian
   b. Sanskrit
   c. the language of the Indus Valley civilization
   d. Kannada

   1. ______

2. In "Hundred Questions," from the *Mahabharata*, what is the purpose of the series of questions to Yudhistira?
   a. to test his strength of mind
   b. to test his supernatural powers
   c. to stall for time
   d. to test his honesty

   2. ______

3. In "Philosophy and Spiritual Discipline," from the *Bhagavad-Gita*, what is the purpose of the dialogue between Arjuna and Lord Krishna?
   a. to prepare Arjuna for death in battle
   b. to explain the origins of the dispute within Arjuna's family
   c. to eliminate Arjuna's concerns about doing his sacred duty
   d. to instruct Arjuna in the use of supernatural weapons

   3. ______

4. What is the theme of "Right-Mind and Wrong-Mind," from the *Panchatantra?*
   a. Gods are superior to humans.
   b. Goodness turns the tables on evil.
   c. Two wrongs don't make a right.
   d. Animal stories are more effective than stories about gods and goddesses.

   4. ______

5. At the end of "Rama and Ravana in Battle," from the *Ramayana*, when Rama has killed Ravana, what do we learn about Rama?
   a. He is part god and part human.
   b. He is Indra, the god of war.
   c. He is punitive and unforgiving.
   d. He is a noble and generous victor.

   5. ______

(continued)

B. Identifying Characters. Each description below refers to a main character in one of the selections you have just read. Identify the characters by choosing the letter of the best answer. Write the letter in the space provided. *(8 points each)*

6. I was accused of a crime of which I was innocent.
   a. Arjuna
   b. Rama
   c. Wrong-Mind
   d. Right-Mind

   6. ______

7. When my four brothers were killed by a god, I passed a test and saved them.
   a. Arjuna
   b. Yudhistira
   c. Bhima
   d. Rama

   7. ______

8. I was the greatest living warrior, with my many arms and heads, until I met my match.
   a. Ravana
   b. Wrong-Mind
   c. Rama
   d. Yudhistira

   8. ______

9. When I pitied the relatives I would kill, I was counseled about my sacred duty.
   a. Yudhistira
   b. Rama
   c. Arjuna
   d. Krishna

   9. ______

10. I responded to my opponent's asthras with supernatural weapons of my own, ultimately killing him.
    a. Ramayana
    b. Ravana
    c. Right-Mind
    d. Rama

    10. ______

C. Composition. Choose *one* of these topics and write a brief essay on a separate piece of paper. *(20 points)*

1. In "Rama and Ravana in Battle," the warriors use a variety of weapons, including asthras, weapons of supernatural power. Describe some of these weapons, and compare them to modern, future, or science-fiction weaponry.
2. Pick one of the following: Yudhistira, Arjuna, or Rama. Write a short essay in which you identify the character, the selection, the character's conflict, and the way the conflict is resolved.

NAME ______________________ CLASS ______________________ DATE __________ SCORE __________

UNIT 5: INDIAN LITERATURE

CRITICAL THINKING AND WRITING/Applying Skills II

A. Reading Poetry. Read the poems below carefully. Then answer the questions that follow.

from SPEAKING OF SIVA

translated by
A. K. RAMANUJAN

70

As a mother runs
close behind her child
with his hand on a cobra
or a fire,

the lord of the meeting rivers
stays with me
every step of the way
and looks after me.

—*Basavanna*

144

The crookedness of the serpent
is straight enough for the snake-hole.

The crookedness of the river
is straight enough for the sea.

And the crookedness of our Lord's men
is straight enough for our Lord!

—*Basavanna*

42

A man filled grain
in a tattered sack
and walked all night
fearing the tollgates

but the grain went through the tatters
and all he got was the gunny sack.

It is thus
with the devotion
of the fainthearted

O Rāmanātha.

—*Dēvara Dāsimayya*

144

Suppose you cut a tall bamboo
in two;
make the bottom piece a woman,
the headpiece a man;
rub them together
till they kindle:
tell me now,
the fire that's born,
is it male or female,

O Rāmanātha?

—*Dēvara Dāsimayya*

(continued)

B. Analyzing Poetry. In the space provided, write the letter of the best answer to each question. *(6 points each)*

1. Which of the following words best describes the mother in Basavanna's poem #70?
   a. manipulator
   b. protector
   c. interferer
   d. preventer

   1. ______

2. What figure of speech is used in poem #70?
   a. metaphor
   b. apostrophe
   c. simile
   d. onomatopoeia

   2. ______

3. Which of these items best describes the nature of "the lord of the meeting rivers" in Basavanna's poem #70?
   a. having unlimited power
   b. having unlimited knowledge
   c. devouring everything
   d. being ever-watchful and protective

   3. ______

4. Which of these words is the best synonym for the word *crookedness* in line 5 of Basavanna's poem #144?
   a. imperfection
   b. poison
   c. curving
   d. slyness

   4. ______

5. Which pair of words best describes the themes of Basavanna's two poems?
   a. comfort and acceptance
   b. suffering and danger
   c. animals and humans
   d. companionship and traveling

   5. ______

6. In Dēvara Dāsimayya's poem #42, the poet expresses the importance of
   a. taking care of one's possessions
   b. exercising devotion
   c. caution in journeying through life
   d. proper behavior in religious rites

   6. ______

(continued)

7. In poem #42, why does Dāsimayya compare the sack-bearer to the faint-hearted?
   a. They have nothing in common.
   b. They both lose something.
   c. They both carry sacks.
   d. They both ignore tollgates.

7. ______

8. What does the grain symbolize in poem #42?
   a. the fruits of labor
   b. the source of flour and bread
   c. love of one's god
   d. the food of the world

8. ______

9. In poem #144 by Dāsimayya, the poet implies a comparison between a fire and something else. Which of the items below best completes the comparison?
   a. love
   b. anger
   c. bamboo
   d. jealousy

9. ______

10. Which set of words best expresses the differences between the themes of the first three poems and the theme of the last poem?
    a. explaining vs. inquiring
    b. commonplace vs. unusual
    c. childhood vs. adulthood
    d. mothers vs. snakes

10. ______

C. Writing About Poetry.

Basavanna and Dēvara Dāsimayya, known as *vacana* poets, wrote in tenth-century India. At that time, Hindus worshipped many gods. In these poems, however, the poets express a belief in one god—the Lord Shiva (Siva), also known as "Rāmanātha" or "lord of the meeting rivers." On a separate sheet of paper, write one paragraph describing Lord Shiva as he is depicted by the two poets. In your answer, consider (a) whether Lord Shiva is seen as a wrathful or a gentle god, (b) how tolerant he is to the mistakes of humans, and (c) what demands Lord Shiva makes of humans. Be sure to include specific details from the poems. *(40 points)*

UNIT 5: INDIAN LITERATURE

UNIT INTRODUCTION TEST

(Textbook pages 446–453)

1. c	5. d	8. c
2. b	6. a	9. b
3. b	7. d	10. c
4. a		

NIGHT, *from the* RIG VEDA

translated by Wendy Doniger O'Flaherty
(Textbook page 456)

REVIEW AND RESPONSE WORKSHEET

Reviewing the Selection

1. near
2. around
3. on her glories
4. spaces, depths, and heights
5. the darkness
6. the twilight aside
7. wolves and thieves
8. waves

Reader's Response

Responses will vary. Possible sentences:
1. She brings warmth and light.
2. She looks into darkened streets and homes.
3. She speaks of cocks crowing.
4. She rushes across continents and oceans.
5. She withdraws slowly, sadly.

HUNDRED QUESTIONS *from the* MAHABHARATA

translated by R. K. Narayan
(Textbook page 461)

VOCABULARY ACTIVITY WORKSHEET

Developing Vocabulary

Responses will vary.

VOCABULARY TEST

A.	1. c	3. d	5. e
	2. a	4. b	
B.	6. C	8. C	10. I
	7. I	9. C	

REVIEW AND RESPONSE WORKSHEET

Reviewing the Selection

1. They are retrieving prayer articles for a brahman which were carried off by the deer.
2. They fall down, lifeless.
3. a forest divinity who is really Yama, the God of Justice, and father of Yudhistira
4. He is testing Yudhistira's strength of mind.

Reader's Response

Responses will vary. Students should not reproduce Yudhistira's answers verbatim, but some may be influenced by his responses. Other students may have very different notions of the meaning of these concepts.

(continued)

SELECTION TEST

Reading Comprehension

1. a	5. b	8. c
2. d	6. c	9. a
3. d	7. a	10. b
4. c		

PHILOSOPHY AND SPIRITUAL DISCIPLINE *from the* BHAGAVAD-GITA

translated by Barbara Stoler Miller
(Textbook page 469)

VOCABULARY ACTIVITY WORKSHEET

Developing Vocabulary

Responses will vary.

VOCABULARY TEST

A. 1. f	5. j	8. b
2. g	6. a	9. e
3. h	7. c	10. d
4. i		

B. 11 immutable 12. diffuse
13. mundane 14. lucid 15. impartial

REVIEW AND RESPONSE WORKSHEET

Reviewing the Selection

1. Arjuna is sad at the thought of having to kill his elder relatives during the upcoming battle.
2. Responses may vary slightly. Krishna explains that although a body may be killed, the embodied self lives forever. It is simply reborn in another body.
3. b, c
4. Responses will vary. A sage is one who has achieved inner peace, one who does not crave pleasure and who feels no fear, anger, or attraction for worldly things.

Reader's Response

Responses will vary, depending upon what individual students feel is sacred. Some might believe that military service, when called for by the government, is sacred; others may feel that their highest duty is to their family or their god.

LANGUAGE SKILLS WORKSHEET

Subject-Verb Agreement

Exercise 1

1. C	5. C	8. I
2. C	6. C	9. I
3. I	7. C	10. I
4. I		

Exercise 2

1. is	5. prepares	8. addresses
2. loses	6. have	9. avoids
3. go	7. concerns	10. is
4. wants		

Exercise 3

Krisha *argues* that it *is* the warrior's dharma to fight. Shame and cowardice *await* the warrior who will not fight. A warrior who *fights* in the battles *has* no reason to be sad about killing his enemies. Although their bodies *are* killed, their embodied selves endure forever. The embodied self *leaves* the dead body and *takes* on a new one. If the warrior is killed in battle while doing his sacred duty, he *wins* heaven.

SELECTION TEST

Reading Comprehension

1. b	5. b	8. a
2. c	6. d	9. d
3. a	7. c	10. a
4. b		

(continued)

RIGHT-MIND AND WRONG-MIND *from the* PANCHATANTRA

translated by Arthur William Ryder
(Textbook page 480)

VOCABULARY ACTIVITY WORKSHEET

Developing Vocabulary

Responses will vary.

VOCABULARY TEST

A. 1. d 3. e 5. c
2. b 4. a

B. 6. b 8. c 10. b
7. a 9. a

REVIEW AND RESPONSE WORKSHEET

Reviewing the Selection

1. Wrong-Mind says that burying the treasure will preserve their friendship and allow the two of them to test their virtue.
2. Wrong-Mind steals it.
3. Wrong-Mind's father tells a fable called "A Remedy Worse Than the Disease," which demonstrates that schemes that are poorly thought out can be disastrous to the schemer.
4. He sets fire to the hole to force Wrong-Mind's father out. The father then confesses.

Reader's Response

Responses will vary. Students may reason that the father bowed to his son's wishes out of blind love or greed to share the treasure. Some students might think that Wrong-Mind's father should have let Wrong-Mind bear the responsibility for his own wrongdoing.

LANGUAGE SKILLS WORKSHEET

Perfect Tenses

Exercise 1

1. a 5. a 8. b
2. b 6. b 9. a
3. c 7. b 10. c
4. b

Exercise 2

1. has trusted
2. will have been
3. had recited
4. had planned
5. has tried

Exercise 3

The *Panchatantra has been* a source of wisdom in India for centuries; even today, parents in India tell the stories to their children. For in India, as in most parts of the world, storytellers *have understood* the value of fables as teaching tools for a long time. Even before the *Panchatantra* found a mass audience, however, it *had been* used to teach the art of governance to young Indian nobles. Although it was written in Sanskrit originally, the *Panchatantra had appeared* in Persian by the sixth century A.D. By the Renaissance, scholars *had translated* it into Arabic, Greek, Hebrew, Latin, German, and Italian. With a new emphasis on world literature in American schools, thousands of American high school students *will have read* excerpts from the *Panchatantra* by the end of this decade!

SELECTION TEST

Reading Comprehension

1. b 5. d 8. a
2. a 6. c 9. d
3. c 7. b 10. c
4. b

(continued)

RAMA AND RAVANA IN BATTLE *from the* RAMAYANA

translated by R. K. Narayan
(Textbook page 486)

VOCABULARY ACTIVITY WORKSHEET

Developing Vocabulary
Responses will vary.

VOCABULARY TEST

A. 1. b	6. i	**B.** 11. d	
2. e	7. h	12. c	
3. d	8. a	13. e	
4. g	9. j	14. b	
5. f	10. c	15. a	

REVIEW AND RESPONSE WORKSHEET

Reviewing the Selection

1. Rama
2. Ravana has many heads and arms.
3. They send down a special chariot and charioteer.
4. The asthras are supernatural weapons with a variety of unique and powerful effects. They affect the senses, attack vulnerabilities, and so on.

Reader's Response

Responses will vary. Students may offer their personal methods of mustering inner strength: prayer, a talk with a friend, a "psych-up" exercise, and so on.

LANGUAGE SKILLS WORKSHEET

Essential and Nonessential Clauses

Exercise 1

1. which was written some 2,000 years ago, who is the incarnation of Vishnu
2. that relates the final battle between Ravana and Rama
3. who is Rama's wife
4. who has spent his lifetime destroying others, that his forces are losing
5. which are powerful supernatural weapons
6. that seeks out the enemy's weakness
7. whose qualities include strength and courage
8. whom Rama eventually defeats, whose battle is the subject of this selection
9. who is the creator of the universe, that enables him to win the battle
10. who is Rama's faithful wife

Exercise 2

Responses will vary slightly. Sample sentences:

1. The woman whose kidnapping results in the battle is named Sita.
2. Conventional weapons have little effect upon Ravana, who has many heads and arms.
3. Both Ravana and Rama use the supernatural weapons that are known as *asthras.*
4. Ravana, who misjudges his enemy, thinks Rama is mortal.
5. Rama, whom Indians still consider a hero, is an honorable person.

Exercise 3

After his weakness-seeking asthra kills Ravana, Rama approaches Ravana's lifeless body, which is covered with blood from his many wounds. Ravana's faces, which have always reflected anger, conceit, and cruelty,

(continued)

now reflect serenity and peace. On Ravana's back, Rama is shocked to see a bloodstained scar that seems proof of Ravana's retreating. There is no glory in killing someone who has turned his back. Vibishana, who is Ravana's brother, steps forward to ease Rama's concern. The scar is the result of a goring from a divine elephant that was protecting itself from an attack by Ravana. The scar appears to be fresh because of the blood that is flowing out of it.

SELECTION TEST

Reading Comprehension

1. c
2. d
3. a
4. b
5. b
6. a
7. d
8. c
9. b
10. b

WORD ANALOGIES/Extending Vocabulary

1. c (dispel : rumor :: arrest : gossip)
   Relationship: action to object
   One *dispels*, or figuratively "scatters," *rumors* just as one *arrests gossip*. The analogy is strengthened by the fact that *rumor* and *gossip* have similar meanings, as do *dispel* (in this sense) and *arrest*.
2. a (intermittent : continuous :: periodic : steady)
   Relationship: antonyms
   Intermittent, "ending and beginning again at intervals," is an antonym of *continuous*. *Periodic* and *steady* are also antonyms. The analogy is strengthened by the fact that *intermittent* and *periodic* are synonyms, as are *continuous* and *steady*.
3. b (vanquish : enemy :: defeat : opponent)
   Relationship: action to object
   One acts to *vanquish*, "conquer," an *enemy*. One acts to *defeat* an *opponent*. The analogy is strengthened by the fact that *vanquish* and *defeat* are synonyms, as are *enemy* and *opponent*.
4. b (residue : remainder :: remnant : leavings)
   Relationship: synonyms
   Residue, *remainder*, *remnant*, and *leavings* are all synonyms for "leftover portion."
5. d (reflect : thought :: ponder : idea)
   Relationship: action to object
   One acts to *reflect*, "contemplate seriously," on a *thought*. One acts to *ponder* an idea. The analogy is strengthened by the fact that *reflect* and *ponder* are synonyms, as are *thought* and *idea*.
6. c (pilgrimage : pilgrim :: excursion : tourist)
   Relationship: action to person
   An action of a *pilgrim* is to make a *pilgrimage*, "a trip to a holy place" or "a long journey." An action of a *tourist* is to make an *excursion*. The analogy is strengthened by the fact that *pilgrimage* and *excursion* are closely related in meaning, as are *pilgrim* and *tourist*.
7. a (sanction : denial :: permission : refusal)
   Relationship: antonyms
   Sanction, "approval," is an antonym of *denial*. *Permission* is an antonym of *refusal*. The analogy is strengthened by the fact that *sanction* and *permission* are synonyms, as are *denial* and *refusal*.
8. d (impartial: judge:: biased: prosecutor)
   Relationship: Characteristic to person
   One expects a *judge* to be *impartial*, "not favoring either side in a dispute or contest." One expects a *prosecutor* to be *biased*.
9. d (immutable : unalterable :: lasting : permanent)
   Relationship: synonyms
   All four words are synonyms of each other sharing the meaning "unchangeable."
10. b (lucid : statement :: clear : sky)
    Relationship: characteristic to object
    One ideally expects a *statement* to be *lucid*, "clear." One ideally expects the *sky* to be *clear*.

(continued)

UNIT REVIEW TEST/Applying Skills I

A. Reading Comprehension

1. b
2. a
3. c
4. b
5. d

B. Identifying Characters

6. d
7. b
8. a
9. c
10. d

C. Composition

1. Responses will vary. Students may mention any of the following asthras, or supernatural weapons: Danda, a gift from Shiva, which flames along in pursuit of its target until it pulverizes it; Maya, which creates illusions and confuses the enemy; Gnana, which means "wisdom" or "perception," and which makes illusions vanish; Thama, which comes down as arrows with fiery faces, creates total darkness in all worlds, paralyzes all of creation, creates a deluge of rain on one side, a rain of stones on the other, an intermittent hailstorm, and a tornado; Shivasthra, which counteracts Thama; a trident with extraordinary destructive power; a weapon that issues serpents spitting fire and venom; Garuda, which has the form of thousands of eagles that eat serpents; Brahmasthra, the most powerful, which Rama aims at Ravana's heart.

2. Responses will vary. Students may choose any of the following: (a) the eldest Pandava brother, Yudhistira, who insightfully answers the hundred questions of the yaksha (his father, the god of justice, disguised as a minor forest god), restoring his four brothers to life and gaining a divine boon (the ability to go unrecognized) that will enable the brothers to complete successfully the final conditions of their exile (from *Hundred Questions);* (b) Arjuna, the third Pandava brother, who has a dialogue with his charioteer, Krishna, that helps Arjuna to understand his sacred duty, overcome his sorrow and unwillingness, and fight his cousins, the Kauravas, so that the Pandavas can regain their inheritance and Arjuna can attain "the pure calm of infinity" (from the *Bhagavad-Gita);* (c) Rama, a semidivine incarnation of Vishnu, who counteracts an arsenal of supernatural weapons and defeats the demon king Ravana in order to win back Sita (Rama's wife, whom Ravana has abducted) and return to his own kingdom as ruler (from the *Ramayana*).

CRITICAL THINKING AND WRITING/
Applying Skills II

B. Analyzing Poetry

1. b
2. c
3. d
4. a
5. a
6. b
7. b
8. c
9. a
10. a

C. Writing About Poetry

Students' paragraphs will vary. Basavanna's poem #70 suggests that Lord Shiva is a gentle, protective god, similar to the God of the New Testament. This poem also suggests a personal involvement on Shiva's part with humankind. Basavanna's poem #144, in which the "crookedness" of humans is compared with that of things of nature, indicates a tolerance on the part of Lord Shiva to human imperfection. The themes of devotion in Basavanna's poem #70 and Dāsimayya's poem #42 suggest that Lord Shiva requires the unaffected devotion of his followers.

NAME ______________________ CLASS ______________________ DATE ________ SCORE ________

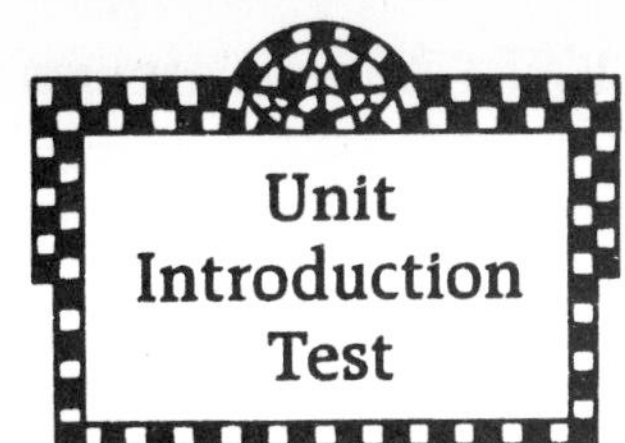

UNIT 6: CHINESE AND JAPANESE LITERATURES

(Textbook pages 506–511)

INTRODUCTION/The Literature of China

Directions: In the space provided, write the letter of the best answer to each question. *(10 points each)*

1. Of all the literary forms, the Chinese hold the highest regard for
   a. biographies
   b. short stories
   c. poetry
   d. drama

   1. ______

2. The origin of Chinese fiction and drama goes back to
   a. people passing along stories by word of mouth
   b. foreigners bringing books into the country
   c. the poetry collection *The Book of Songs*
   d. the development of a Chinese alphabet

   2. ______

3. When a country is ruled by a dynasty,
   a. free elections are held
   b. political power is passed down through a family
   c. local government officials are chosen by the people
   d. the government maintains high ethical standards

   3. ______

4. The Chinese alphabet differs from ours in that it
   a. has fewer letters
   b. contains more than three thousand characters
   c. did not develop until very late in Chinese history
   d. represents a relatively new language

   4. ______

5. Politically, China can be said to be
   a. generally stable
   b. always at war
   c. a model for the rest of the world to follow
   d. in a continuous cycle of peace and upheaval

   5. ______

6. Beginning with the Ming dynasty, China sought to heighten its culture by practicing
   a. isolationism
   b. communism
   c. free trade
   d. cultural exchange with other countries

   6. ______

(continued)

7. Which of the following items describes Buddhism?
   a. The teaching emphasizes the importance of worshiping one god.
   b. It is a system of belief that emphasizes material values.
   c. It began in the year A.D. 1000.
   d. It stresses the importance of seeking earthly peace through enlightenment. 7. ______

8. The teachings of Confucius primarily embraced
   a. a love of nature
   b. advancement in government
   c. the importance of government control
   d. ethical values 8. ______

9. The concept of *yin* and *yang* holds that the conflicting sides of nature
   a. fight each other
   b. create a life constantly in turmoil
   c. depend on and balance each other
   d. cause spirits to rule the earth 9. ______

10. Due to the influence of Chinese philosophy and religion, Chinese poets such as Li Po and Tu Fu wrote many poems about
    a. nature
    b. war
    c. the government
    d. Buddhism 10. ______

NAME ______________________ CLASS ______________ DATE ________ SCORE ________

from THE BOOK OF SONGS

translated by Arthur Waley

(Textbook page 515)

REVIEWING THE SELECTIONS

1. Circle the three words that best describe the feelings of the speaker in the poem "What Plant Is Not Faded?"

   angry lonely content conceited mistreated indifferent

2. What do the speakers in both "O Oriole, Yellow Bird" and "What Plant Is Not Faded?" want to do?

   ____

3. List three specific complaints each speaker has about his or her situation.

   A. Song 103: "O Oriole, Yellow Bird"

      1. ____

      2. ____

      3. ____

   B. Song 130: "What Plant Is Not Faded?"

      1. ____

      2. ____

      3. ____

Reader's Response

Of the two speakers—the woman in "O Oriole, Yellow Bird" or the soldier in "What Plant Is Not Faded?"—with whom do you sympathize the most? Write two or three sentences explaining why you feel as you do.

____

____

____

____

NAME ______________________ CLASS ______________________ DATE __________ SCORE __________

Poems of Li Po

Li Po
translated by Arthur Cooper

(Textbook page 520)

REVIEWING THE SELECTIONS

Li Po uses images of nature to describe his feelings. Complete the following paragraph about his poems by filling in the blanks with the words below. You will use each word only once.

silkworms	peach	frost	moon
spring	mulberry	fields	stream

Even if you didn't know the title, you would know that "Quiet Night Thoughts" takes place at night because Li Po says the moonlight looks like ______________________ on the ground. He watches the ______________________ before falling asleep and dreaming about his home. You know that "Letter to His Two Small Children" takes place in ______________________ because he talks about the green ______________________ leaves and the stages that the ______________________ have gone through. He also says that it is time to sow the ______________________. In the letter to his children, he tells them about how he dreams of the leaves on the ______________________ tree he planted before he left home. He knows that the children, who have grown as fast as the tree, miss him too, and he aches as he thinks about his daughter's tears flowing like a running ______________________.

Reader's Response

The poems of Li Po are filled with emotional images, such as the bright moonlight that makes him think of home in "Quiet Night Thoughts." Write one or two sentences explaining which of the images in either of the two poems on textbook pages 520 and 521 has the greatest emotional effect on you. Explain why you feel the way you do.

____

____

____

____

NAME ______________________ CLASS ______________________ DATE ________ SCORE ________

POEMS OF TU FU

Tu Fu
translated by Arthur Cooper
and Kenneth Rexroth

(Textbook page 528)

DEVELOPING VOCABULARY

Directions: Read carefully the explanation of each word. Then write a sentence of your own using that word. In your sentences, include clues to the word's meaning.

grizzled (griz′əld) ***adj.*** Gray, especially in reference to hair. ▶ This word stems from the Old French *gris*, meaning "gray." ▪ Grizzled and wind–battered after many years at sea, the old man enjoyed telling stories of his adventures. **Page 528**

ORIGINAL SENTENCE ____

____

sequence (sē′kwəns) ***n.*** The following of one thing after another in some logical order. ▶ *Subsequent*, a related adjective, means "coming after." ▪ Bill had trouble remembering the sequence of events that led to the car wreck. **Page 528**

ORIGINAL SENTENCE ____

____

courtier (kôrt′ē·ər) ***n.*** An attendant in a court of royalty . ▶ This word can also refer to someone who uses flattery to get something or to win favor . ▪ The queen's favorite courtier never left her side. **Page 530**

ORIGINAL SENTENCE ____

____

pathos (pā′thäs′) ***n.*** The quality in something experienced or observed that moves one to feelings of pity or sorrow. ▶ The Greek word *pathos* means "suffering, disease, or feeling." ▪ The pathos of the movie's ending, in which the character loses everything, moved the audience to tears. **Page 530**

ORIGINAL SENTENCE ____

____

imperceptible (im′pər·sep′tə·bəl) ***adj.*** Not easily sensed. —**imperceptibly** ***adv.*** ▶ This word should not be confused with *imperceptive*, which means "lacking in perception," as in "a stupid and *imperceptive* person." ▪ The flaw in the diamond was almost imperceptible, visible only with a jeweler's special glass. **Page 530**

ORIGINAL SENTENCE ____

____

NAME ______________________ CLASS ____________________ DATE ________ SCORE ______

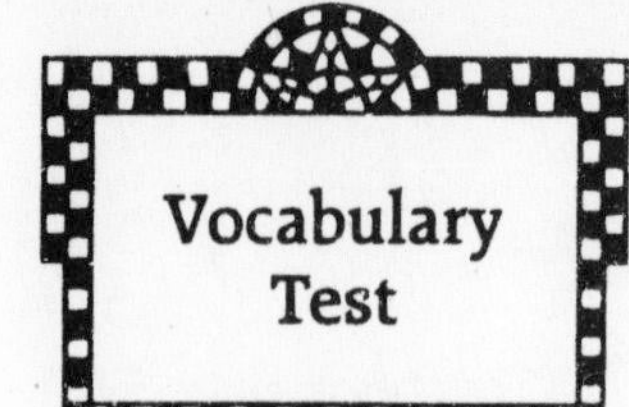

POEMS OF TU FU

Tu Fu
translated by Arthur Cooper
and Kenneth Rexroth

(Textbook page 528)

VOCABULARY TEST

A. Match each word in column I with the correct definition in column II. Place the letter of the definition you choose in the space provided. *(10 points each)*

I	II
______ 1. courtier	a. a quality that stirs pity
______ 2. grizzled	b. an attendant in a royal court
______ 3. imperceptible	c. the following of one thing after another
______ 4. pathos	d. gray
______ 5. sequence	e. not easily sensed

B. From the vocabulary words listed below, choose the word that best completes the sentence. Write the appropriate word in the blank provided. *(10 points each)*

grizzled pathos sequence
courtiers imperceptible

6. The ______________________ of the situation of homeless people brought tears to Jacob's eyes.

7. The old sailor had long, ______________________ hair and scars on his face.

8. In previous centuries, ______________________ would write love poems and distribute them among the nobility for their amusement.

9. The slight dent in the car was ______________________ to a casual observer.

10. The experiment was ruined because the lab technician added the chemicals in the wrong ______________________.

NAME ______________________ CLASS ______________ DATE ________ SCORE ______

Poems of Tu Fu

Tu Fu
translated by Arthur Cooper
and Kenneth Rexroth

(Textbook page 528)

REVIEWING THE SELECTIONS

1. In "For Wei Pa, in Retirement," who are the ghosts Tu Fu talks about?

____

2. Circle the words that best describe the poet's feelings in "Night Thoughts Afloat."

   melancholy   happy   angry   lonely   insignificant

3. In "Jade Flower Palace," what one item remains as a symbol of the prince's past glory?

____

4. Circle the one saying that might be applied to each of these poems.
   a. A friend for life is a joy to cherish.
   b. Nothing remains the same forever.
   c. A life of work without play is meaningless.

Reader's Response

There is a sadness to each of these poems of Tu Fu. Which poem do you think carries the saddest message? What is it about the poem that makes you feel this way? Write two or three sentences explaining your answer.

____
____
____
____
____
____
____
____
____

NAME ______________________ CLASS ________________ DATE ________ SCORE ______

Peonies

Li Ch'ing-chao
translated by Kenneth Rexroth
and Ling Chung

(Textbook page 534)

REVIEWING THE SELECTION

1. During what time of year is this poem set?

____

2. Circle the words that describe the woman in the poem.

   beautiful   silly   old   modest   indifferent

3. What is the meaning of the word "twilight" in the last line of the poem?

____

4. Circle the letter of the sentence that best describes the speaker's thoughts.
   a. Both fresh flowers and beautiful women are part of palace life.
   b. No flower lasts as long as a beautiful palace.
   c. Like a flower, physical beauty will fade with time.

Reader's Response

This poem was written more than eight hundred years ago. Do you think people today still share some of the speaker's feelings about female beauty? Write one or two sentences explaining your answer.

____

____

____

____

____

____

____

____

____

NAME ______________________ CLASS ______________________ DATE __________ SCORE __________

from the ANALECTS

Confucius

translated by Arthur Waley

(Textbook page 538)

DEVELOPING VOCABULARY

Directions: Read carefully the explanation of each word. Then write a sentence of your own using that word. In your sentence, include clues to the word's meaning.

docile (däs'əl) ***adj.*** Easily managed or controlled; submissive. ▶ This word derives from *docilis*, "easily taught," which itself derives from *docere*, "to teach." The familiar word *doctor*, which also comes from *docere*, originally meant "teacher." ▪ Although Bingo could be savage to an intruder, he made a docile pet. **Page 539**

ORIGINAL SENTENCE ____

____

dictate (dik'tāt') ***n.*** A guiding principle; something required by authority. ▶ This word comes from the Latin verb *dictare*. ▪ An important dictate for Confucius was to achieve moderation in all things. **Page 539**

ORIGINAL SENTENCE ____

____

filial (fil' ē·əl) ***adj.*** Of, referring to, or appropriate for one's children. ▶ The Latin words *filius*, "son," and *filia*, "daughter," are the ancestors of this term. ▪ Janet felt that respect for her mother was her filial duty. **Page 539**

ORIGINAL SENTENCE ____

____

intent (in·tent') ***adj.*** Directed or fixed—**intent on** or **upon** ***adj.*** Having the attention fixed; strongly directed. ▶ The noun *intent* means "purpose or aim." ▪ Matt was so intent upon his studies that he forgot about his date that evening. **Page 539**

ORIGINAL SENTENCE ____

____

dispense (di·spens') ***v.*** To exempt—**dispense with** ***v.*** To eliminate. ▶ The Latin root of this word is *pendere* (to weigh). A *dispenser* weighs, measures, or divides something and then distributes it. ▪ Cheryl, who was busy every minute of the day, wished she could dispense with sleep altogether. **Page 539**

ORIGINAL SENTENCE ____

____

NAME ______________________ CLASS ______________ DATE ________ SCORE ________

from the ANALECTS

Confucius

translated by Arthur Waley

(Textbook page 538)

VOCABULARY TEST

A. Match each word in column I with the correct definition in column II. Place the letter of the definition you choose in the space provided. *(10 points each)*

I	II
_____ 1. dictates	a. easily managed
_____ 2. dispense	b. purposeful
_____ 3. docile	c. to exempt
_____ 4. filial	d. guiding principles
_____ 5. intent	e. appropriate for one's children

B. From the words listed below, choose the word that best completes the sentence. Write the appropriate word in the blank provided. *(10 points each)*

intent	dictates	dispense
filial	docile	

6. The ______________________ lamb would eat grass out of the children's hands.

7. Although he lived far from his family, Clifton never neglected his ______________________ duties.

8. The ______________________ of Confucius were designed to create social harmony.

9. Susan was ______________________ on winning first place in the swim meet.

10. The executives decided to ______________________ with formalities and eat a fast-food informal lunch.

NAME ______________ CLASS ______________ DATE ________ SCORE ________

from the ANALECTS

Confucius

translated by Arthur Waley

(Textbook page 538)

REVIEWING THE SELECTION

1. Confucius said one idea from *The Book of Songs* covers all his teaching. Circle the letter of the sentence that best expresses that idea.
   a. You should not have evil in your thoughts.
   b. You will not find happiness in material possessions.
   c. Speak softly, but carry a big stick.

2. How does Confucius define knowledge?

   ____

   ____

3. Circle the letter of the one teaching that Confucius says a person can follow all day, every day.
   a. Love your mother and father.
   b. Do not do to other people what you would not want them to do to you.
   c. Recognize your weaknesses, but do not brag about your successes.

4. Circle the words that describe the ideals that Confucius says are important.

trust	prestige	wealth	personality
humility	power	honesty	consideration

Reader's Response

If you were to choose just one of the sayings in the *Analects* to follow faithfully, which one would you choose? Write one or two sentences explaining your choice.

____

____

____

____

____

____

NAME ______________________ CLASS ____________________ DATE ________ SCORE ______

from the TAO TE CHING

Lao-tzu

translated by Stephen Mitchell

(Textbook page 543)

REVIEWING THE SELECTION

In these passages, Lao-tzu teaches the principles of Taoism. The following are thoughts that the poet may or may not have included in his writing. If the thought is included in these passages, write *yes* in the blank before it. If the thought is not included, write *no.*

______ 1. People will respect you if you just act like yourself.

______ 2. Strive for greatness, and you will be great.

______ 3. Simple thinking results in poor work.

______ 4. Enjoy the work you do.

______ 5. Do not worry about things you cannot change.

______ 6. For good to exist, evil must also exist.

______ 7. There is a time for everything.

______ 8. Respect the balance of nature.

______ 9. A woman's work is never done.

______ 10. The world is ours to control.

Reader's Response

If you were to choose one of these passages as a guide for your life, which one would best express your beliefs? Write three or four sentences explaining your choice. Include details from the passage in your answer.

____

____

____

____

____

NAME ______________________ CLASS ______________________ DATE __________ SCORE __________

Taoist Anecdotes

translated by Moss Roberts (Textbook page 548)

REVIEWING THE SELECTIONS

1. Circle the word that best describes Chuang Tzu's attitude about his life in "Wagging My Tail in the Mud."

   bored   content   lonely   ambitious   self-sacrificing

2. In "The Butterfly," what is the butterfly in Chuang Tzu's dream doing?

   ____

3. In "Gold, Gold," what mistake does the thief make?

   ____

4. How does the man in "The Missing Axe" view his neighbor's son when his axe is lost?

   ____

   ____

5. In "The Lost Horse," how does the disaster of the son's fall from a horse turn into a blessing?

   ____

Reader's Response

Do the Taoist anecdotes apply to modern life? Can we still learn lessons from them? Choose one of the anecdotes and state whether you think the lesson learned is just as important today as it was when it was written. Write two or three sentences explaining your answer.

____

____

____

____

____

NAME ______________ CLASS ______________ DATE ________ SCORE ________

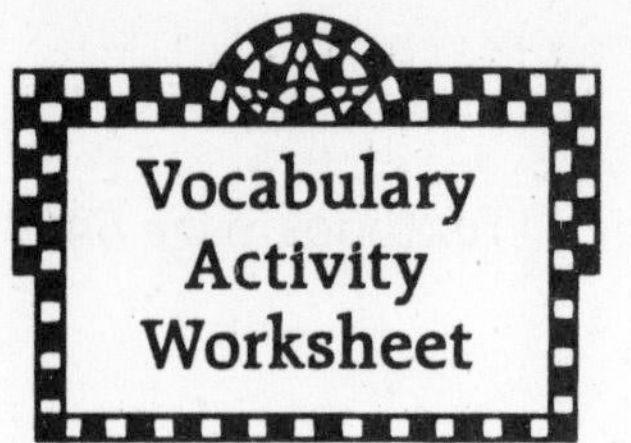

NIEH CHENG, *from* RECORDS OF THE HISTORIAN

Ssu-ma Ch'ien
translated by Burton Watson (Textbook page 553)

DEVELOPING VOCABULARY

Directions: Read carefully the explanation of each word. Then write a sentence of your own using that word. In your sentence, include clues to the word's meaning.

retaliate (ri·tal'ē·āt') ***v.*** To do something to get revenge for an injury or evil—**retaliation *n.*** ▶ The Latin *talio,* "punishment in kind," is the ancestor of this word. ▪ After being scolded, the dog retaliated by biting its owner. **Page 553**

ORIGINAL SENTENCE ______________________________

____

valor (val'ər) ***n.*** Bravery. ▶ *Valor* derives from the Latin *valere,* which means "to be strong." ▪ Maureen was given a medal for her valor in battle. **Page 553**

ORIGINAL SENTENCE ______________________________

____

etiquette (et'i·kit) ***n.*** Established rules of behavior in society or a profession. ▶ The word *etiquette* comes from an Old French word that meant "a document to provide lodging for soldiers." ▪ As the old rules of etiquette change, women now frequently invite men out and pay for the evening's entertainment. **Page 554**

ORIGINAL SENTENCE ______________________________

____

profound (prō'found') ***adj.*** **1.** Deeply felt. **2.** Having great intellectual depth. ▶ This word derives from the Latin *fundus,* "bottom," which is also the origin of *fundamental.* ▪ Coleman has such a profound fear of snakes that he cannot bear even to look at a picture of them. **Page 556**

ORIGINAL SENTENCE ______________________________

____

apprehension (ap'rē·hen'shən) ***n.*** A sudden anxious expectation; dread. ▶ *Apprehension* can also mean "arrest." ▪ Teresa, filled with anxiety and apprehension, refused to jump off the diving board into the pool. **Page 556**

ORIGINAL SENTENCE ______________________________

____

NAME ______________________ CLASS ______________________ DATE ________ SCORE ________

NIEH CHENG, *from* RECORDS OF THE HISTORIAN

Ssu–ma Ch'ien

translated by Burton Watson (Textbook page 553)

VOCABULARY TEST

A. Match each word in column I with the correct definition in column II. Place the letter of the definition you choose in the space provided. *(10 points each)*

	I	II
______	1. apprehension	a. rules of behavior
______	2. etiquette	b. to get even with
______	3. profound	c. dread
______	4. retaliate	d. deeply felt
______	5. valor	e. bravery

B. From the words listed below, choose the word that best completes the sentence. Write the appropriate word in the blank provided. *(10 points each)*

valor   retaliation   profound
etiquette   apprehension

6. The ______________________ of the soldiers was praised in popular folk songs.

7. The young philosophy students had a ______________________ respect for the sayings of the ancient thinkers.

8. The United States declared war on Japan in ______________________ for the bombing of Pearl Harbor.

9. Doug was filled with ______________________ as he hesitantly opened the door to the dilapidated house.

10. Proper ______________________ requires that you write a thank-you note when you receive a birthday gift.

NAME ______________________ CLASS ______________________ DATE __________ SCORE __________

NIEH CHENG, *from* RECORDS OF THE HISTORIAN

Ssu–ma Ch'ien
translated by Burton Watson

(Textbook page 553)

REVIEWING THE SELECTION

On line 1 below is an event that happens early in the story. On line 5 is an event that happens at the end. On lines 2, 3, and 4, list three important events that occur between the events given. List these events in the order in which they happen in the story.

1. Yen Chung-tzu flees to Ch'i.
2. ______________________________
3. ______________________________
4. ______________________________
5. Nieh Cheng's sister saves her brother's name.

Reader's Response

The sister paid a high price to save her brother's name. Do you think she was brave or foolish to do what she did? Write two or three sentences explaining your answer.

____

NAME ______________________ CLASS ______________ DATE ________ SCORE ________

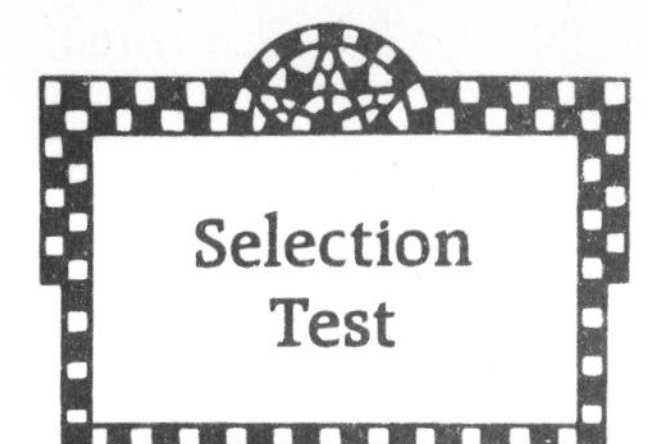

NIEH CHENG, *from* RECORDS OF THE HISTORIAN

Ssu–ma Ch'ien

translated by Burton Watson (Textbook page 553)

READING COMPREHENSION

Directions: In the space provided, write the letter of the best answer to each question. *(10 points each)*

______ 1. Why did Nieh Cheng move to Ch'i?
   a. Someone in Deep Well tried to kill him.
   b. His mother and sister lived there.
   c. He had killed a man in Deep Well.
   d. He wanted to kill someone who lived there.

______ 2. What was Nieh Cheng's new occupation?
   a. butcher
   b. architect
   c. shepherd
   d. farmer

______ 3. What did Yen Chung-tzu want Nieh Cheng to do?
   a. teach him a new trade
   b. return to Deep Well
   c. assassinate Han Hsia-lei
   d. allow Yen Chung-tzu to marry Nieh Cheng's sister

______ 4. What did Nieh Cheng do with the gold Yen Chung-tzu offered Nieh Cheng's mother?
   a. refused to allow his mother to accept it
   b. took it for himself
   c. sold it
   d. bought it

______ 5. At what point did Nieh Cheng agree to do what Yen Chung-tzu asked of him?
   a. after Yen Chung-tzu offered even more gold
   b. after Yen Chung-tzu agreed to pay his expenses
   c. after Yen Chung-tzu promised to go with him
   d. after Nieh Cheng's mother died

______ 6. Why did Nieh Cheng decide to go alone on his mission to kill Han Hsia-lei?
   a. He always worked alone.
   b. There was no one he could trust.
   c. He was afraid word would leak out.
   d. Yen Chung-tzu advised him against it.

(continued)

______ 7. What weapon did Nieh Cheng use?
a. a gun
b. poison
c. a sword
d. his hands

______ 8. What happened to Nieh Cheng after he carried out his mission?
a. He was killed by the guards.
b. He mutilated and killed himself.
c. Yen Chung-tzu hired someone to kill him.
d. He escaped and returned to Ch'i.

______ 9. Why did the ruler of Han expose Nieh Cheng's body in the marketplace and offer a reward?
a. to learn Nieh Cheng's identity
b. to humiliate Nieh Cheng's family
c. to learn the whereabouts of Yen Chung-tzu
d. to warn others of what happens when one commits murder

______ 10. Why did Nieh Cheng's sister put her own life in jeopardy?
a. to collect the reward
b. to let others know that it was all Yen Chung-tzu's idea
c. to let others know that she had nothing to live for
d. to save her brother's good name

NAME ______________________ CLASS ______________________ DATE ________ SCORE ________

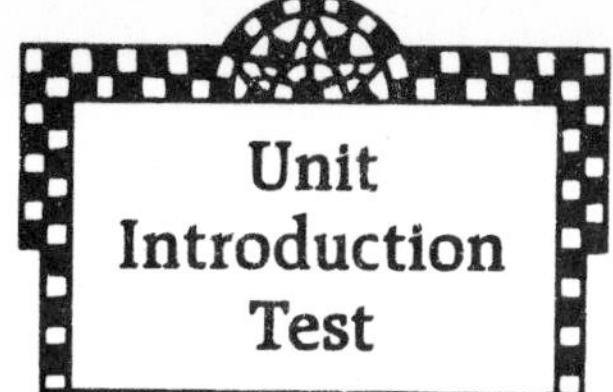

UNIT 6: CHINESE AND JAPANESE LITERATURES

(Textbook pages 558–563)

INTRODUCTION / The Literature of Japan

Directions: In the space provided, write the letter of the best answer to each question. *(10 points each)*

1. In the fourth century A.D., the Yamato clan introduced Japan to
   a. lyric poetry called *tanka*
   b. East African music and dance
   c. Chinese culture, philosophy, and political structure
   d. a priest who ruled over the samurai — 1. ______

2. Samurai are
   a. young emperors
   b. professional warriors
   c. royal jugglers
   d. poets — 2. ______

3. Beginning with Yoritomo in the twelfth century, Japan was governed by
   a. Chinese emperors
   b. shoguns
   c. chivalric knights
   d. Buddhist monks — 3. ______

4. From the late 1500s, the biggest concern of the shogun was
   a. Western invasions and internal revolts
   b. the growing influence of Christianity
   c. the collapse of the Chinese government
   d. the influence of Roman literature and music — 4. ______

5. After the 1853 arrival of Commodore Matthew Perry of the U.S. Navy,
   a. Japan kept itself isolated from the Western world
   b. Japan became a colony of the United States
   c. Japan began trading with Western countries
   d. Japan conquered the United States — 5. ______

6. Shintoism is
   a. a form of martial arts that was popular in the twelfth century
   b. a sect of Buddhism
   c. the ancient religion of Japan
   d. an innovative method of gardening — 6. ______

(continued)

7. Japanese poetry
   a. is deeply influenced by Western literature
   b. has not always been respected by the imperial Japanese government
   c. is mostly narrative poetry
   d. is very compressed
   7. ______

8. Lady Murasaki Shikibu is
   a. a famous Japanese writer and the author of *The Tale of Genji*
   b. a shogun
   c. the author of *The Pillow Book*
   d. a well-known Japanese actress
   8. ______

9. The Heian period marked
   a. the most violent time in Japanese history
   b. the most productive period of Japanese prose writing
   c. a time of terrible poverty and illness
   d. the beginning of trade between Korea and France
   9. ______

10. Noh and kabuki are two styles of Japanese
    a. martial arts
    b. drama
    c. clothing
    d. music
    10. ______

NAME ______________________ CLASS __________________ DATE ________ SCORE ________

Tanka Poems

translated by Geoffrey Bownas and Anthony Thwaite

(Textbook page 569)

REVIEWING THE SELECTIONS

1. Circle the letters of the images that are described in any of the five tanka poems.
   a. an elegant feast
   b. a person yearning for a friend
   c. the moonlight shining on a changing world
   d. a person daydreaming under the shade of a tree

2. What is the speaker doing in the tanka "The End of My Journey"?

____

____

3. To what does the speaker compare his friend in the tanka "Now, I Cannot Tell"?

____

____

4. Which tanka connects the image of a severed reed with a body?

____

Reader's Response

Choose one of the five tanka poems on textbook pages 569 and 570, and write your response to it. How does the poem make you feel? How does it apply to your own life? Which image in the poem seems the most powerful?

____

____

____

____

____

____

NAME ______________ CLASS ______________ DATE ________ SCORE ________

TANKA POETRY

translated by Geoffrey Bownas and Anthony Thwaite

(Textbook page 564)

READING COMPREHENSION

Directions: In the space provided, write the letter of the best answer to each question. *(10 points each)*

1. Tanka poetry is
   a. a new form of Japanese poetry
   b. a form of dramatic writing
   c. a modern form of Japanese prose
   d. an ancient form of Japanese poetry

   1. ______

2. Traditional tanka are
   a. three syllables and three lines
   b. five syllables and thirty-one lines
   c. thirty-one syllables and five lines
   d. fifteen syllables and three lines

   2. ______

3. Tanka poetry inspired the invention of
   a. epic poetry
   b. Chinese poetry
   c. the sonnet
   d. haiku

   3. ______

4. The *Manyōshū,* or *Collection of Ten Thousand Leaves,* is
   a. a history of Japanese gardening
   b. a book about tea ceremonies
   c. an anthology of poetry
   d. a Chinese religious text

   4. ______

5. The early Japanese poets wrote poems in
   a. French
   b. Chinese
   c. Sanskrit
   d. Japanese

   5. ______

6. What are the common themes in traditional and modern tanka?
   a. war, religion, politics, industry
   b. nature, solitude, love, the impermanence of life
   c. epic heroes, mythology, the supernatural
   d. music, painting, drama, dance

   6. ______

(continued)

7. During the Heian period, tanka were often used as
   a. declarations of war
   b. religious texts
   c. expressions of love between aristocrats
   d. political documents
   7.______

8. The poems in the *Kokinshū* reflect
   a. the politics of court life in the Heian period
   b. an earthy, rustic quality
   c. the wit and elegance of the Heian society that created them
   d. great Chinese lyrical poetry
   8.______

9. Why did medieval tanka poets use repetition in their poems?
   a. The poets were uneducated.
   b. Few Japanese words existed at the time.
   c. They wanted to create an emotional effect with word sounds.
   d. They were influenced by Chinese epic poets.
   9.______

10. Tanka poetry
    a. is a brief and cherished poetic form in Japan
    b. always rhymes
    c. is a lengthy and complicated poetic form
    d. was originally orally transmitted
    10.______

NAME ______________________ CLASS ______________________ DATE __________ SCORE __________

HAIKU

translated by Harold G. Henderson, Peter Beilenson, and Harry Behn

(Textbook page 576)

REVIEWING THE SELECTIONS

1. What seasonal image does Bashō connect with the crow on a branch?

____

2. What sings to the wild cherries in Uejima Onitsura's haiku?

____

3. What nature image does Taniguchi Buson connect with a woman reading in the moonlight?

____

4. In Kobayashi Issa's haiku, what transforms a simple hut into a beautiful place?

____

Reader's Response

Bashō's haiku is filled with imagery drawn from nature. Is this nature imagery relevant today—at a time when many people are living surrounded by concrete in large cities? If you were to write haiku today, what three subjects might you choose? Write your choices on the blanks below with a brief explanation for each choice.

1. ____

____

2. ____

____

3. ____

____

HAIKU

translated by Harold G. Henderson,
Peter Beilenson, and Harry Behn (Textbook page 572)

READING COMPREHENSION

Directions: In the space provided, write the letter of the best answer to each question. *(10 points each)*

1. A haiku is composed of
   a. an unspecified number of lines
   b. one hundred lines
   c. three lines
   d. seventeen lines 1.______

2. When was the haiku form mastered?
   a. during the late seventeenth century
   b. during the Heian period
   c. during the early 1970s
   d. during the Iron Age 2.______

3. The greatest haiku poet was
   a. Sei Shōnagon
   b. Bashō
   c. Li Po
   d. Princess Nukada 3.______

4. What contributes to the enduring quality of haiku?
   a. nature imagery
   b. religious principles
   c. specific historical references
   d. humor and irony 4.______

5. Haiku poetry
   a. juxtaposes, or places together, contrasting images
   b. traditionally rhymes
   c. has never been translated from the original Japanese
   d. uses complex images few readers can understand 5.______

6. How is the Japanese language different from the English language?
   a. All words have fourteen syllables.
   b. There are no articles.
   c. There are more pronouns than nouns.
   d. There are no words for the elements in nature. 6.______

(continued)

7. How many syllables are in the first and last lines of classical haiku?
   a. fifty
   b. five
   c. seven
   d. three
   7. ______

8. Haiku are traditionally
   a. stories of unreturned love
   b. short unrhymed poems
   c. performed
   d. long unrhymed poems
   8. ______

9. Many haiku incorporate references to
   a. the emperor
   b. Chinese literature
   c. cherry trees
   d. Japanese customs and culture
   9. ______

10. Haiku are difficult to translate because
    a. they are very long
    b. they were written on tablets, and many have been lost
    c. they leave a great deal unsaid and often have many interpretations
    d. they were never written down
    10. ______

NAME ______________________ CLASS ______________________ DATE __________ SCORE __________

from THE PILLOW BOOK

Sei Shōnagon

translated by Ivan Morris

(Textbook page 581)

DEVELOPING VOCABULARY

Directions: Read carefully the explanation of each word. Then write a sentence of your own using that word. In your sentence, include clues to the word's meaning.

wisp (wisp) ***n.*** A slender, filmy fragment or strand. ▶ A *will–o'–the–wisp* is a filmy, shifting light seen over the marshes at night. ▪ The smoke alarm sounded as the first wisp of smoke went up from the old trash can. **Page 581**

ORIGINAL SENTENCE ____

____

insignificant (in' sig·nif' i·kənt) ***adj.*** Unimportant; of no meaning or consequence. ▶ The adjective *significant* means "having meaning." ▪ All their work seemed insignificant when their candidate lost the election. **Page 582**

ORIGINAL SENTENCE ____

____

stealthy (stel' thē) ***adj.*** Intentionally secretive or sly.—**stealthily** ***adv.*** ▶ The noun *stealth* derives from an Old English word meaning "to steal." ▪ A stealthy exchange of fake jewels for real ones is a typical plot device of mystery stories. **Page 584**

ORIGINAL SENTENCE ____

____

convulse (kən · vuls') ***v.*** To cause to tremble or shake, as with pain or laughter. ▶ This verb comes from a Latin word meaning "to pluck up." ▪ The children would convulse with laughter when the magician pulled coins from behind their ears. **Page 584**

ORIGINAL SENTENCE ____

____

intimate (in' tə· mət) ***adj.*** **1.** Innermost or personal. **2.** Closely acquainted, very familiar. ▶ This adjective comes from a Latin word meaning "inmost" or "within." ▪ The spies had sophisticated equipment that allowed them to listen in on intimate conversations between top-level officials. **Page 585**

ORIGINAL SENTENCE ____

____

NAME ______________________ CLASS ____________________ DATE ________ SCORE ________

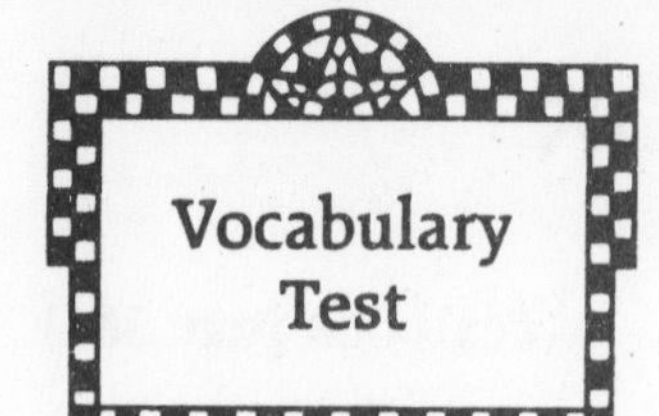

from THE PILLOW BOOK

Sei Shōnagon

translated by Ivan Morris

(Textbook page 581)

VOCABULARY TEST

A. Match each word in column I with the correct definition in column II. Place the letter of the definition you choose in the space provided. *(10 points each)*

	I	II
______	1. convulse	a. closely acquainted
______	2. insignificant	b. secret
______	3. intimate	c. a thin, filmy strand
______	4. stealthy	d. to cause to shake
______	5. wisp	e. having little or no importance

B. In the space provided, write the letter of the word or phrase closest in meaning to the word in italics. *(10 points each)*

______ 6. The captains of the basketball and tennis teams are *intimate* friends; they've known each other for years.
a. close b. casual c. interesting

______ 7. The book was filled with *insignificant* details about the author's habits that had nothing to do with the work itself.
a. brilliant b. famous c. meaningless

______ 8. Berenice *convulsed* with laughter as she watched the school play, even though it wasn't meant to be funny.
a. glowed b. tightened c. shook

______ 9. A barely visible *wisp* of smoke rose from the chimney.
a. thin strand b. enormous cloud c. smoggy exhaust

______ 10. The jewel thief approached the display case in a *stealthy* manner and removed a diamond without anyone noticing.
a. magical b. sneaky c. dangerous

NAME ______________________ CLASS ______________ DATE ________ SCORE ______

from THE PILLOW BOOK

Sei Shōnagon

translated by Ivan Morris

(Textbook page 581)

REVIEWING THE SELECTION

1. In the section "In Spring It Is the Dawn," what does Sei Shōnagon find beautiful about the summer? What does she like most about winter?

____

____

2. In the section "Things That Cannot Be Compared," what are some things in nature that Sei Shōnagon says cannot be compared?

____

____

3. What are two things about Masahiro that cause people to laugh at him?

____

____

4. In the section "Pleasing Things," what does the Empress sometimes do that especially pleases Sei Shōnagon?

____

____

Reader's Response

In *The Pillow Book*, Sei Shōnagon points out many things that delight and disturb her. Suppose you were writing your own pillow book. What might your lists be like? On the blanks below, write three things that you enjoy. Then, write three things that fill you with insecurity or that disturb you.

Things You Like	*Things You Dislike*
1. ____________	1. ____________
2. ____________	2. ____________
3. ____________	3. ____________

NAME ______________________ CLASS ______________________ DATE __________ SCORE __________

from THE PILLOW BOOK

Sei Shōnagon
translated by Ivan Morris

(Textbook page 581)

PRONOUNS

A **pronoun** is a word used in place of one or more nouns or other pronouns.

EXAMPLES Sei Shōnagon tells about *her* experiences in *The Pillow Book*, *which* is a type of diary. *Everyone*, including Sei Shōnagon *herself*, is a possible subject.

There are different types of pronouns. Follow these rules to decide which type of pronoun to use.

1. Use a **personal pronoun** to refer to people.

   I me you he him she her it we us they them

EXAMPLE *She* wrote in *The Pillow Book* about things that interested *her*.

Personal pronouns also have **possessive** and **reflexive** forms. Use the *possessive* form to show possession or ownership: *my, mine, your, yours, his, her, hers, its, their, theirs.*

EXAMPLE *Her* observations differ from *yours* or *mine.*

The reflexive form ends in *-self* or *-selves.* Use the reflexive form to refer to or emphasize the person, people, thing, or things named in the sentence: *myself, yourself, herself, himself, itself, ourselves, yourselves,* and *themselves.*

EXAMPLE Sei Shōnagon reveals a lot about *herself* in *The Pillow Book.*

2. Use a **relative pronoun** to introduce a subordinate clause. There are five relative pronouns: *who, whom, whose, which,* and *that.*

EXAMPLE *The Pillow Book, which* consists of Sei Shōnagon's private thoughts, was found and printed.

3. Use an **indefinite pronoun** to refer to people, places, and things in a general sense. Indefinite pronouns include those in the following list.

all	both	few	none	some
another	each	many	no one	somebody
any	either	more	one	someone
anybody	everybody	neither	other	something
anyone	everyone	nobody	several	such

EXAMPLE *Many* would be embarrassed at the publication of private thoughts.

4. Use a **demonstrative** pronoun to point out a particular person, place, or thing. There are four demonstrative pronouns: *this, that, these,* and *those.*

EXAMPLE *This* is an interesting way to learn about life in feudal Japan.

(continued)

Exercise 1. Identifying Pronouns

Underline all the personal, relative, indefinite, and demonstrative pronouns in the following sentences about *The Pillow Book.* The number in parentheses indicates the number of pronouns you should underline.

1. Sei Shōnagon, who wrote *The Pillow Book,* says dawn is the most beautiful time of day for her. (2)
2. Sei Shōnagon writes about anybody who attracts her attention. (3)
3. She writes about herself indirectly when she comments on others. (4)
4. She observes animals and birds and seems drawn by the beauty that is their natural environment. (3)
5. Sei Shōnagon is not one to be generous toward people who act foolishly. (2)
6. Masahiro frequently puts himself into ridiculous situations, causing others to laugh at him. (3)
7. This is an interesting excerpt that provides insight into life in feudal Japan. (2)
8. Sei Shōnagon is very proud of herself when the empress summons her in front of others. (3)
9. Sei Shōnagon's skills as an observer match those of anyone who is writing today. (3)
10. She uses imagery to help us see Heian Japan ourselves. (3)

Exercise 2. Adding Pronouns for Variety

The following sets of sentences are about *The Pillow Book.* Rewrite the sentences, adding at least two pronouns to each set. You may change words and combine sentences freely.

EXAMPLE Sei Shōnagon writes about hateful things and embarrassing things. Hateful things and embarrassing things seem particularly to interest Sei Shōnagon. Sei Shōnagon also writes about beautiful things, however.

Sei Shōnagon writes about hateful things and embarrassing things. These seem particularly to interest her. She also writes about beautiful things, however.

1. Sei Shōnagon dislikes not being able to get rid of visitors. The visitors talk nonstop. The visitors do not endear the visitors to Sei Shōnagon.

____

____

2. Sei Shōnagon says Sei Shōnagon cannot compare a person Sei Shōnagon once loved with a person Sei Shōnagon stopped loving. These two people seem like two different people.

____

____

(continued)

3. Sei Shōnagon does not think of servants as people like Sei Shōnagon. Sei Shōnagon believes servants should confine servants to creeping around the palace silently.

____

____

4. A person wonders how Sei Shōnagon could have observed so much through the curtain. The curtain kept women in feudal Japan from being observed by men and strangers. Men and strangers might approach the women.

____

____

5. The rest of Shōnagon's diary contains different kinds of lists. Different kinds of lists reveal even more of Sei Shōnagon's personality. Sei Shōnagon's personality already shines through the selected excerpts.

____

____

Exercise 3. Revising a Paragraph

Revise the following paragraph about *The Pillow Book* by adding pronouns to provide variety and to eliminate repetition. Change words and combine sentences freely. Part of the paragraph is revised for you as a sample.

Masahiro is an artistocrat at the palace, ~~Masahiro~~ who attracts Sei Shōnagon's attention with ~~Masahiro's~~ his antics. Masahiro dresses Masahiro elegantly, but other aristocrats in the palace find his attire humorous. Masahiro's attire might not seem funny on someone else. Sometimes Masahiro says things. People seem to find these things amusing. When Masahiro is required to report for night duty, for example, Masahiro asks two servants to collect Masahiro's things. A servant assures Masahiro that one servant can carry Masahiro's things alone. Masahiro objects to the servant's opinion, and asks how one person can carry a load meant for two people. Sometimes, Masahiro does things. These things amuse other aristocrats. Masahiro speaks in a funny way to Sei Shōnagon, for example. Masahiro drags the cloth under the lamp around with Masahiro's foot. Masahiro is also found eating in public.

NAME ______________________________ CLASS ______________________ DATE ________ SCORE ________

from THE PILLOW BOOK

Sei Shōnagon

translated by Ivan Morris

(Textbook page 581)

READING COMPREHENSION

Directions: In the space provided, write the letter of the best answer to each question. *(10 points each)*

1. Sei Shōnagon believes that during the spring, dawn
   a. is the ugliest time of day
   b. is the best time for sleep
   c. is the most beautiful time of day
   d. does not exist
   1. ______

2. Sei Shōnagon says that listening to a person discuss many subjects as if he knew everything is
   a. inspiring
   b. hateful
   c. the most relaxing way to spend an afternoon
   d. the best way to acquire new information
   2. ______

3. Among her list of "Hateful Things," Sei Shōnagon includes
   a. looking at the frosty ground on a winter morning
   b. getting a piece of gravel stuck in an inkstick
   c. receiving a beautiful new comb
   d. hearing a famous poet recite a new poem
   3. ______

4. Sei Shōnagon believes that many aspects of nature, such as day and night,
   a. are old-fashioned and will eventually be replaced
   b. should be more similar
   c. should be avoided at all costs
   d. cannot be compared
   4. ______

5. Sei Shōnagon is embarrassed
   a. by the crows asleep in a garden of evergreens
   b. by speaking about someone who overhears her
   c. by being told that someone she loves has recovered from an illness
   d. when something nice happens to a person she loves
   5. ______

6. Sei Shōnagon lists reasons why Masahiro is considered
   a. the oldest man at court
   b. a laughing stock
   c. the finest cook in Japan
   d. a great scholar
   6. ______

(continued)

7. By recounting different stories, Sei Shōnagon makes fun of
   a. herself
   b. teachers
   c. warriors
   d. Masahiro

7. ______

8. Sei Shōnagon is pleased when
   a. she hears someone make fun of her appearance
   b. she hears that something bad happened to someone she does not like
   c. she hears that something bad happened to someone she loves
   d. she hears that a friend is ill

8. ______

9. What is included among Sei Shōnagon's list of "Pleasing Things"?
   a. losing an important love letter
   b. watching someone eat an entire cake alone
   c. having a bad dream
   d. acquiring nice white paper

9. ______

10. Judging from her diary entries, Sei Shōnagon is a woman who
   a. appreciates small, beautiful things
   b. is bored by court life
   c. is tolerant of boring and silly people
   d. complains about the weather

10. ______

NAME ____________________ CLASS ____________________ DATE __________ SCORE __________

ZEN PARABLES

translated by Paul Reps

(Textbook page 591)

DEVELOPING VOCABULARY

Directions: Read carefully the explanation of each word. Then write a sentence of your own using that word. In your sentence, include clues to the word's meaning.

precipice (pres'i·pis) ***n.*** A high, steep cliff. ▶ To describe something that is steep, use the adjective form *precipitous*. ▪ To view the ocean from the highest point, we drove up the coastal road and parked at the edge of the precipice. **Page 591**

ORIGINAL SENTENCE ____

____

surpass (sər·pas') ***v.*** To excel; outdo all others. ▶ This verb comes from the French word meaning "to pass over." ▪ The students were able to surpass expectations and make high scores on their math exams. **Page 593**

ORIGINAL SENTENCE ____

____

mediocre (mē'dē·ō'kər) ***adj.*** **1.** Average; ordinary. **2.** Of inferior quality. ▶ *Mediocre* comes from two Latin words meaning "middle" and "peak." ▪ The cheap turquoise jewelry available in the mall was mediocre compared with the authentic necklaces and bracelets sold at the Santa Clara pueblo. **Page 593**

ORIGINAL SENTENCE ____

____

anticipate (an·tis'ə·pāt') ***v.*** To expect. ▶ This verb can also mean "to prevent." ▪ By early June, students across the United States anticipate the end of classes and the beginning of summer. **Page 593**

ORIGINAL SENTENCE ____

____

intensive (in·ten'siv) ***adj.*** Thorough; deep; concentrated.—**intensively** ***adv.*** ▶ The word forms a compound adjective in the sentence "*Intensive*-care units treat seriously ill patients." ▪ The teacher expected the students to do intensive research for their essays, but many of them did little reading. **Page 593**

ORIGINAL SENTENCE ____

____

NAME ______________________ CLASS ______________________ DATE __________ SCORE __________

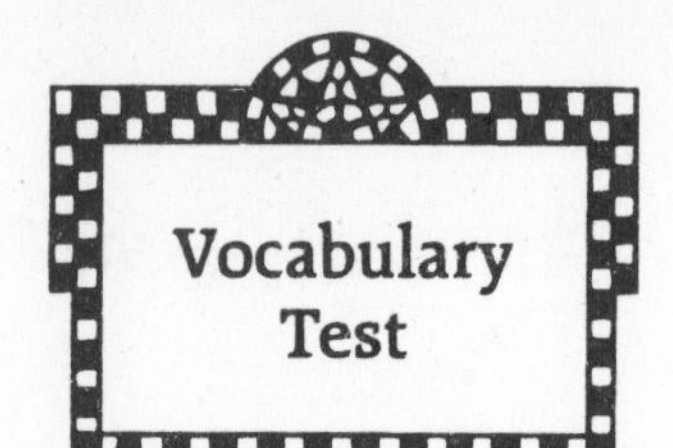

ZEN PARABLES

translated by Paul Reps

(Textbook page 591)

VOCABULARY TEST

A. Match each word in column I with the correct definition in column II. Place the letter of the definition you choose in the space provided. *(10 points each)*

I	II
______ 1. anticipated	a. thorough
______ 2. intensive	b. to excel
______ 3. mediocre	c. a steep cliff
______ 4. precipice	d. expected
______ 5. surpass	e. ordinary

B. Complete each sentence below with a word from column I above. Write the appropriate word in the blank provided. *(10 points each)*

6. Martin stood on the top of the ______________________ and threw stones down into the ravine.

7. The musicians ______________________ a crowd, but only a few people attended the concert.

8. The zookeeper announced that a(n) ______________________ search throughout the zoo uncovered the missing ape.

9. Julio read two mysteries on the train; the first was very exciting, but the second was only ______________________.

10. This semester, Ruby was able to ______________________ her earlier low grade-point average and join the honor society.

NAME ______________________ CLASS ______________________ DATE __________ SCORE __________

ZEN PARABLES

translated by Paul Reps

(Textbook page 591)

REVIEWING THE SELECTIONS

1. What action of Tanzan disturbs Ekido in the parable "Muddy Road"? How does Tanzan reply to Ekido's accusation?

____

____

2. In "A Parable," why does the strawberry taste especially sweet?

____

____

3. What are Tetsugen's three sets of sutras?

____

____

4. In "The Taste of Banzo's Sword," Matajuro wants to become a master swordsman. What is it about Matajuro's longing that so bothers Banzo?

____

____

Reader's Response

Choose one of the Zen parables on textbook pages 591–594 and explain what it means to you. Does it apply to your own daily life, or is it simply a quaint story? Write several sentences explaining your answer.

____

____

____

____

NAME ______________________ CLASS ______________________ DATE ________ SCORE ________

ZEN PARABLES

translated by Paul Reps

(Textbook page 591)

VARYING SENTENCE BEGINNINGS

The typical English sentence has this structure: subject, verb, complement.

EXAMPLE Parables (s) teach (v) moral lessons (c).

You can avoid a boring and monotonous writing style by sometimes varying your sentence structure so that not every sentence begins with the subject. The following sentences illustrate a variety of sentence beginnings.

prepositional phrase *On the road,* the rain water forms wide pools.
clause *As two tigers wait for him,* the man eats the strawberry.
participial phrase *Working diligently,* Tetsugen collected money for his project.
infinitive phrase *To thank Shichiri,* the thief becomes his disciple.
single-word modifier *Eventually,* Matajuro learns how to use a sword.

Exercise 1. Identifying Sentence Beginnings

Each of the following sentences is about the Zen parables. Write the letter of the item that identifies the type of beginning used in each sentence.

a. prepositional phrase b. single-word modifier c. clause
d. participial phrase e. infinitive phrase

EXAMPLE To frighten Shichiri, the thief carries a sharp sword. __e__

1. Happily, the thief takes the money, thanks Shichiri, and leaves. ______
2. To raise money, Tetsugen travels throughout the countryside. ______
3. Pausing at the intersection, Tanzan asks the girl if she needs help. ______
4. As the rain falls, the girl hurries on her way. ______
5. After many hours, Ekido expresses his dismay. ______
6. Suddenly, the tiger leaps out of the bushes. ______
7. To escape from the tiger, the man grabs the vine and jumps. ______
8. While the man hangs from the vine, he sees another tiger below him. ______
9. Under Banzo's supervision, Matajuro becomes a great swordsman. ______
10. Waiting patiently, Matajuro learns an important lesson. ______

(continued)

Exercise 2. Writing Sentences with Varied Beginnings

Each of the following sentences about Zen begins with a subject. Rewrite each sentence so that it has the type of beginning that is indicated. You may add or change words.

EXAMPLE Many kinds of people use Zen to help reduce stress. (infinitive phrase)
To help reduce stress, many kinds of people use Zen.

1. Millions of people around the world use Zen today. (single-word modifier)

____

____

2. A Zen practitioner meditates for long periods and finds inner peace. (participle phrase)

____

____

3. Japanese children receive half-hour lessons in *zazen* to learn meditation. (infinitive phrase)

____

____

4. A Zen monk meditates under the rap of an "awakening" stick. (prepositional phrase)

____

____

5. Zen monks focus on the inner self, and they do not preach sermons about good and evil. (clause)

____

____

(continued)

Exercise 3. Revising a Paragraph

The sentences in the following paragraph about parables all begin with the subject. Revise the paragraph so that the sentences have a variety of beginnings. You may add or change words. The first sentence has been revised as an example.

Zen parables illustrate universal and timeless truths and present entertaining anecdotes. The parables provide insight into individuals and society with moral lessons. The parables often appear simple and focus on common experiences. They are like fables and encourage readers to apply the morals to their own lives. People of all ages apply these experiences and learn important lessons about subjects such as greed, generosity, and patience.

To illustrate universal and timeless truths, Zen parables present entertaining anecdotes.

NAME ______________________ CLASS ______________ DATE ________ SCORE ______

ZEN PARABLES

translated by Paul Reps (Textbook page 591)

READING COMPREHENSION

Directions: In the space provided, write the letter of the best answer to each question. *(10 points each)*

1. Whom do Tanzan and Ekido meet as they walk down a muddy road?
   a. a famous warrior with golden armor
   b. a girl wearing a silk kimono
   c. their teacher
   d. a priest 1. ______

2. Why does the man in "A Parable" grab the vine and swing over the edge?
   a. He is practicing for the Olympics.
   b. A tiger is chasing him.
   c. He is searching for the perfect dessert.
   d. He is late for his meditation at the monastery. 2. ______

3. While swinging on the vine, the man in "A Parable" plucks at
   a. the mice chewing on the vine
   b. the tiger's fur
   c. a splinter in his finger
   d. a luscious strawberry 3. ______

4. What does Tetsugen decide to publish?
   a. a collection of tanka and haiku
   b. a series of martial arts comic books
   c. his autobiography
   d. the Zen sutras 4. ______

5. What does Tetsugen do when famine and epidemic threaten his people?
   a. He moves to a new country where everyone is healthy.
   b. He gives away the money he has collected to the sick and hungry.
   c. He becomes a doctor.
   d. He opens a restaurant and feeds the sick and hungry. 5. ______

6. In "The Thief Who Became a Disciple," Shichiri tells the thief
   a. that he will make sure the thief is thrown in jail
   b. to take everything Shichiri owns
   c. that the thief is the cleverest person he has ever met
   d. to thank Shichiri for the money he is taking 6. ______

(continued)

7. When called as a witness, Shichiri tells the court
   a. that he has never seen the man before
   b. to throw the thief in jail
   c. that Shichiri gave the money to the man and the man thanked him
   d. that the thief stole the shirt off his back

   7. ______

8. The thief became a disciple after
   a. serving time in prison
   b. traveling around the world
   c. stealing from Shichiri a second time
   d. robbing a bank

   8. ______

9. Matajuro in "The Taste of Banzo's Sword" wants to become
   a. Banzo's servant
   b. a master swordsman
   c. a famous politician
   d. a thief

   9. ______

10. How long does Matajuro serve Banzo before beginning his training?
    a. a few weeks
    b. three years
    c. a century
    d. five minutes

    10. ______

NAME ______________________ CLASS ______________________ DATE __________ SCORE __________

ATSUMORI

Seami Motokiyo

translated by Arthur Waley

(Textbook page 600)

DEVELOPING VOCABULARY

Directions: Read carefully the explanation of each word. Then write a sentence of your own using that word. In your sentence, include clues to the word's meaning.

guise (gīz) ***n.*** **1.** Manner or way of dressing. **2.** Deceiving or false appearance. ▶ The word *disguise* comes from this thirteenth-century noun. ▪ In the movie *To Kill a Mockingbird*, the main character, Scout, dresses in the unusual guise of a ham for the school fair. **Page 601**

ORIGINAL SENTENCE ______________________________

____

knoll (nōl) ***n.*** Small hill. ▶ In some parts of the country, a *knoll* is known as a *dune* or a *mesa*. ▪ Gravy ran down the knoll of mashed potatoes into the brilliant array of carrots and peas. **Page 601**

ORIGINAL SENTENCE ______________________________

____

estrange (e·strānj′) ***v.*** **1.** To keep apart or separate. **2.** To make hostile or unfriendly. ▶ Both "estrange" and "stranger" come from the Latin word *extraneus*. ▪ Cassy became estranged from all her old friends when she moved to a new neighborhood. **Page 602**

ORIGINAL SENTENCE ______________________________

____

interlude (in′tər·lo͞od′) ***n.*** Entertainment between the acts of a play. ▶ The prefix *inter-* means "between" or "in the middle." ▪ The performance was so boring that most people enjoyed the interlude more than the actual play. **Page 604**

ORIGINAL SENTENCE ______________________________

____

clan ***n.*** A tribal division; extended family. ▶ This word is Gaelic in origin. ▪ The families that make up each Scottish clan are descended from the same ancestor. **Page 606**

ORIGINAL SENTENCE ______________________________

____

NAME ______________________ CLASS ______________________ DATE __________ SCORE __________

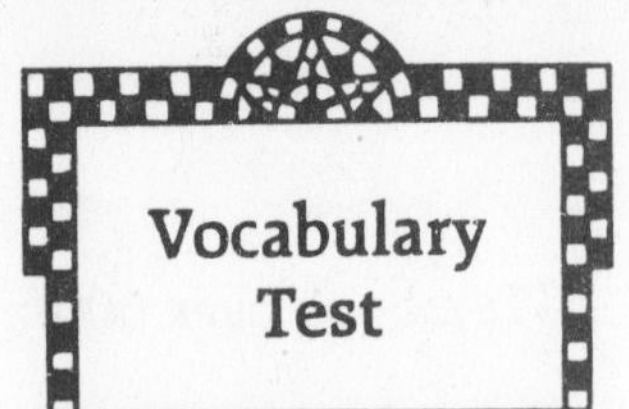

ATSUMORI

Seami Motokiyo
translated by Arthur Waley

(Textbook page 600)

VOCABULARY TEST

A. Match each word in column I with the correct definition in column II. Place the letter of the definition you choose in the space provided. *(10 points each)*

	I	II
______	1. clan	a. extended family
		b. small hill
______	2. estrange	c. performance between the acts of a play
		d. to keep apart
______	3. guise	e. deceiving appearance
______	4. interlude	
______	5. knoll	

B. In the space provided, write the letter of the word or phrase closest in meaning to the word in italics. *(10 points each)*

______ 6. The audience enjoyed the comic *interlude* more than the feature performance.

a. rehearsal b. intermission c. performance between acts

______ 7. Sylvia stood on the grassy *knoll* and photographed the view.

a. field b. hilltop c. meadow

______ 8. The movie star slipped away from the crowd in the *guise* of a police officer.

a. costume b. truck c. shadow

______ 9. By moving to California, Hakim would *estrange* himself from his family in New York.

a. distance b. entertain c. protect

______ 10. Every July, the Hunley *clan* gathers in Prospect Park for a barbecue.

a. heroes b. travelers c. relatives

NAME ________________ CLASS ________________ DATE ________ SCORE ________

ATSUMORI

Seami Motokiyo

translated by Arthur Waley

(Textbook page 600)

REVIEWING THE SELECTION

1. Why has Rensei come to Ichi no tani?

____

____

2. What does Rensei hear when he arrives at Ichi no tani?

____

____

3. Why is the ghost of Atsumori dressed as a young warrior?

____

____

4. At the end of the play, how does the relationship between Atsumori and Rensei change?

____

____

Reader's Response

In *Atsumori*, Rensei, who killed Atsumori in an act of war, asks the ghost of Atsumori for forgiveness. Do you find this behavior strange, or can you understand what motivates Rensei? Write two or three sentences explaining your answer.

____

____

____

____

____

NAME ______________________ CLASS ______________________ DATE __________ SCORE __________

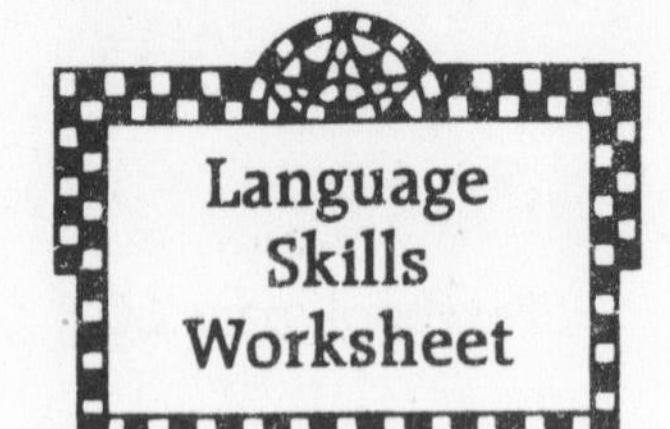

ATSUMORI

Seami Motokiyo

translated by Arthur Waley (Textbook page 600)

SENTENCE FRAGMENTS

A **sentence fragment** is a group of words that does not express a complete thought. You can usually change a fragment into a complete sentence by adding it to the sentence that comes before or after it.

FRAGMENT Along the path. He hears the sound of a flute.

CORRECTED Along the path, he hears the sound of a flute.

A complete sentence must have a subject and a verb and express a complete thought. Common types of fragments include *phrases, subordinate clauses,* and *appositives.*

FRAGMENT *Calling himself a priest.* He goes to Ichi no tani. (participial phrase)

CORRECTED Calling himself a priest, he goes to Ichi no tani.

FRAGMENT *As Rensei travels.* He thinks about Atsumori. (subordinate clause)

CORRECTED As Rensei travels, he thinks about Atsumori.

FRAGMENT The reapers speak to Rensei. *The man who killed Atsumori.* (appositive)

CORRECTED The reapers speak to Rensei, the man who killed Atsumori.

Exercise 1. Identifying Sentence Fragments

The information in the following sentences is from *Atsumori.* In the space provided, write *S* if the item is a complete sentence. Write *F* if it is a fragment.

EXAMPLE __F__ Listening to the reaper's story.

______ 1. He lives in sadness.

______ 2. Speaking to the reapers.

______ 3. From the clan of Atsumori.

______ 4. Atsumori, the young warrior.

______ 5. Rensei prays to save him.

______ 6. Like caged birds, they long for freedom.

______ 7. Although the warriors sing before the battle.

______ 8. Watching from the shore.

(continued)

______ 9. Whose horse is in the waves.

______ 10. Atsumori is abandoned by his clan.

Exercise 2. Correcting Sentence Fragments

Correct the sentence fragments in each of the following items about *Atsumori*. First, decide which part of the item is a sentence fragment. Then, correct it by adding it to the sentence before or after it. Write your new sentence on the blanks.

EXAMPLE Rensei and Atsumori fight. Until the boy dies. Later, Rensei finds salvation for his enemy. Rensei and Atsumori fight until the boy dies.

1. Atsumori carries the flute around his neck. He is wearing it when he dies. At the hands of Rensei.

____

____

2. Racing into the sea. Atsumori tries to reach the soldiers' boats. As he watches, the boats sail away without him.

____

____

3. Atsumori knows he can't escape from the enemy. Who is following him. As a samurai warrior, Atsumori knows his enemy intends to kill him.

____

____

4. Riding on his horse. Atsumori bravely turns and faces his enemy. They fight in the waves and in the surf along the shore.

____

____

5. Now a ghost, Atsumori makes his peace with Rensei. Once his enemy. Because they make peace, they will be reborn together.

____

____

(continued)

Exercise 3. Revising Paragraphs

Read the following paragraphs about *Atsumori* and correct the sentence fragments by joining them to the sentences that precede or follow them. The first fragment has been corrected for you.

Though the story of Atsumori is uplifting, it is sad as well. The death of a brave boy is always a tragedy. It is terrible to think about Atsumori's clan. Sailing away without him. I imagine that he must have felt very frightened as he watched the boats. Preparing to depart. I wonder if Atsumori's father wanted to wait for his son. To reach the ship. Perhaps the father wanted to turn back, but the soldiers would not let him. I am sure his father hoped that Atsumori would escape. Into the hills away from the enemy.

When Rensei follows the young warrior, Atsumori stops. And turns toward his enemy. Atsumori faces his death with courage. An important trait for a samurai. Perhaps his courage makes it especially hard for Rensei to kill him. According to Rensei, he does not want to hurt the boy. If Rensei had let Atsumori escape. Someone else would have killed him. Rensei's lifelong sadness about Atsumori shows that he truly regrets his actions. And hopes that he can make peace with the spirit of Atsumori.

NAME ______________________ CLASS ________________ DATE ________ SCORE ______

ATSUMORI

Seami Motokiyo

translated by Arthur Waley

(Textbook page 600)

READING COMPREHENSION

Directions: In the space provided, write the letter of the best answer to each question. *(10 points each)*

1. Why does Rensei come to Ichi no tani?
   a. to eat dinner with an old friend
   b. to become a priest
   c. to kill Atsumori
   d. to obtain the salvation of Atsumori's soul — 1. ______

2. How does Rensei want to save Atsumori?
   a. He wants to exorcise Atsumori's spirit.
   b. He wants to pray for him.
   c. He wants to give Atsumori a proper burial.
   d. He wants to give him his own life. — 2. ______

3. Whom does Rensei meet when he arrives at Ichi no tani?
   a. a monk
   b. two reapers
   c. a group of old warriors
   d. an emperor — 3. ______

4. Atsumori first speaks to the priest Rensei
   a. to ask directions
   b. to condemn Rensei as a murderer
   c. as a ghost
   d. in the guise of a flute-playing reaper — 4. ______

5. How does the ghost of Atsumori later appear before Rensei?
   a. dressed as a warrior
   b. in a long, flowing robe
   c. pale and sad
   d. angrily, bearing his sword — 5. ______

6. When Rensei and Atsumori first met they were
   a. classmates
   b. wandering travelers
   c. musicians
   d. enemies — 6. ______

(continued)

7. What did Atsumori have with him when he died?
   a. a mask
   b. a flute
   c. a priest's robe
   d. the enemy's uniform

   7.______

8. The night before battle, what did Rensei hear from the enemy camp?
   a. music
   b. screaming ghosts
   c. guns firing
   d. a pack of howling wolves

   8.______

9. What has brought Atsumori back to the living world?
   a. desire for revenge
   b. the wheel of fate
   c. loneliness
   d. boredom

   9.______

10. At the end of the play, what does Atsumori ask Rensei to do?
    a. ride his horse into the sea
    b. tell his family that he is alive and well
    c. pray for him again
    d. go home

    10.______

NAME ______________________ CLASS ______________________ DATE __________ SCORE __________

Unit 6: Chinese and Japanese Literatures

WORD ANALOGIES/Extending Vocabulary

Directions: In the space provided, write the letter of the pair of words with the relationship that is closest to that of the capitalized words. *(10 points each)*

1. INTENT : DETERMINED ::
   a. weak : firm
   b. willing : undecided
   c. flexible : fixed
   d. hesitant : uncertain — 1. ______

2. KNOLL : HILL ::
   a. fin : fish
   b. highway : road
   c. wave : ocean
   d. water : lake — 2. ______

3. VALOR : BRAVE ::
   a. honesty : truth
   b. coward : afraid
   c. courage : bold
   d. virtue : beautiful — 3. ______

4. DOCILE : REBELLIOUS ::
   a. loyal : dutiful
   b. obedient : unruly
   c. stubborn : uncooperative
   d. anxious : nervous — 4. ______

5. INTIMATE : FRIEND ::
   a. distant : sibling
   b. secret : spy
   c. personal : confidante
   d. demanding : employee — 5. ______

6. ETIQUETTE : MANNERS ::
   a. game : players
   b. host : guests
   c. code : laws
   d. grammar : nouns — 6. ______

7. STEALTHY : CONCEAL ::
   a. quick : disappear
   b. clever : bright
   c. unseen : observe
   d. sly : hide — 7. ______

8. APPREHENSION : FEAR ::
   a. relief : fright
   b. anxiety : dread
   c. escape : harm
   d. trust : doubt — 8. ______

9. PATHOS : SADNESS ::
   a. grief : death
   b. sorrow : happiness
   c. bliss : joy
   d. sympathy : unkindness — 9. ______

10. MEDIOCRE : AVERAGE ::
   a. superior : great
   b. major : minor
   c. outstanding : little
   d. inferior : large — 10. ______

NAME ______________________ CLASS ______________ DATE ________ SCORE ________

UNIT 6: CHINESE AND JAPANESE LITERATURES

UNIT REVIEW TEST/Applying Skills I

A. Reading Comprehension. In the space provided, write the letter of the best answer to each question. *(8 points each)*

______ 1. The speakers in the poems of Chinese poet Li Po, "Quiet Night Thoughts" and "Letter to His Two Small Children," are
a. anxious to travel to strange new lands
b. pleased with the situation
c. unmarried
d. homesick

______ 2. According to the Chinese philosopher Confucius in the *Analects*, the one thing a ruler must have is
a. enough food
b. the people's trust
c. enough weapons
d. the people's obedience

______ 3. In *Records of the Historian*, Yen Chung-tzu seeks out Nieh Cheng because he wants
a. to give Nieh Cheng's mother gold
b. to become a butcher
c. Nieh Cheng as a friend
d. Nieh Cheng to kill a man

______ 4. The six haiku poems are similar in that each of them refers to something in
a. Japanese philosophy
b. literature
c. nature
d. Japanese history

______ 5. In the Zen parable, "The Taste of Banzo's Sword," Banzo believes that a person who is in a hurry will probably
a. be slain by a sword
b. learn quickly
c. not learn very quickly
d. not be a very good servant

(continued)

______ 6. In the Noh play *Atsumori,* Rensei has become a priest
   a. to atone the sin of killing Atsumori
   b. to retire from the world's affairs
   c. because he expects to die soon
   d. because he is in mourning

B. Identifying Characters. Each description below refers to a main character in one of the selections you have just read. Identify the character by choosing the letter of the best answer. Write the letter in the space provided. *(8 points each)*

______ 7. His foolish actions make him a laughing stock.
   a. Masahiro in *The Pillow Book*
   b. Wei Pa in "For Wei Pa, in Retirement"
   c. Tetsugen in the parable "Publishing the Sutras"
   d. the man in the Taoist anecdote "Wagging My Tail in the Mud"

______ 8. He spends his life trying to make up for killing a young man in battle.
   a. the soldier in Song 130 of *The Book of Songs*
   b. Rensei in *Atsumori*
   c. Tzu-kung in the *Analects*
   d. Ekido in the parable "Muddy Road"

______ 9. She is willing to die rather than have her brother's name be forgotten.
   a. the master in the poem from the *Tao Te Ching*
   b. Jung in "Nieh Cheng"
   c. Sei Shōnagon in *The Pillow Book*
   d. the princess in Song 103 of *The Book of Songs*

______ 10. He learned that disasters often turn into blessings, and vice versa.
   a. the speaker in Tu Fu's "Jade Flower Palace"
   b. Yen Chung-Tzŭ in "Nieh Cheng"
   c. Atsumori in *Atsumori*
   d. the man in the Taoist anecdote "The Lost Horse"

C. Composition. Choose *one* of these topics and write a brief essay on a separate piece of paper. *(20 points)*

1. Both the *Analects* and the Zen parables teach lessons. Compare and contrast the two forms of teachings. Consider the origin and purpose of both forms and the way the lessons are presented. Use examples from each form to support your essay.

2. The poetry in the Chinese *The Book of Songs* and the Japanese tanka poems are both forms of lyrical poetry. Compare and contrast the two forms of poetry. Consider the poets' use of poetic devices and images to create a mood. Consider, too, the purpose of lyrical poetry in Chinese and Japanese cultures. Use examples from each form to support your essay.

NAME ______________ CLASS ______________ DATE ________ SCORE ________

UNIT 6: CHINESE AND JAPANESE LITERATURES

CRITICAL THINKING AND WRITING/Applying Skills II

A. Reading a Novel Excerpt. Read the passage below carefully, and answer the questions that follow.

from THE TALE OF GENJI

Lady Murasaki Shikibu

translated by

ARTHUR WALEY

In this tenth-century Japanese novel—widely considered the world's first novel—Genji is the son of the Emperor and a woman of humble birth whom the Emperor deeply loved. Princess Fujitsubo, who reminds the Emperor of Genji's dead mother, has recently come to court as a consort of the Emperor. Genji finds himself deeply attracted to Princess Fujitsubo, who is referred to, in this excerpt, only as "she" and as the "girl at the Palace." As this excerpt opens, Genji prepares to undergo the initiation ceremony that marks his transition to manhood.

Though it seemed a shame to put so lovely a child into man's dress, he was now twelve years old and the time for his Initiation was come. The Emperor directed the preparations with tireless zeal and insisted upon a magnificence beyond what was prescribed. The Initiation of the Heir Apparent, which had last year been celebrated in the Southern Hall, was not a whit more splendid in its preparations. The ordering of the banquets that were to be given in various quarters, and the work of the Treasurer and Grain Intendant he supervised in person, fearing lest the officials should be remiss; and in the end all was perfection. The ceremony took place in the eastern wing of the Emperor's own apartments, and the Throne was placed facing towards the east, with the seats of the Initiate-to-be and his Sponsor (the Minister of the Left) in front.

Genji arrived at the hour of the Monkey.[1] He looked very handsome with his long childish locks, and the Sponsor, whose duty it had just been to bind them with the purple filet,[2] was sorry to think that all this would soon be changed and even the Clerk

1. **hour of the monkey:** 3 P.M.
2. **filet:** headband.

(continued)

of the Treasury seemed loath to sever those lovely tresses with the ritual knife. The Emperor, as he watched, remembered for a moment what pride the mother would have taken in the ceremony, but soon drove the weak thought from his mind.

Duly crowned, Genji went to his chamber and changing into man's dress went down into the courtyard and performed the Dance of Homage, which he did with such grace that tears stood in every eye. And now the Emperor, whose grief had of late grown somewhat less insistent, was again overwhelmed by memories of the past.

It had been feared that his delicate features would show to less advantage when he had put aside his childish dress; but on the contrary he looked handsomer than ever.

His sponsor, the Minister of the Left, had an only daughter whose beauty the Heir Apparent had noticed. But now the father began to think he would not encourage that match, but would offer her to Genji. He sounded the Emperor upon this, and found that he would be very glad to obtain for the boy the advantage of so powerful a connection.

When the courtiers assembled to drink the Love Cup, Genji came and took his place among the other princes. The Minister of the Left came up and whispered something in his ear; but the boy blushed and could think of no reply. A chamberlain now came over to the Minister and brought him a summons to wait upon His Majesty immediately. When he arrived before the Throne, a Lady of the Wardrobe handed to him the Great White Inner Garment and the Maid's Skirt,[3] which were his ritual due as Sponsor to the Prince. Then, when he had made him drink out of the Royal Cup, the Emperor recited a poem in which he prayed that the binding of the purple filet might symbolize the union of their two houses; and the Minister answered him that nothing should sever this union save the fading of the purple band. Then he descended the long stairs and from the courtyard performed the Grand Obeisance.[4] Here too were shown the horses from the Royal Stables and the hawks from the Royal Falconry, that had been decreed as presents for Genji. At the foot of the stairs the Princes and Courtiers were lined up to receive their bounties, and gifts of every kind were showered upon them. That day the hampers and fruit baskets were distributed in accordance with the Emperor's directions by the learned Secretary of the Right, and boxes of cake and presents lay about so thick that one could scarcely move. Such profusion had not been seen even at the Heir Apparent's Initiation.

That night Genji went to the Minister's house, where his betrothal was celebrated with great splendor. It was thought that the little Prince looked somewhat childish and delicate, but his beauty astonished everyone. Only the bride, who was four years older, regarded him as a mere baby and was rather ashamed of him.

The Emperor still demanded Genji's attendance at the Palace, so he did not set up a house of his own. In his inmost heart he was always thinking how much nicer *she* was than anyone else, and only wanted to be with people who were like her, but alas no one was the least like her. Everyone seemed to make a great deal of fuss about Princess Aoi, his betrothed; but he could see nothing nice about her. The girl at the Palace now filled all his childish thoughts and this obsession became a misery to him.

Now that he was a "man" he could no longer frequent the women's quarters as he had been wont to do. But sometimes when an entertainment was afoot he found

---

3. **Great . . . Skirt:** symbols of unmanliness, indicating that Genji has put aside the life of childhood.
4. **Grand Obeisance** (ō·bā'·səns): an elaborate kowtow in which one kneels so that the forehead touches the ground in a gesture of respect.

(continued)

comfort in hearing her voice dimly blending with the sound of zithern or flute and felt his grown-up existence to be unendurable. After an absence of five or six days he would occasionally spend two or three at his betrothed's house. His father-in-law attributing this negligence to his extreme youth was not at all perturbed and always received him warmly. Whenever he came the most interesting and agreeable of the young people of the day were asked to meet him and endless trouble was taken in arranging games to amuse him.

The Shigeisa, one of the rooms which had belonged to his mother, was allotted to him as his official quarters in the Palace, and the servants who had waited on her were now gathered together again and formed his suite. His grandmother's house was falling into decay. The Imperial Office of Works was ordered to repair it. The grouping of the trees and disposition of the surrounding hills had always made the place delightful. Now the basin of the lake was widened and many other improvements were carried out. "If only I were going to live here with someone whom I liked," thought Genji sadly.

B. Analyzing a Novel Excerpt. In the space provided, write the letter of the best answer to each question. *(6 points each)*

1. The preparations for Genji's initiation ceremony suggest that
   a. the Emperor feels sorry for Genji because his mother is dead
   b. the Emperor does not want the Heir Apparent to be jealous of Genji
   c. the Minister of the Left does not like Genji
   d. Genji is a favorite of the Emperor 1. ______

2. The description of the Initiation creates a mood, or feeling, of
   a. bitterness and discontent
   b. silliness and humor
   c. danger and violence
   d. festivity and excitement 2. ______

3. When Genji dresses as a man,
   a. he loses his childish appeal
   b. he still has long hair
   c. he looks more handsome
   d. he no longer reminds the Emperor of his dead consort 3. ______

4. To recreate the initiation and betrothal ceremonies for readers, Lady Murasaki uses
   a. conflict
   b. wit
   c. assonance, or repeated vowel sounds
   d. descriptive imagery 4. ______

(continued)

5. Genji is betrothed to the Princess Aoi because
   a. he is madly in love with her
   b. her father is powerful, and the marriage will improve Genji's position in Court
   c. the marriage was arranged at the time of Genji's birth
   d. Princess Fujitsubo has rejected him

   5.______

6. Princess Aoi
   a. is somewhat ashamed of her husband-to-be
   b. is very much in love with Genji
   c. says she will not marry Genji
   d. is indifferent toward Genji

   6.______

7. After his betrothal, Genji feels
   a. very happy
   b. miserable
   c. grown-up
   d. angry

   7.______

8. Lady Murasaki creates Genji as a round, or well-developed, character by
   a. describing his appearance
   b. describing his initiation ceremony
   c. revealing his complex thoughts and feelings
   d. showing his speech

   8.______

9. What tone, or feeling, does Lady Murasaki suggest as Genji looks over his quarters at the end of the excerpt?
   a. joy and peace
   b. sorrow and loneliness
   c. anger and vengeance
   d. excitement and expectation

   9.______

10. The descriptions in *The Tale of Genji* reflect
    a. the social, economic, and political complexities of Japanese court life
    b. the relationship between royalty and peasants in tenth-century Japan
    c. the lifestyle of the average tenth-century Japanese
    d. the lifestyle of servants in tenth-century Japan

    10.______

C. Writing About a Novel Excerpt. On a separate sheet of paper, write one or two paragraphs describing the character of Genji. Remember that Japanese writers place great importance on suggestion as well as on concrete description. In your paragraph(s), explain (a) which characteristics are actually described, and (b) which qualities are suggested through descriptions of setting, plot, and other characters. Use specific examples from the excerpt. *(40 points)*

UNIT 6: CHINESE AND JAPANESE LITERATURES

UNIT INTRODUCTION TEST

INTRODUCTION/ The Literature of China
(Textbook pages 506–511)

1. c	5. d	8. d
2. a	6. a	9. c
3. b	7. d	10. a
4. b		

from THE BOOK OF SONGS

translated by Arthur Waley
(Textbook page 515)

REVIEW AND RESPONSE WORKSHEET

Reviewing the Selections

1. angry, lonely, mistreated
2. return home
3. Responses may vary. Possible responses:
   A. 1. People do not treat her well.
      2. She misses her kinfolk.
      3. She doesn't understand the ways of the people.
   B. 1. There is little respect for soldiers.
      2. A soldier is placed in the wilderness, like an animal.
      3. A soldier doesn't get enough rest.

Reader's Response

Responses will vary, depending upon which character the student most sympathizes with.

POEMS OF LI PO

Li Po
translated by Arthur Cooper
(Textbook page 520)

REVIEW AND RESPONSE WORKSHEET

Reviewing the Selections

The words should appear in the blanks in this order: frost, moon, spring, mulberry, silkworms, fields, peach, stream.

Reader's Response

Responses will vary, depending upon which image they choose to discuss.

POEMS OF TU FU

Tu Fu
translated by Arthur Cooper and Kenneth Rexroth
(Textbook page 528)

VOCABULARY ACTIVITY WORKSHEET

Developing Vocabulary

Responses will vary.

VOCABULARY TEST

A. 1. b	3. e	5. c
2. d	4. a	
B. 6. pathos	8. courtiers	10. sequence
7. grizzled	9. imperceptible	

REVIEW AND RESPONSE WORKSHEET

Reviewing the Selections

1. friends, family, and acquaintances who have died

(continued)

2. melancholy, lonely, insignificant
3. a stone horse
4. b

Reader's Response

Responses will vary depending on which poem a student finds the saddest.

PEONIES

Li Ch'ing–chao
translated by Kenneth Rexroth and Ling Chung
(Textbook page 534)

REVIEW AND RESPONSE WORKSHEET

Reviewing the Selection

1. spring
2. beautiful, modest
3. old age
4. c

Reader's Response

Responses will vary. Answers may depend upon whether students believe a woman's physical appearance is a measure of her value.

from the ANALECTS

Confucius
translated by Arthur Waley
(Textbook page 538)

VOCABULARY ACTIVITY WORKSHEET

Developing Vocabulary

Answers will vary.

VOCABULARY TEST

A. 1. d 2. c 3. a 4. e 5. b

B. 6. docile 7. filial 8. dictates 9. intent 10. dispense

REVIEW AND RESPONSE WORKSHEET

Reviewing the Selection

1. a
2. recognizing what you know and what you do not know
3. b
4. trust, humility, consideration, honesty

Reader's Response

Responses will vary depending on which saying students choose to write about.

from the TAO TE CHING

Lao-tzu
translated by Stephen Mitchell
(Textbook page 543)

REVIEW AND RESPONSE WORKSHEET

Reviewing the Selection

1. yes (#8)
2. no
3. no
4. yes (#8)
5. yes (#8,#29)
6. yes (#2)
7. yes (#29)
8. yes (#2,#29)
9. no
10. no

Reader's Response

Responses will vary depending on which passage students choose to write about.

TAOIST ANECDOTES

translated by Moss Roberts
(Textbook page 548)

REVIEW AND RESPONSE WORKSHEET

Reviewing the Selections

1. content
2. floating freely in the air

(continued)

3. He is so blinded by his love of gold that he takes foolish chances to obtain it—he steals it in front of other people.
4. He imagines that the boy walks, looks, and acts like a thief.
5. Because he is lame, the son does not have to go to war.

Reader's Response

Responses will vary depending on which anecdote students choose to write about.

NIEH CHENG, *from* RECORDS OF THE HISTORIAN

Ssu–ma Ch'ien
translated by Burton Watson
(Textbook page 553)

VOCABULARY ACTIVITY WORKSHEET

Developing Vocabulary

Responses will vary.

VOCABULARY TEST

A. 1. c   3. d   5. e
   2. a   4. b

B. 6. valor   8. retaliation   10. etiquette
   7. profound   9. apprehension

REVIEW AND RESPONSE WORKSHEET

Reviewing the Selection

Responses will vary. These are possible responses.

2. Yen Chung–tzu convinces Nieh Cheng to kill Han Hsia–lei.
3. Nieh Cheng mutilates and kills himself.
4. Nieh Cheng's body is exposed in the marketplace.

Reader's Response

Responses will vary depending on students' opinions of the sister's actions.

SELECTION TEST

Reading Comprehension

1. c   5. d   8. b
2. a   6. c   9. a
3. c   7. c   10. d
4. a

UNIT INTRODUCTION TEST

INTRODUCTION/ The Literature of Japan (Textbook pages 558–563)

1. c   5. c   8. a
2. b   6. c   9. b
3. b   7. d   10. d
4. a

TANKA POEMS

translated by Geoffrey Bownas and Anthony Thwaite
(Textbook page 569)

REVIEW AND RESPONSE WORKSHEET

Reviewing the Selections

1. b, c, d
2. resting in the shade of a tree on a mountain
3. He compares the friend to plum petals.
4. "How Helpless My Heart!"

Reader's Response

Responses will vary according to the poem they choose.

SELECTION TEST

Reading Comprehension

1. d   5. b   8. c
2. c   6. b   9. c
3. d   7. c   10. a
4. c

(continued)

HAIKU

translated by Harold G. Henderson,
Peter Beilenson, and Harry Behn
(Textbook page 576)

REVIEW AND RESPONSE WORKSHEET

Reviewing the Selections

1. He connects the crow with nightfall in the autumn.
2. Stones in mountain water sing to the wild cherries.
3. He connects the image of pear blossoms.
4. A blossoming morning-glory vine transforms the hut.

Reader's Response

Responses will vary. Possible responses include flowers growing on windowsills of apartment buildings, the sound of thunder before a city storm, the reflections of car lights on wet city streets. (Rural and suburban students may find no reason to revise Bashō's choice of imagery.)

SELECTION TEST

Reading Comprehension

1. c
2. a
3. b
4. a
5. a
6. b
7. b
8. b
9. d
10. c

from THE PILLOW BOOK

Sei Shōnagon
translated by Ivan Morris
(Textbook page 581)

VOCABULARY ACTIVITY WORKSHEET

Developing Vocabulary

Responses will vary.

VOCABULARY TEST

A. 1. d
2. e
3. a
4. b
5. c

B. 6. a
7. c
8. c
9. a
10. b

REVIEW AND RESPONSE WORKSHEET

Reviewing the Selection

1. She finds the nights especially beautiful. She likes early mornings most in winter.
2. Students might mention any two of the following pairs of items: summer and winter, night and day, rain and sunshine, youth and age, laughter and anger, the indigo plant and the philodendron, black and white, love and hatred, rain and mist, crows in the middle of the night and crows during the daytime. She also mentions the feeling of falling out of love with someone.
3. Students might mention any two of the following items: his dress, the way he speaks, his peculiar actions.
4. The Empress sometimes calls Sei Shōnagon to the Empress's side in front of other women, who have to make way for Sei Shōnagon.

Reader's Response

Responses will vary.

LANGUAGE SKILLS WORKSHEET

Pronouns

Exercise 1

1. who, her
2. anybody, who, her
3. She, herself, she, others
4. She, that, their
5. one, who
6. himself, others, him
7. This, that

(continued)

8. herself, her, others
9. those, anyone, who
10. She, us, ourselves

Exercise 2

Responses will vary. These are possible sentences.

1. Sei Shōnagon dislikes not being able to get rid of visitors who talk nonstop. They do not endear themselves to her.
2. Sei Shōnagon says she cannot compare a person she once loved with someone she has stopped loving. They seem like two different people.
3. Sei Shōnagon does not think of servants as people like herself. She believes they should confine themselves to creeping around the palace silently.
4. One wonders how Sei Shōnagon could have observed so much through the curtain that kept women in feudal Japan from being observed by men and strangers who might approach them.
5. The rest of Sei Shōnagon's diary contains different kinds of lists. These reveal even more of her personality, which already shines through the selected excerpts.

Exercise 3

Students' paragraphs will vary. Here is one possible paragraph.

Masahiro is an aristocrat at the palace who attracts Sei Shōnagon's attention with his antics. He dresses himself elegantly, but others find even his attire, which might not seem funny on someone else, humorous. Sometimes he says things that people seem to find amusing. When he is required to report for night duty, for example, he asks for two servants to collect his things. One servant assures Masahiro that he can carry all of Masahiro's things himself, to which Masahiro responds by asking how one can carry a load meant for two. Sometimes Masahiro does things that amuse others. He speaks in a funny way to Sei Shōnagon, for example. He drags the cloth under the lamp around with his foot, and he is found eating in public.

SELECTION TEST

Reading Comprehension

1. c	5. b	8. b
2. b	6. b	9. d
3. b	7. d	10. a
4. d		

ZEN PARABLES

translated by Paul Reps
(Textbook page 591)

VOCABULARY ACTIVITY WORKSHEET

Developing Vocabulary

Responses will vary.

VOCABULARY TEST

A. 1. d　3. e　5. b
　2. a　4. c

B. 6. precipice　8. intensive　10. surpass
　7. anticipated　9. mediocre

REVIEW AND RESPONSE WORKSHEET

Reviewing the Selections

1. Ekido objects to Tanzan carrying the girl. Tanzan says that although he carried her, he can forget her, whereas Ekido, who didn't touch her, is still thinking about her.
2. The man eats it as he faces death.
3. The first two sets are his invisible sutras, that is, the sutras that he would have published had he not twice given away all his money to help people suffering from famine and epidemic. The third set is the set actually published.

(continued)

4. Matajuro is impatient and wants to become a master quickly; he doesn't understand that impatience hinders mastery.

Reader's Response

Students' reponses will vary according to the parable they choose.

LANGUAGE SKILLS WORKSHEET

Varying Sentence Beginnings

Exercise 1

1. b	5. a	8. c
2. e	6. b	9. a
3. d	7. e	10. d
4. c		

Exercise 2

Students' sentences may vary slightly. These are possible sentences.

1. Today, millions of people around the world use Zen.
2. Meditating for long periods, a Zen practitioner finds inner peace.
3. To learn meditation, Japanese children receive half-hour lessons in *zazen.*
4. Under the rap of an "awakening" stick, a Zen monk meditates.
5. Rather than preach sermons about good and evil, Zen monks focus on the inner self.

Exercise 3

Students' paragraph revisions may vary. This is one possible revision.

To illustrate universal and timeless truths, Zen parables present entertaining anecdotes. With moral lessons, the parables provide insight into individuals and society. Often appearing simple, the parables focus on common experiences. Like fables, they encourage readers to apply the morals to their own lives. As people of all ages apply these experiences, they learn important lessons about subjects such as greed, generosity, and patience.

SELECTION TEST

Reading Comprehension

1. b	5. b	8. a
2. b	6. d	9. b
3. d	7. c	10. b
4. d		

ATSUMORI

Seami Motokiyo

translated by Arthur Waley

(Textbook page 600)

VOCABULARY ACTIVITY WORKSHEET

Developing Vocabulary

Responses will vary.

VOCABULARY TEST

A. 1. a	3. e	5. b
2. d	4. c	
B. 6. c	8. a	10. c
7. b	9. a	

REVIEW AND RESPONSE WORKSHEET

Reviewing the Selection

1. He has come to pray for the soul of Atsumori.
2. He hears the reapers playing flutes.
3. because Atsumori died as a young warrior
4. They are no longer enemies.

Reader's Response

Responses will vary.

(continued)

LANGUAGE SKILLS WORKSHEET

Sentence Fragments

Exercise 1

1. S	5. S	8. F
2. F	6. S	9. F
3. F	7. F	10. S
4. F		

Exercise 2

Students should write the following new sentences.

1. He is wearing it when he dies at the hands of Rensei.
2. Racing into the sea, Atsumori tries to reach the soldiers' boats.
3. Atsumori knows he can't escape from the enemy who is following him.
4. Riding on his horse, Atsumori bravely turns and faces his enemy.
5. Now a ghost, Atsumori makes his peace with Rensei, once his enemy.

Exercise 3

Though the story of Atsumori is uplifting, it is sad as well. The death of a brave boy is always a tragedy. It is terrible to think about Atsumori's clan sailing away without him. I imagine that he must have felt very frightened as he watched the boats preparing to depart. I wonder if Atsumori's father wanted to wait for his son to reach the ship. Perhaps the father wanted to turn back, but the soldiers would not let him. I am sure his father hoped that Atsumori would escape into the hills away from the enemy.

When Rensei follows the young warrior, Atsumori stops and turns toward his enemy. Atsumori faces his death with courage, an important trait for a samurai. Perhaps his courage makes it especially hard for Rensei to kill him. According to Rensei, he does not want to hurt the boy. If Rensei had let Atsumori escape, someone else would have killed him. Rensei's lifelong sadness about Atsumori shows that he truly regrets his actions and hopes that he can make peace with the spirit of Atsumori.

SELECTION TEST

Reading Comprehension

1. d	5. a	8. a
2. b	6. d	9. b
3. b	7. b	10. c
4. d		

WORD ANALOGIES/Extending Vocabulary

1. d (intent : determined :: hesitant : uncertain)
   Relationship: synonyms
   Intent and *determined* are synonyms sharing the meaning "directed or fixed." *Hesitant* and *uncertain* are synonyms sharing the meaning "undecided." The analogy is strengthened by the fact that *intent* and *hesitant* are antonyms of each other, as are *determined* and *uncertain.*
2. b (knoll : hill :: highway : road)
   Relationship: species to class
   A *knoll* is a kind of *hill.* A *highway* is a kind of *road.*
3. c (valor : brave :: courage : bold)
   Relationship: quality to characteristic
   One who has the quality of *valor* is likely to be *brave.* One who has the quality of *courage* is likely to be *bold.* The analogy is strengthened by the fact that *valor* and *courage* are synonyms, as are *brave* and *bold.*
4. b (docile : rebellious :: obedient : unruly)
   Relationship: antonyms
   Docile, "easily managed or controlled," is an antonym of *rebellious. Obedient,* "obeying willingly," is an antonym of *unruly.* The analogy is strengthened by

(continued)

the fact that *docile* and *obedient* are synonyms, as are *rebellious* and *unruly.*

5. c (intimate : friend :: personal : confidante)
   Relationship: characteristic to object
   A *friend* is—at least relatively—*intimate,* and a *confidante* is *personal.* The analogy is strengthened by the fact that *friend* and *confidante* are synonyms, as are *intimate* and *personal.*
6. c (etiquette : manners :: code : laws)
   Relationship: general to specific
   Manners are the individual items that make up *etiquette. Laws* are the individual items that make up a *code.*
7. d (stealthy : conceal :: sly : hide)
   Relationship: characteristic to action
   One who is *stealthy* is likely to *conceal.* One who is *sly* is likely to *hide.* The analogy is strengthened by the fact that *stealthy* and *sly* are synonyms, as are *conceal* and *hide.*
8. b (apprehension : fear :: anxiety : dread)
   Relationship: synonyms
   All four words are synonyms of each other sharing the meaning "unease" or "misgiving."
9. c (pathos : sadness :: bliss : joy)
   Relationship: synonyms
   Pathos and *sadness* are synonyms sharing the meaning "sorrow." *Bliss* and *joy* are synonyms sharing the meaning "happiness." The analogy is strengthened by the fact that *pathos* and *bliss* are antonyms of each other, as are *sadness* and *joy.*
10. a (mediocre : average :: superior : great)
    Relationship: synonyms
    Mediocre and *average* are synonyms sharing the meaning "limited compared with others." *Superior* and *great* are synonyms sharing the meaning "bigger or better compared with others." The analogy is strengthened by the fact that *mediocre* and *superior* are differ by the same degree as do *average* and *great.*

UNIT REVIEW TEST/Applying Skills I

A. 1. d   2. b   3. d   4. c   5. c   6. a
B. 7. a   8. b   9. b   10. d
C. Responses will vary. Students may include the following in their essays:
   1. Both works use a philosophical approach to teach moral lessons of behavior, conduct, and honor. They differ in that the *Analects* depict the teachings of Confucius and the Zen parables are based on Buddhism; the *Analects* contain direct statements from Confucius and the parables are told in story form. The *Analects* put forth a direct message while the parables have hidden or indirect meanings.
   2. Both are forms of lyrical poetry, meant to be sung; both convey human feelings, especially of moodiness and loneliness; both use images of nature. Major differences are that the tanka poems all have five lines while the Songs vary in length; the Songs have repetitive words and phrases while the tanka poems feature assonance.

CRITICAL THINKING AND WRITING/
Applying Skills II

B. Analyzing a Novel Excerpt
1. d   2. d   3. c   4. d   5. b   6. a   7. b   8. c   9. b   10. a

C. Writing About a Novel Excerpt
Students' paragraphs will vary. Lady Murasaki describes Genji as a very handsome and sensitive boy, whom others in the palace admire greatly. In describing his

(continued)

feelings for Princess Fujitsubo, Lady Murasaki suggests there is a great sadness about Genji. His activities and his response to his official palace quarters indicate that he is very lonely. He is drawn to familiar people in the palace, but he dislikes Princess Aoi. In the description of his dutiful visits to Princess Aoi's home, Genji appears respectful and responsible, though sad.

NOTES

NAME ______________________ CLASS ______________ DATE ______ SCORE ______

Unit 7: Persian and Arabic Literatures

(Textbook pages 622–629)

INTRODUCTION/Persian and Arabic Literatures

Directions: In the space provided, write the letter of the best answer to each question. *(10 points each)*

1. The Persian Empire had its beginnings in
   a. the migration of Indians into Africa
   b. the migration of Central Asian tribes into the Middle East
   c. Rome
   d. rebellious Greek warriors — 1. ______

2. The Persian religion Zoroastrianism taught that
   a. one all-powerful and good god ruled the universe
   b. one good god and one evil god struggled for power
   c. there were many gods
   d. one god ruled the desert and one god ruled the mountains — 2. ______

3. The Arabic religion of Islam was founded in the seventh century by
   a. Alexander the Great
   b. Zarathustra
   c. Mohammed
   d. Caliph Abbas — 3. ______

4. Islam has ________ and stresses ________.
   a. one God; community, charity, and submission to God
   b. many gods; war, conquest, and sacrifices to the gods
   c. one God; the falseness of human prophets
   d. three gods; the Trinity — 4. ______

5. When the Arabic Empire conquered Persia
   a. the Abbasid Caliphate destroyed Persian traditions
   b. Persians never again spoke their own language
   c. the joining of the two cultures produced a civilization of high achievement
   d. a and b — 5. ______

(continued)

6. Some important legacies that Arabic culture gave to later European culture are
   a. a number system, algebra, astronomy, and translation of classical Greek and Roman writings
   b. agriculture, Roman numerals, irrigation
   c. alchemy, anesthesia, psychology, and translation of Egyptian hieroglyphic writing
   d. knowledge of the first humans and their tools 6.______

7. In the Arabic culture, literature
   a. was purely religious
   b. was popular with the people but not considered an important endeavor
   c. was highly respected and had both a strong oral and written tradition
   d. was not written down until the fifteenth century 7.______

8. During the Samanid dynasty of the ninth and tenth centuries,
   a. Islamic law was abolished
   b. Persian art forms were forbidden
   c. a great revival of Persian writing occurred
   d. the first Persian kings were crowned 8.______

9. Sufism is
   a. a Persian epic
   b. a mystical sect that believes a direct, personal experience with Allah can be achieved through intuition
   c. an orthodox sect that outlaws mysticism
   d. a type of ode 9.______

10. Animal fables, sayings, philosophical and historical works, and didactic stories are all examples of
    a. the writings of Omar Khayyám
    b. Zoroastrian achievements
    c. the writings of the prophet Mohammed
    d. Persian prose writings 10.______

NAME ______________ CLASS ______________ DATE ________ SCORE ________

On Her Brother

al-Khansa
translated by Willis Barnstone

(Textbook page 631)

REVIEWING THE SELECTION

1. What feeling, or emotion, is most present in the poem? What phrases or lines convey this feeling?

____

____

2. In the poem, what might be an answer to the question al-Khansa asks in lines 7 and 8?

____

____

3. List two phrases that show what kind of warrior the poet's brother was.

____

____

4. How does al-Khansa describe those who probably killed her brother?

____

Reader's Response

"On Her Brother" is an elegy, a lament for someone or something lost. Choose a current issue, involving loss, about which you feel deeply. For example, you might write an "Elegy for the Rain Forests." List words and images that tell what you feel about the issue and that might be used in a poem.

Issue: ____

Feelings: ____

Images: ____

____

____

NAME ______________________ CLASS ____________________ DATE ________ SCORE ________

from the KORAN

translated by N. J. Dawood (Textbook page 635)

DEVELOPING VOCABULARY

Directions: Read carefully the explanation of each word. Then write a sentence of your own using that word. In your sentence, include clues to the word's meaning.

admonition (ad·mə·nish′ən) ***n.*** A warning or scolding. ▶ This word can also mean simply "an urging or advising to do something," but it usually carries the meaning of at least mild disapproval. The verb is *admonish.* ■ The coach issued an admonition to all team members to attend study period or face a penalty. **Page 636**

ORIGINAL SENTENCE ____

____

abhor (ab·hôr′) ***v.*** To draw back in hatred or disgust. ▶ The Latin root of this word is *horrere*, meaning "to bristle or to stand on end" (said of hair). ■ I abhor people who mistreat animals, and I will have nothing to do with them. **Page 636**

ORIGINAL SENTENCE ____

____

chide (chīd) ***v.*** To scold mildly. ▶ This word comes from an Old English word meaning "strife." ■ Rosa knew we would chide her for forgetting to clean the hamsters' cage. **Page 636**

ORIGINAL SENTENCE ____

____

renown (ri·noun′) ***n.*** Illustrious reputation; great fame. ▶ This word is derived from the Old French *renommer*, a verb meaning "to make famous" or "to name again." ■ Lily's great renown as a runner had spread all over the city. **Page 636**

ORIGINAL SENTENCE ____

____

fervor (fur′vər) ***n.*** Strong, warm feeling. ▶ This word comes from a Latin word meaning "to boil." ■ They danced with such fervor that the audience grew tired just watching them. **Page 636**

ORIGINAL SENTENCE ____

____

NAME ______________________ CLASS ______________ DATE ________ SCORE ________

from the KORAN

translated by N. J. Dawood

(Textbook page 635)

VOCABULARY TEST

A. Match each word in column I with the correct definition in column II. Place the letter of the definition you choose in the space provided. *(10 points each)*

	I	II
______	1. abhor	a. to express disapproval
		b. high reputation
______	2. admonition	c. to draw back in hatred or disgust
		d. a warning or scolding
______	3. chide	e. strong, warm feeling
______	4. fervor	
______	5. renown	

B. In the space provided, write the letter of the word closest in meaning to the word in italics. *(10 points each)*

______ 6. She displayed such *fervor* on the topic of in-line skating that I was unable to change the subject.

a. bitterness b. enthusiasm c. apathy

______ 7. It was difficult to *chide* the tearful children for their naughty behavior.

a. praise b. admire c. scold

______ 8. The general's cruelty made both his enemies and his own soldiers *abhor* him.

a. despise b. respect c. leave

______ 9. The *renown* of the new professor of philosophy has increased the popularity of the class.

a. fame b. obscurity c. weirdness

______ 10. The director issued an *admonition* about following proper procedure.

a. document b. lecture c. caution

NAME ______________________ CLASS ______________________ DATE __________ SCORE __________

from the KORAN

translated by N. J. Dawood

(Textbook page 635)

REVIEWING THE SELECTION

1. In "The Exordium," the speaker gives praise to Allah and asks for guidance. What in particular is he asking for guidance about?

   ____

2. In "The Cessation," the speaker talks about what will happen when the earth comes to an end. Name two of the things that will signal the end of the world.

   ____

3. In "Daylight," the speaker discusses the life to come. How does he say that the life to come will compare with this one?

   ____

4. In "Comfort," the speaker talks about comfort and ease. What does he suggest you do when your task is ended?

   ____

Reader's Response

The Koran uses much **figurative language,** in which one thing stands for another and has more than its literal meaning. Moral uprightness is called a straight path, and sin or troubles are weighty burdens carried on the back. Below, write whether you found the figurative language *clear and vivid* or *confusing and difficult.* Explain your response with an example.

____

____

____

____

____

____

NAME ______________________ CLASS ______________ DATE ________ SCORE ________

from the KORAN

translated by N. J. Dawood (Textbook page 635)

PRONOUN AND ANTECEDENT AGREEMENT

Pronouns are words such as *her, she, it, them,* and *someone* that take the place of nouns. The word that a pronoun replaces, or refers to, is called its **antecedent.** Pronouns must agree with their antecedents in number (singular or plural) and in gender (masculine, feminine, or neuter).

EXAMPLES The *city* of Medina is known for *its* mosque. (singular, neuter)
The *woman* embraced Islam when *she* heard the Koran read. (singular, feminine)
Muslims face Mecca when *they* pray. (plural, either gender)
Each Muslim faces Mecca when *he* or *she* prays. (singular, either gender)

The following rules will help you with common problems in pronoun reference.

1. Two antecedents joined by *and* require a plural pronoun.

EXAMPLES Both *Abraham and Jesus* are considered prophets, and *they* are honored in the Koran.
The stars and the sun will cease to give *their* light.

2. Two antecedents joined by *or* or *nor* require a pronoun that agrees with the nearest antecedent. If the nearest antecedent is singular, use a singular pronoun; if it is plural, use a plural pronoun.

EXAMPLES A *rich man or a poor man* will find *his* errors judged fairly.
Neither *a mother nor her children* should fear for *their* protection.

3. When the following **indefinite pronouns** are antecedents, they require a singular pronoun: *each, either, neither, one, everyone, everybody, no one, nobody, anyone, anybody, someone, somebody.*

EXAMPLES
Incorrect: *Each* of the men in the world will know what *they* have done. (The plural noun *men* in the prepositional phrase is not the antecedent. The pronoun *each [man]* is.)
Correct: *Each* of the men in the world will know what *he* has done.

When the antecedent refers to either gender, you may use "he or she" or reword the sentence.

EXAMPLES
Incorrect: *Everyone* who reads the Koran will find wisdom *they* can live by.
Correct: *Everyone* who reads the Koran will find wisdom *he or she* can live by.
Reworded: *Everyone* who reads the Koran will find wisdom to live by.

4. **Ambiguous,** or unclear, reference occurs when a pronoun may refer to more than one antecedent and the reader is not sure which one is meant. In this case, reword the sentence.

(continued)

EXAMPLES

Unclear: When *beasts* are brought together and *souls* reunite, then *they* will be judged. (Will the beasts, the souls, or both be judged? The reference of *they* is ambiguous.)

Clear: When beasts are brought together and souls reunite, then all souls will be judged.

Exercise 1. Identifying Pronouns and Antecedents

Find and circle each pronoun in the sentences below about the Koran. Then find and underline the pronoun's antecedent. Remember that an antecedent may be an indefinite pronoun such as *someone.*

EXAMPLE Although Mohammed was prosperous, (he) was also troubled.

1. Mohammed's childhood was filled with hardship, and by the age of six he was an orphan.
2. The faithful memorized Mohammed's speeches and jotted them down on leaves or scraps of leather.
3. Because the angel Gabriel is thought to have dictated the Koran from Allah's tablets in heaven, Muslims consider it perfect and unalterable.
4. The Koran urges that everyone be responsible for his or her neighbors if they are in need.
5. "The Cessation" alludes to pre-Islamic times, when the parents of an unwanted infant girl might bury her alive.

Exercise 2. Using Correct Pronoun-Antecedent Agreement

In each sentence, circle the correct pronoun.

1. The exploding mountains and the bright falling star will unleash (its / their) fury on Judgment Day.
2. How might submission or obedience offer (its / their) rewards to the followers of Islam?
3. The Koran states that neither the wealthy person nor the famous person will be able to use (his or her / their) position to escape judgment.
4. Numerous Muslim scholars have devoted (his or her / their) lives to the study of the Koran.
5. People may have (his or her / their) own interpretations of the Koran.
6. No one can escape the consequences of (his or her / their) actions in life.
7. Translations of the Koran cannot be used in religious ceremonies because (its / their) rewordings only approximate Allah's word.

(continued)

8. Islam is the state religion of many countries; each enforces (its / their) laws according to guidelines set forth in the Koran.

9. The Koran portrays Allah as fair and compassionate in (his / its) judgments of human beings.

10. Every person is told to rejoice, for Allah has eased (his / his or her) burdens.

Exercise 3. Revising Sentences

Rewrite the sentences to eliminate ambiguous pronoun reference. You may combine sentences or reword them in any way necessary. Be prepared to explain the possible confusion in each original sentence.

EXAMPLE: Orthodox Muslims believe that translations alter the Koran's meaning, so they are banned from ceremonies.

Orthodox Muslims believe that translations alter the Koran's meaning and so ban their use in ceremonies.

1. Early Muslims feared that Mohammed's words would be lost forever if they were not gathered in one place.

____

____

2. Mohammed was disturbed by the sufferings of the poor, though he was surrounded by wealthy people. Their plight caused him to withdraw to the mountains to meditate.

____

____

3. Mohammed and Gabriel were in a hillside cave when he began to dictate the words of Allah.

____

4. Mohammed received numerous visions, some containing images of Judgment Day. They were the source of his preaching.

____

5. When the angel Gabriel appeared, Mohammed's wife told him to accept what was happening.

____

NAME ______________________ CLASS ______________ DATE ________ SCORE ______

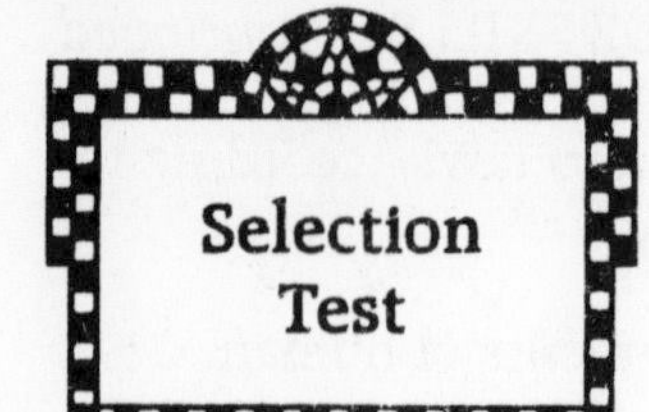

from the KORAN

translated by N. J. Dawood

(Textbook page 635)

READING COMPREHENSION

Directions: In the space provided, write the letter of the best answer to each question. *(20 points each)*

1. In the line that opens each chapter of the Koran, Allah is described as
   a. the Judge, the Destroyer
   b. the Compassionate, the Merciful
   c. the Humble, the Meek
   d. the Orphan, the Beggar
   1. ______

2. In "The Cessation," how does Mohammed explain his unusual knowledge of burning seas, a dark sun, Paradise brought near, and other wonders?
   a. He is Allah.
   b. He is mad.
   c. An angel and messenger has told him.
   d. An accursed devil has told him.
   2. ______

3. On the day of these wonders, Mohammed says that every soul will know its actions in life. This day is best called
   a. Creation Day
   b. Judgment Day
   c. the Day of Birth
   d. the Day of Turning Planets
   3. ______

4. In "Daylight," Mohammed says that the life to come holds more riches than the present life. Which of the following is the best statement of his meaning?
   a. Wealth is important.
   b. Spiritual knowledge in the afterlife is a richer prize than the world's wealth.
   c. No matter how rich you are, you will be richer in the afterlife.
   d. You will never be rich.
   4. ______

5. In "Comfort," what does Mohammed probably mean by emphasizing that hardship is always followed by ease?
   a. If you work hard, you will make more money.
   b. If you work hard, others will praise you.
   c. If you strive to serve Allah, he will bless you.
   d. If you strive to serve Allah, you will make more money.
   5. ______

NAME ______________ CLASS ______________ DATE ________ SCORE ________

from THE THIRD VOYAGE OF SINDBAD THE SAILOR

translated by N. J. Dawood (Textbook page 640)

DEVELOPING VOCABULARY

Directions: Read carefully the explanation of each word. Then write a sentence of your own using that word. In your sentence, include clues to the word's meaning.

rend ***v.*** [past tense *rent*] To rip up or tear apart violently. ▶ This word can be used figuratively, as in "The thunder *rent* the sky." ▪ Suzanna rent the dress in two when she saw how unevenly she'd sewn the seams. **Page 640**

ORIGINAL SENTENCE ______________________________

____

disconsolate (dis·kän′sə·lit) ***adj.*** Inconsolable; terribly unhappy. —**disconsolately** ***adj.*** ▶ The root word is *consolate*, from the Latin *consolari*, meaning "to console." ▪ The disconsolate children could not even be comforted by our offer of ice cream. **Page 641**

ORIGINAL SENTENCE ______________________________

____

corpulent (kôr′pyo͞o·lənt) ***adj.*** Obese; excessively fat. ▶ This word is derived from the Latin *corpus*, meaning "body." The noun form, *corpulence*, means "stoutness." ▪ The hamster became so corpulent after eating that it could no longer squeeze through the bars of its cage. **Page 641**

ORIGINAL SENTENCE ______________________________

____

ogre (ō′gər) ***n.*** A monster or giant who eats people. ▶ This word, borrowed from French, was first used in 1697 by Charles Perrault, author of many of the Mother Goose tales and rhymes. ▪ Tom dressed as an ogre on Halloween to terrify the other children. **Page 641**

ORIGINAL SENTENCE ______________________________

____

approbation (ap·rə·bā′shən) ***n.*** Official approval. ▶ This word contains the Latin root *probus*, "good." ▪ Mario needed approbation from the media center director to organize a video and film club at school. **Page 643**

(continued)

ORIGINAL SENTENCE ____

____

martyr (märt'ər) ***n.*** **1.** A person who prefers to suffer or die rather than deny his or her principles or beliefs. **2.** A person who undergoes immense pain or suffering for a long time. ▶ The second meaning is more common today. ▪ Those on the picket line were prepared to become martyrs, for the strike could mean weeks without wages. **Page 643**

ORIGINAL SENTENCE ____

____

spit ***n.*** A thin, pointed rod used to hold meat over a fire. ▶ The words *spit, spike,* and *spine* are all related through a common Indo-European base word. ▪ At camp, Jenny learned how to roast meat on a spit. **Page 641**

ORIGINAL SENTENCE ____

____

nimble ***adj.*** Moving about in a quick or light manner.—**nimbly** ***adv.*** ▶ *Nimble* comes from the Old English word *niman,* meaning "able to take." ▪ The pianist's fingers moved nimbly over the keys, barely seeming to touch them. **Page 643**

ORIGINAL SENTENCE ____

____

stupendous (stōō·pen'dəs) ***adj.*** Amazing; astonishing in magnitude or scope. ▶ This word comes from the Latin word *stupere,* "to be stunned." It was originally used to describe anything to be wondered at. ▪ The space shuttle lifted off with stupendous power, making the ground shudder. **Page 643**

ORIGINAL SENTENCE ____

____

contrive (kən·trīv') ***v.*** To bring about; manage. ▶ This word comes from the Old French word *controver,* which meant "to invent fraudulently or falsely." ▪ Alan had to contrive a way to sneak out of the house early. **Page 643**

ORIGINAL SENTENCE ____

____

NAME ______________________ CLASS ____________________ DATE ________ SCORE ________

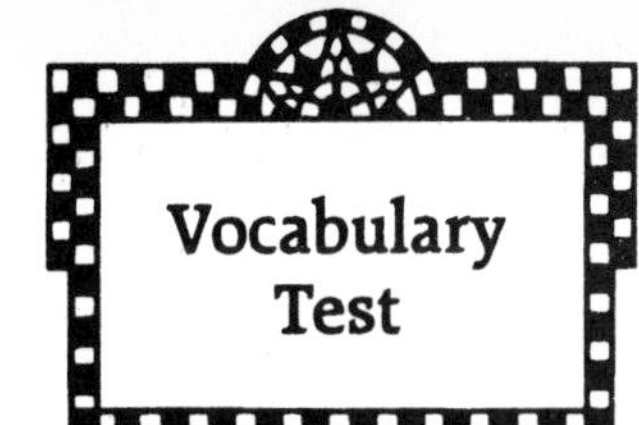

from THE THIRD VOYAGE OF SINDBAD THE SAILOR

translated by N. J. Dawood (Textbook page 640)

VOCABULARY TEST

Directions: In the space provided, write the letter of the word or phrase closest in meaning to the word in italics. *(10 points each)*

______ 1. I was amazed to get such *approbation* for my project proposal.

a. disapproval b. approval c. response

______ 2. José will always *contrive* to study with a good student.

a. fail b. attempt c. manage

______ 3. The poodle was too *corpulent* to lie down comfortably.

a. fat b. wet c. cramped

______ 4. The members of the chess club were *disconsolate* when they heard the match was canceled.

a. elated b. dejected c. surprised

______ 5. Alan became a *martyr* for the cause by joining the hunger strike.

a. annoyance b. winner c. sufferer

______ 6. Her fingers were surprisingly *nimble* as she worked on the costume.

a. quick b. slow c. accurate

______ 7. The fairy tale included a princess and an *ogre*.

a. animal b. prince c. monster

______ 8. Maria's first impulse was to *rend* the rejection letter.

a. discard b. tear c. hide

______ 9. Ellen removed the *spit* from the dying fire.

a. cooking rod b. coal c. ash

______ 10. The fireworks provided a *stupendous* end to the evening.

a. bright b. happy c. marvelous

NAME ________________ CLASS ________________ DATE ________ SCORE ________

from THE THIRD VOYAGE OF SINDBAD THE SAILOR

translated by N. J. Dawood (Textbook page 640)

REVIEWING THE SELECTION

1. From what city does Sindbad set sail? Who is traveling with him?

____

2. How do Sindbad and the others get onto the island?

____

____

3. Name two items in the deserted courtyard that might have been a warning to Sindbad.

____

4. Sindbad and his companions blind the giant. How does the giant still manage to drown many of them?

____

____

Reader's Response

Seafaring adventure stories are often full of vivid descriptions. Complete the chart below with your own descriptions of characters from "The Third Voyage of Sindbad the Sailor." Use precise sensory words (coal-red eyes), specific qualities (cunning), and, if you like, colorful comparisons (plump as a juicy goose).

CHARACTERS	DESCRIPTIVE DETAILS
the dwarves	
the captain	
the giant	
Sindbad	

NAME ______________________ CLASS ________________ DATE ________ SCORE ______

from THE THIRD VOYAGE OF SINDBAD THE SAILOR

translated by N. J. Dawood (Textbook page 640)

ORNATE STYLE AND PLAIN STYLE

Style refers to a writer's way of using language. Style involves word choice, sentence length and structure, and the use of literary devices.

Some writers use an **ornate style,** characterized by elegant words, indirect statements, and long sentences with many clauses or unusual structures such as inversions. Ornate writing may also include many literary devices, such as figurative language (metaphor, personification, and simile) and allusions. The following example shows a purposely exaggerated ornate style.

EXAMPLE Ere twelve new moons had risen in the starry firmament, I felt myself oppressed by the need to travel more. Therefore did I hie me, with the swiftness of the restless wind, to an acquaintance, to ascertain whether any mercantile ventures were afoot.

Notice the elegant words (*firmament, ascertain, mercantile, afoot*); the indirect way of referring to time (*Ere twelve new moons had risen*); the long sentences, including one in which subject and verb are inverted (*Therefore did I hie me*); and the use of simile (*with the swiftness of the restless wind*).

A **plain style** is characterized by shorter, simpler words, sentences with fewer modifiers, and straightforward statements. If literary devices are used, they are briefer and less frequent than in ornate writing.

EXAMPLE Before a year had passed, I longed to travel again. I asked a friend if he knew of any merchant ships I could work on.

Notice the shorter words and everyday constructions, the direct way of stating things, the briefer sentences, and the lack of modifiers and figurative language.

Authors may choose the plain style when they want their writing to appear matter-of-fact, simple, or understated. They may choose the ornate style when they want their writing to sound complex, exotic, or sophisticated. In "The Third Voyage of Sindbad the Sailor," the translator uses an ornate style to recreate the exotic flavor of the original.

Exercise 1. Identifying Plain and Ornate Style

In the blank before each sentence, write *P* if the style is plain, or *O* if the style is ornate. The sentences are based on "The Third Voyage of Sindbad the Sailor."

EXAMPLE __P__ The ship rocked with a gentle motion.

______ 1. His eyes seemed to be illuminated from within by the fire of a mighty furnace; the bellow of his voice when he roared seemed to signify that there was indeed an inferno within.

______ 2. He was huge and furious, and we were small and frightened.

______ 3. The pair of them hurled rocks at us from the beach.

(continued)

______ 4. It was a sad sight to see the well-fed rotundity of our erstwhile commander turning slowly over the red-hot coals.

______ 5. The fruit tree was marvelous to behold as it overhung the limpid waters of the inland pool; but for all the beauty of the luscious fruit, I would rather have sunk my teeth into a pomegranate bought from the meanest market stall at home.

______ 6. The giant's deafening snores made sleep impossible.

______ 7. The storm clouds gathered in the western sky with the stealth of a band of thieves meeting for no good purpose.

______ 8. The creatures were hideously malformed, and I was transfixed with horror at the sight of the multitude swarming across the water like hairy four-legged spiders.

______ 9. While the giant slept, we made our plans for escape.

______ 10. Our raft drifted out of range of the giant, and I looked toward the open sea.

Exercise 2. Using Plain Style and Ornate Style

Rewrite each of the following sentences as directed, changing plain style to ornate or ornate to plain. Notice that plain writing can be as detailed as ornate writing, though it is briefer. Feel free, however, to add details as you feel necessary.

EXAMPLE The ship was laden with riches beyond compare, from priceless rubies and sea-green emeralds to the rarest of aromatic spices.
Plain style: The ship was filled with precious cargo: rubies, emeralds, and spices.

1. The troll was spectacular in his ugliness, and the cold pool of his eyes shone with pure malice.

Plain style: ____

____

2. The palace seemed empty as we approached.

Ornate style: ____

____

3. With very little conviction, I suggested to my terrified companions that we attempt to foil the greedy ogre's plan to devour us all.

Plain style: ____

____

(continued)

4. We could barely hear the ocean lapping on the shore.

   Ornate style: ____

   ____

5. As ever, the colorful sights and clangorous sounds, the unending bustle and heady fragrances of the Baghdad market, delighted me as if I had been a small child.

   Plain style: ____

   ____

Exercise 3. Revising a Paragraph

Revise the following paragraph. Focus on simplifying the elevated vocabulary and complex sentence structure of the ornate style to create a plain style. You may add or change words, move words around, or make other changes. Some sample revisions are shown.

The men ~~went about their task with the practiced~~ *worked* stealth*ily, for they knew they* ~~of those accustomed to living under the shadow of~~ *would face* death *if they were caught.* ~~as if with every breath their allotted time on earth shrank visibly~~. Despite the furious heat of the mid-afternoon sun and the buzzing distraction of swarms of stinging insects, they somehow contrived to gather enough wood for a raft stout enough to bear us away from that cursed isle. As the great orange orb of the sun sank slowly into the distant depths of the ocean and we still had not finished the raft, we began to despair of ever completing the task which now seemed not only difficult, but well nigh hopeless. When we finally finished, not even Noah himself could have looked with more delight on his great ark than we looked upon the rough-hewn vessel that was to save us from a fate we could only imagine, but which we hoped never to experience.

NAME ______________ CLASS ______________ DATE ________ SCORE ________

from THE THIRD VOYAGE OF SINDBAD THE SAILOR

translated by N. J. Dawood (Textbook page 640)

READING COMPREHENSION

Directions: In the space provided, write the letter of the best answer to each question. *(10 points each)*

1. Why does Sindbad want to go to sea again?
   a. He is bored and wants profit and adventure.
   b. He is being hunted by the authorities in Baghdad.
   c. He wants to learn more about foreign customs.
   d. He wants to escape a troubled marriage. 1. ______

2. Why does the captain of the ship get upset when the wind drives them off course?
   a. He doesn't know how to navigate.
   b. He isn't sure where they are.
   c. They are dangerously near the island of the dwarves.
   d. They have passed the island of the dwarves. 2. ______

3. What do the dwarves do after they board Sindbad's ship?
   a. They leave Sindbad and the crew on the island and steal the ship.
   b. They kill Sindbad's crew.
   c. They offer Sindbad and the crew a feast on the island.
   d. They throw Sindbad and the crew into the ocean. 3. ______

4. When Sindbad and his companions enter the palace courtyard, what sight is a hint of their danger?
   a. a lion in a cage
   b. an ebony knife
   c. a table laid with fattening foods
   d. a large heap of bones 4. ______

5. Why does the giant pass over Sindbad and choose another victim?
   a. Sindbad is too strong.
   b. Sindbad is hiding.
   c. Sindbad is too thin.
   d. Sindbad outsmarts him. 5. ______

(continued)

6. What does the giant do to his victims?
   a. He makes them wrestle a lion.
   b. He roasts and eats them.
   c. He stabs them with a huge knife.
   d. He feeds them until they cannot walk. 6.______

7. Why don't Sindbad and the others hide from the giant?
   a. They can find nowhere on the island to hide.
   b. They are under the giant's spell and cannot leave.
   c. The giant locks them inside the palace.
   d. The giant ties them all together. 7.______

8. How do Sindbad and his companions try to stop the giant?
   a. by tying him up as he sleeps
   b. by putting a spell on him
   c. by thrusting hot iron spits into his eyes and blinding him
   d. by poisoning him 8.______

9. How does Sindbad's good planning allow him to escape the island?
   a. He thinks of building a signal fire, and it alerts a passing ship.
   b. He thinks of building a canoe, and in it he escapes alone.
   c. He thinks of blinding the giant, and he then swims to a safe island.
   d. He thinks of building a raft, and on it he and others row away. 9.______

10. What final surprise does the giant have for Sindbad?
    a. The giant has a third hidden eye.
    b. He and a hag chase Sindbad and his crew to the shore and throw boulders at the raft.
    c. He leaps on the lion's back and follows Sindbad.
    d. He signals the dwarves to return. 10.______

NAME ______________________ CLASS ______________ DATE ________ SCORE ________

from THE TRAGEDY OF SOHRÁB AND ROSTÁM

Ferdowsi

translated by Jerome W. Clinton

(Textbook page 649)

DEVELOPING VOCABULARY

Directions: Read carefully the explanation of each word. Then write a sentence of your own using that word. In your sentence, include clues to the word's meaning.

sever (sev'ər) ***v.*** **1.** To cut off by force. **2.** To separate; divide. ▶ This word comes from an Old French word meaning "cut apart." ▪ James wanted to sever his connection to the drama club after the play flopped. **Page 650**

ORIGINAL SENTENCE ____

____

abase (ə · bās') ***v.*** To humble, humiliate. ▶ *Abase* sometimes has the more specific meaning of "to lower a person's rank." ▪ Martha didn't wish to abase herself by admitting her error in front of the class. **Page 650**

ORIGINAL SENTENCE ____

____

perplexed (pər · plekst') ***adj.*** Puzzled; confused. ▶ This word comes from the Latin *perplexus*, which means "interwoven or entangled." ▪ Although she had studied hard, Janine was perplexed by the final question on the test. **Page 651**

ORIGINAL SENTENCE ____

____

tumult (to͞o'mult) ***n.*** Noisy commotion and uproar; violent disturbance. ▶ You may be familiar with the adjective *tumultuous*, meaning "noisy and disorderly." ▪ The tumult issuing from the apes' cage was earsplitting. **Page 651**

ORIGINAL SENTENCE ____

____

prostrate (präs'trāt) ***adj.*** Lying face down. ▶ The related noun, *prostration*, can mean "exhaustion." ▪ The boxer was prostrate after the knockout punch. **Page 652**

ORIGINAL SENTENCE ____

____

NAME ______________________ CLASS ______________ DATE ________ SCORE ________

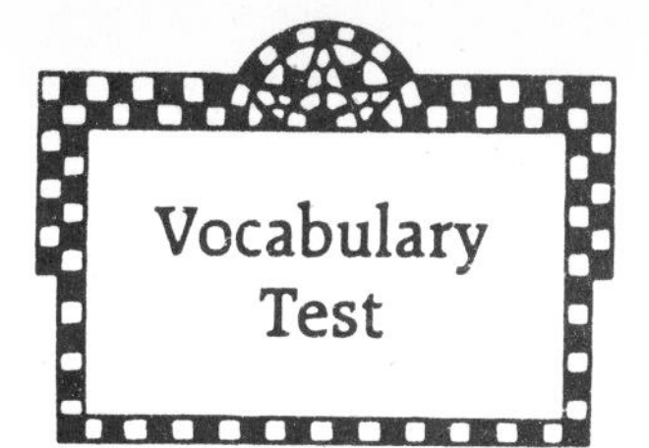

from THE TRAGEDY OF SOHRÁB AND ROSTÁM

Ferdowsi

translated by Jerome W. Clinton

(Textbook page 649)

VOCABULARY TEST

A. Match each word in column I with the correct definition in column II. Place the letter of the definition you choose in the space provided. *(10 points each)*

I	II
______ 1. abase	a. lying face down
______ 2. perplexed	b. commotion; uproar
______ 3. prostrate	c. to humiliate; lower
______ 4. sever	d. confused; puzzled
______ 5. tumult	e. to separate; cut off

B. Complete each sentence below with a word from column I above. Write the appropriate word in the blank provided. *(10 points each)*

6. The contestant refused to ______________________ himself by wearing the clown suit and riding a tricycle.

7. The panting dog lay ______________________ on the cool flagstone floor.

8. Nothing could ______________________ the strong bonds between the two sisters.

9. The deafening ______________________ in the street went on all night.

10. Andrew was ______________________ by the unfriendly behavior of his teammates.

NAME ________________ CLASS ________________ DATE ________ SCORE ________

from THE TRAGEDY OF SOHRÁB AND ROSTÁM

Ferdowsi

translated by Jerome W. Clinton

(Textbook page 649)

REVIEWING THE SELECTION

1. Sohráb and Rostám meet in hand-to-hand combat. Which one is mortally wounded?

____

2. What does Sohráb have with him to show to Rostám? Why?

____

____

3. How does Rostám feel after talking with Sohráb? What does he do as a result?

____

____

4. For which side does Sohráb fight, the Turks or Irán?

____

Reader's Response

The tragedy that befalls Sohráb and Rostám is partly the result of a communication problem. Both suspect the other's identity but for various reasons—distrust, misinformation—do not stop their clash. Write three sentences about a communication problem you've observed recently, whether in life or a story. Sum up both parties' points of view. Then explain how the problem was (or was not) resolved.

First person's viewpoint: ____

____

Second person's viewpoint: ____

____

Outcome or resolution: ____

____

NAME ______________________ CLASS ______________________ DATE __________ SCORE __________

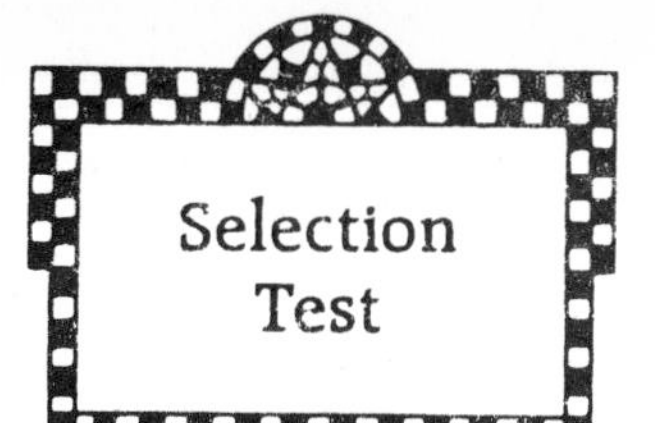

from THE TRAGEDY OF SOHRÁB AND ROSTÁM

Ferdowsi

translated by Jerome W. Clinton

(Textbook page 649)

READING COMPREHENSION

Directions: In the space provided, write the letter of the best answer to each question. *(10 points each)*

1. *Dramatic irony* occurs when readers know something the characters do not. In "The Tragedy of Sohráb and Rostám," the dramatic irony is that readers know
   a. that Irán will win the battle, but Rostám does not know it
   b. that Turan will win the battle, but Sohráb does not know it
   c. that Sohráb and Rostám are son and father, but the characters do not know it
   d. that fate is in control, but Sohráb and Rostám do not believe in fate
   1. ______

2. The poet portrays "evil fortune" as a character that shows its anger. What is the role of evil fortune in the epic?
   a. Evil fortune is the name of Rostám's horse.
   b. Evil fortune is the poet's nickname for Sohráb.
   c. Evil fortune causes terrible things to occur in the epic.
   d. After dying, one of the characters will turn into evil fortune.
   2. ______

3. Why does Sohráb say that his love for his father has ended in his own death?
   a. Sohráb's mother didn't tell him the truth.
   b. Rostám killed Sohráb even though he knew who he was.
   c. Sohráb died before finding his father.
   d. Sohráb's love for his father led him to seek his parent on the battlefield.
   3. ______

4. Why did Sohráb's mother give him a seal to wear on his arm?
   a. The seal would protect him in battle.
   b. It would identify him to his father.
   c. It would identify him to his own men.
   d. He could sell it for a lot of money.
   4. ______

5. Why does Sohráb say that his own luck changed when his companion, the aged warrior Zhende Razm, died?
   a. Zhende Razm was a brave warrior.
   b. Sohráb didn't know anyone else to talk to.
   c. Zhende Razm was supposed to point his father out to him.
   d. Sohráb was afraid.
   5. ______

(continued)

6. Why does Sohráb ask Rostám to loosen his armor and look at his arm?
   a. so that Sohráb can breathe more easily
   b. so that Rostám can see the seal which identifies Sohráb as Rostám's son
   c. so that Rostám can treat Sohráb's wounds
   d. so that Rostám can take Sohráb's armor away with him 6. ______

7. Why does Sohráb feel that what happened was meant to be?
   a. He believes his death was caused by fate and not by Rostám.
   b. He foresaw it in a dream he had about the battle.
   c. His mother predicted this would happen.
   d. He is dying. 7. ______

8. Why does the shah of Irán prepare to mount a wide blow against the Turks?
   a. He believes Rostám has been killed and Sohráb must be stopped.
   b. He believes both Sohráb and Rostám are dead and wants to act quickly.
   c. Rostám signals him to attack.
   d. He gives in to the pleading of the Iranian nobles. 8. ______

9. Why does Rostám tell the army of Irán not to pursue the battle with the Turks?
   a. He is too tired to fight anymore.
   b. He does not think they can win.
   c. He has changed allegiance to the Turks.
   d. Sohráb has asked him to let the Turks go. 9. ______

10. What are Rostám's feelings after Sohráb's death?
    a. He accepts the death calmly because he is a warrior first and foremost.
    b. He is heartbroken at the evil he has done.
    c. He is furious with Sohráb's mother for hiding his son's identity.
    d. He is grieving inside but shows nothing. 10. ______

NAME ______________________ CLASS ______________________ DATE __________ SCORE __________

from the RUBÁIYÁT

Omar Khayyám

translated by Edward FitzGerald

(Textbook page 656)

DEVELOPING VOCABULARY

Directions: Read carefully the explanation of each word. Then write a sentence of your own using that word. In your sentence, include clues to the word's meaning.

destine (des′tin) ***v.*** To predetermine; insure or intend by fate. ▶ This word comes from the French *destiner,* "to make fast or firm." ▪ The two girls' friendship developed so quickly they felt as if they had been destined to meet. **Page 657**

ORIGINAL SENTENCE ____

____

invert (in·vurt′) ***v.*** To place upside down.—**inverted *adj.*** ▶ This word derives from the Latin word *vertere* meaning "to turn." ▪ If you invert the letters of the English alphabet, they look foreign. **Page 658**

ORIGINAL SENTENCE ____

____

impotent (im′pə·tənt) ***adj.*** Powerless, ineffective.—**impotently *adv.*** ▶ The root word for *impotent* is *potent,* meaning "powerful." ▪ When the explosions started, the fire hoses were impotent in the face of the roaring flames. **Page 658**

ORIGINAL SENTENCE ____

____

wax *v.* To grow larger gradually; said of the lighted portion of the moon's face until the full moon is visible. ▶ This word, followed by an adjective, can also mean "to become." ▪ As the moon waxed, the woods around the cabin became brighter and less frightening. **Page 658**

ORIGINAL SENTENCE ____

____

wane *v.* To grow smaller gradually; said of the moon's face after it has been fully lighted. ▶ This word comes from the Old English *wanian,* meaning "to lessen, to grow less." ▪ As his strength waned, the dying soldier called for a priest. **Page 658**

ORIGINAL SENTENCE ____

____

NAME ______________________ CLASS ______________________ DATE __________ SCORE __________

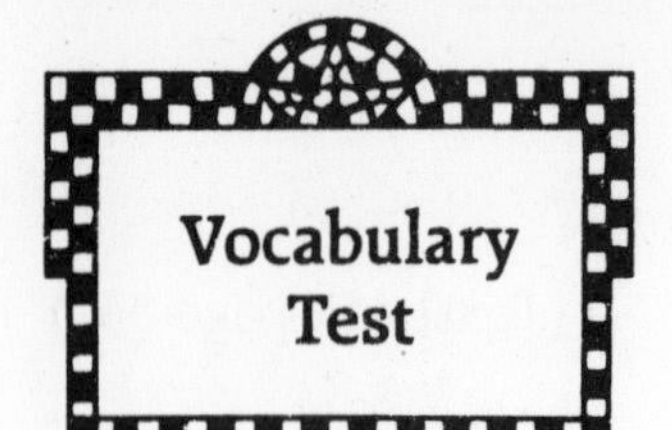

from the RUBÁIYÁT

Omar Khayyám

translated by Edward FitzGerald (Textbook page 656)

VOCABULARY TEST

A. Match each word in column I with the correct definition in column II. Place the letter of the definition you choose in the space provided. *(10 points each)*

	I	II
______	1. destine	a. to place upside down
______	2. impotent	b. to predetermine or insure by fate
______	3. invert	c. to grow smaller gradually
______	4. wax	d. powerless; ineffective
______	5. wane	e. to grow larger gradually

B. In the space provided, write the letter of the word closest in meaning to the word in italics. *(10 points each)*

______ 6. I could see her interest *wane* when Ty left the party.

a. increase b. decrease c. revive

______ 7. If you *invert* the painting, it looks like a smiling cat.

a. raise b. examine c. upend

______ 8. The two athletes' skills surely *destine* them to be rivals.

a. match b. fate c. condition

______ 9. The moon will always *wax* again, no matter how dark it seems tonight.

a. grow full b. inspire c. shine

______ 10. The people in the town felt *impotent* against the wave of crime.

a. angry b. fearful c. helpless

NAME ______________________ CLASS __________________ DATE ________ SCORE ______

from the RUBÁIYÁT

Omar Khayyám

translated by Edward FitzGerald

(Textbook page 656)

REVIEWING THE SELECTION

1. Write what Omar Khayyám uses as a **metaphor** (a comparison) for each of the following. The verse number is in parentheses.

   a. repentance (7): ____________________ b. time (7): ____________________

   c. wisdom (28): ____________________ d. life *or* earth (100): ____________________

2. What are two examples of the *carpe diem* ("seize the day") theme in the verses?

   ____

   ____

3. Put the final line of verse 27 into your own words.

   ____

   ____

4. What are two **images** (sights, sounds, or sensations created by words or phrases) from the verses that emphasize that human life must end?

   ____

Reader's Response

Verse 12 has become so famous that it is now a cliché: paradise as a sort of picnic, with a book of poetry, wine, bread, and a loved one underneath a tree. What is your earthly paradise? Specify at least three objects, a place, and the person or people (if anyone) you are with. You may list items, write a rubá'i, or draw your paradise as a scene or cartoon.

____

____

____

____

____

NAME ______________________________ CLASS ________________________ DATE __________ SCORE ________

Unmarked Boxes

Rumi
translated by John Moyne and
Coleman Barks

(Textbook page 663)

REVIEWING THE SELECTION

1. The poet says that everything you lose comes around in a different form. What is the example he gives of this?

____

____

2. The poet says that one day, God's joy cracks open all of the things it inhabits. What are three things God's joy moves in?

____

____

3. In the third stanza, what are the cypress tree, tulip bed, and grapevines examples of?

____

4. The poet compares wheat and bread to gold and the sun, but says he has neither and is only talking about them. What point do you think he is making?

____

____

Reader's Response

Circle the image below that made the most vivid picture for you of "God's joy." Write a sentence explaining why that image was especially powerful or appealing.

rainwater	flowerbed	rose
rice and fish	vine-covered cliff	horse being saddled

____

____

____

____

NAME ______________________ CLASS ______________________ DATE __________ SCORE __________

THE ANECDOTES AND SAYINGS OF SAADI

Saadi

translated by Idries Shah

(Textbook page 667)

DEVELOPING VOCABULARY

Directions: Read carefully the explanation of each word. Then write a sentence of your own using that word. In your sentence, include clues to the word's meaning.

nurture (nur'chər) ***v.*** To care for, especially by feeding or protecting. ▶ This word comes from the Old French *norreture*, a noun meaning "breeding, upbringing, or training." ■ With such a large litter, the terrier was working hard to nurture her pups as they grew. **Page 667**

ORIGINAL SENTENCE ____

____

lout (lout) ***n.*** An awkward, foolish person; oaf. ▶ This word comes from the Old Norse *lut*, meaning "stooping or awkward." ■ The basketball game was spoiled by three louts who stood up in front of me, heckling the coach. **Page 667**

ORIGINAL SENTENCE ____

____

retinue (ret''n·yoo') ***n.*** A group of assistants and servants who follow an important person. ▶ This word comes from the Old French *retenir*, meaning "to keep, employ, or retain." ■ The king's retinue traveled with him everywhere and took up a whole floor of each hotel. **Page 669**

ORIGINAL SENTENCE ____

____

impassive (im·pas'iv) ***adj.*** Displaying no emotion; calm. ▶ This word contains the prefix *im-*, meaning "not," and the Latin word *passivus*, which means "capable of suffering or feeling." ■ The impassive guards in front of the embassy seem like statues, unmoved by tourists and cameras. **Page 669**

ORIGINAL SENTENCE ____

____

heedless (hēd'lis) ***adj.*** Paying no attention. ▶ This word comes from the verb *heed*, "to listen and consider." ■ The ducklings crossing the road were completely heedless of our frantic honking. **Page 670**

ORIGINAL SENTENCE ____

____

NAME ______________ CLASS ______________ DATE ________ SCORE ________

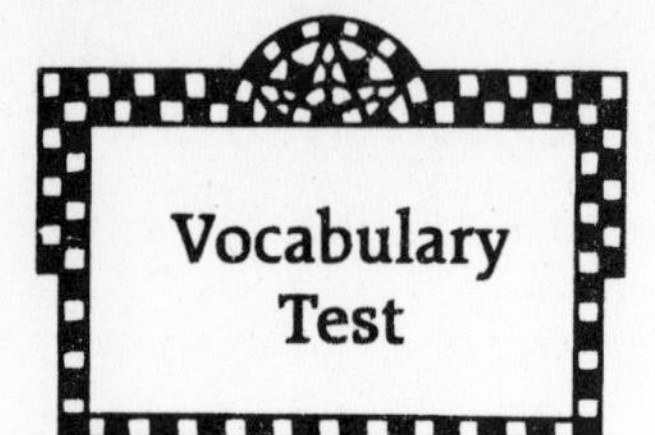

Anecdotes and Sayings of Saadi

Saadi

translated by Idries Shah

(Textbook page 667)

VOCABULARY TEST

A. Match each word in column I with the correct definition in column II. Place the letter of the definition you choose in the space provided. *(10 points each)*

I	II
______ 1. heedless	a. an awkward, foolish person
______ 2. impassive	b. paying no attention
______ 3. lout	c. a group of assistants who follow an important person
______ 4. nurture	d. to care for, especially by feeding or protecting
______ 5. retinue	e. showing no emotion; calm

B. Complete each sentence below with a word from column I above. Write the appropriate word in the blank provided. *(10 points each)*

6. Holly was surprised to see well-behaved William acting like such a ______________ at the dinner party.

7. The movie star and her ______________ arrived at the hotel.

8. Oddly enough, when Josh gets angry, he still manages to look ______________.

9. The tourists, ______________ of the warning sign, walked dangerously near the soft riverbank.

10. Some animals will ______________ a stray newborn if given the chance.

NAME ______________________ CLASS ________________ DATE ________ SCORE ________

Anecdotes and Sayings of Saadi

Saadi

translated by Idries Shah

(Textbook page 667)

REVIEWING THE SELECTION

Match the title of each saying in the left column with the statement of the saying's meaning in the right column. Write the letter in the blank.

______ 1. "Learning"

______ 2. "Relative"

______ 3. "Ambition"

______ 4. "The Dervish Under a Vow of Solitude"

a. The value or quality of a thing must be considered in relation to others like it.

b. The pursuit of power is never satisfied.

c. What you teach others to do, they will do to you.

d. People should not pay homage to those who rule but do not truly serve.

Reader's Response

Saadi's sayings and anecdotes are particularly effective because they illustrate common human failings and problems. Invent a saying or an anecdote of your own. You might begin with a phrase by Saadi, but complete it in your own way. For example, "Brave is she who ..." or "However much you study...."

____

____

____

____

____

____

____

____

____

____

____

NAME ______________________ CLASS ______________________ DATE __________ SCORE __________

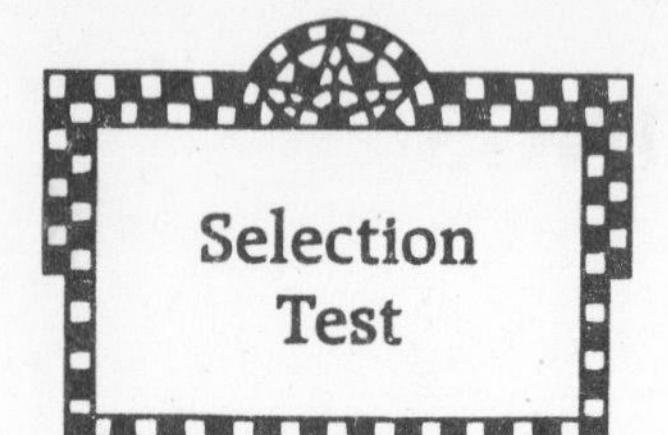

ANECDOTES AND SAYINGS OF SAADI

Saadi
translated by Idries Shah

(Textbook page 667)

READING COMPREHENSION

Directions: In the space provided, write the letter of the best answer to each question. *(20 points each)*

1. In "The Pearl," a raindrop compares itself unfavorably to the sea. For what quality is the raindrop rewarded?
   a. gratitude
   b. beauty
   c. humility
   d. boldness

   1. ______

2. "The Thief and the Blanket" suggests that a Sufi dervish
   a. believes in an eye for an eye
   b. is compassionate and not materialistic
   c. envisions God as warm and comforting
   d. will steal to help the poor

   2. ______

3. In "Information and Knowledge," Saadi's message is that information becomes true knowledge through
   a. study
   b. carrying other's burdens
   c. reading
   d. action

   3. ______

4. "The Destiny of a Wolf-cub" makes a point about a wolf reared among people. Which of these familiar sayings is closest to Saadi's meaning?
   a. Dog is man's best friend.
   b. People who live in glass houses should not throw stones.
   c. A leopard never changes its spots.
   d. One picture is worth a thousand words.

   4. ______

5. In "The Fool and the Donkey," a wise man tells a foolish man not to rave at a donkey. What is the wise man's advice?
   a. Try to understand others in order to deal successfully with them.
   b. Always follow another person's lead.
   c. Treat animals kindly, and you will learn many useful lessons from them.
   d. Follow your own advice, and you will always come out ahead.

   5. ______

NAME ______________________ CLASS ____________________ DATE ________ SCORE ______

Unit 7: Persian and Arabic Literatures

WORD ANALOGIES/Extending Vocabulary

Directions: In the space provided, write the letter of the pair of words with the relationship that is closest to that of the capitalized words. *(10 points each)*

1. PERPLEXED : CONFUSED ::
   a. relieved : frightened
   b. curious : interested
   c. concerned : pleased
   d. cheerful : disappointed 1. ______

2. NIMBLE : BODY ::
   a. strong : quick
   b. laughter : mood
   c. alert : mind
   d. deep : breath 2. ______

3. ABHOR : CHERISH ::
   a. admire : adore
   b. reject : suggest
   c. virtue : faith
   d. hate : love 3. ______

4. WAX : WANE ::
   a. bloom : wither
   b. dim : fade
   c. tide : rise
   d. sun : set 4. ______

5. NURTURE : PROTECT ::
   a. harm : shield
   b. grow : plant
   c. feed : nourish
   d. listen : watch 5. ______

6. CHIDE : SCOLD ::
   a. criticize : admire
   b. respect : blame
   c. reject : accept
   d. approve : favor 6. ______

7. LOUT : CLUMSY ::
   a. graceful : dancer
   b. full : wise
   c. oaf : awkward
   d. clown : jest 7. ______

8. DISCONSOLATE : MISERABLE ::
   a. happy : joyous
   b. sadness : pain
   c. powerful : weak
   d. loneliness : depressed 8. ______

9. TUMULT : MURMUR ::
   a. roar : crowd
   b. outcry : whisper
   c. hum : clap
   d. silence : stillness 9. ______

10. CORPULENT : STOUT ::
   a. slender : tall
   b. heavy : bulky
   c. fat : thin
   d. length : wide 10. ______

NAME ______________________ CLASS ______________ DATE ________ SCORE ______

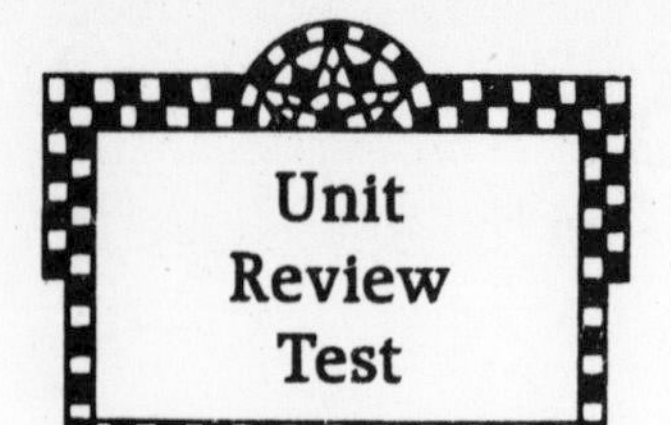

UNIT 7: PERSIAN AND ARABIC LITERATURES

UNIT REVIEW TEST/Applying Skills I

A. Reading Comprehension. In the space provided, write the letter of the best answer to each question. *(8 points each)*

1. The Koran teaches that the path to a blissful afterlife is
   a. to find comfort on earth
   b. to devote oneself to Allah and an upright life
   c. to become a beggar without possessions
   d. to seek a personal relationship with God through mystical intuition — 1. ______

2. In "The Third Voyage of Sindbad the Sailor," Sindbad and his companions are threatened by
   a. cannibal dwarves
   b. a raging tempest
   c. dwarves and a giant cannibal
   d. the evil captain — 2. ______

3. In "The Tragedy of Sohráb and Rostám," how does Sohráb die?
   a. He is killed in battle by a young Turkish soldier.
   b. He is killed in hand-to-hand combat by his father.
   c. He is tied up and stabbed by the sky god.
   d. He is trampled by Rakhsh, a giant horse. — 3. ______

4. In the *Rubáiyát*, Omar Khayyám describes time as
   a. a rose that never fades
   b. a bird that can fly forever and will never stop
   c. a bird already in flight that has only a short way to fly
   d. a jug of wine — 4. ______

5. Which of the following best expresses the central idea in Rumi's poem "Unmarked Boxes"?
   a. We must treat our neighbors well.
   b. All things are essentially one and contain God's joy.
   c. We must work hard all the time.
   d. Dreams are mysterious but important. — 5. ______

(continued)

NAME ______________________ CLASS ________________ DATE ______ SCORE ______

B. Identifying Characters. For each question below, identify the character by choosing the letter of the best answer. *(8 points each)*

6. In "On Her Brother," the poet's brother was
   a. a knight
   b. a shepherd
   c. a camel driver
   d. an athlete

   6. ______

7. In "The Third Voyage of Sindbad the Sailor," who steals the ship from Sindbad and his companions?
   a. the giant
   b. the merchants
   c. the captain
   d. the dwarves

   7. ______

8. In "The Third Voyage of Sindbad the Sailor," whom does the giant kill first?
   a. the captain of the ship
   b. Sindbad
   c. one of the merchants
   d. the ship's cook

   8. ______

9. In "The Tragedy of Sohráb and Rostám," who gave Sohráb an identifying seal to wear upon his arm?
   a. Rostám
   b. Zhende Razm
   c. Sohráb's mother
   d. Sohráb's warriors

   9. ______

10. In "The Tragedy of Sohráb and Rostám," Zhende Razm is
    a. Rostám's bodyguard
    b. Sohráb's mother
    c. Sohráb's companion/guide
    d. Rostám's son

    10. ______

C. Composition. Choose *one* of these topics and write a brief essay on a separate piece of paper. *(20 points)*

1. Both the narrator's brother in al-Khansa's poem "On Her Brother" and Sohráb in "The Tragedy of Sohráb and Rostám" die in battle, leaving grieving relatives behind. Compare and contrast the circumstances of each character's death. Consider where, how, and why each dies, and describe the way each character's grieving relative responds to the death.

2. In the *Rubáiyát* of Omar Khayyám, the speaker recalls how, as a young man, he listened reverently to the discussions of learned doctors and saints but came away none the wiser. In "The Anecdotes and Sayings of Saadi," a person who tries to learn without putting ideas into action is likened to a donkey laden with books. Explain your interpretation of either of these two observations. Use examples from your own experience to illustrate your points.

NAME ______________________ CLASS ______________________ DATE __________ SCORE __________

UNIT 7: PERSIAN AND ARABIC LITERATURES

CRITICAL THINKING AND WRITING / Applying Skills II

A. Reading an Ode. Read the ode below carefully. Then answer the questions that follow.

ODE

Hafiz

translated by

RICHARD LE GALLIENNE

A grievous folly shames my sixtieth year—
My white head is in love with a green maid;
I kept my heart a secret, but at last
I am betrayed.
5 Like a mere child I walked into the snare;
My foolish heart followed my foolish eyes;
And yet, when I was young—in ages past—
I was so wise.

If only she who can such wonders do
10 Could from my cheeks time's calumny° erase,
And change the color of my snow-white locks—
Give a young face
To my young heart and make my old eyes new,
Bidding my outside tell the inward truth!
15 O 'tis a shallow wit wherewith time mocks
An old man's youth!

Ah! it was always so with us who sing!
Children of fancy, we are in the power
Of any dream, and at the bidding we
20 Of a mere flower;
Yet, Hafiz, though full many a foolish thing
Ensnared thy heart with wonder, never thou
Wert wont° imagination's slave to be
As thou art now.

10. **calumny** (kal′ə m·nē): false statement; slander.

23. **wont** (wänt): accustomed.

(continued)

B. Analyzing an Ode. In the space provided, write the letter of the best answer to each question. *(6 points each)*

1. This poem is apparently about
   a. a young woman falling in love with an older man
   b. a young man falling in love with an older woman
   c. an older man falling in love with a young woman
   d. an older woman falling in love with a young man

   1. ______

2. In stanza 1, the speaker in the poem says that his "grievous folly" causes him to feel
   a. ashamed
   b. youthful
   c. wise
   d. confused

   2. ______

3. What do lines 7 and 8 of stanza 1 suggest about age and wisdom?
   a. Age does not necessarily bring more wisdom.
   b. Youth is always wise.
   c. Wisdom increases as age increases.
   d. a and b

   3. ______

4. The **irony**—or unexpected outcome—described in lines 7 and 8 is that
   a. the speaker kept his feelings secret, but now his heart has finally betrayed him
   b. the speaker has lived out his life without ever experiencing love
   c. he looks young, but he is old at heart
   d. the speaker felt wise when he was younger, but now that he is old he feels foolish

   4. ______

5. In stanza 2, what does the speaker in the poem wish his loved one could give him, besides a "young heart"?
   a. time's calumny
   b. a snare
   c. a youthful appearance
   d. inward truth

   5. ______

6. Lines 15 and 16 explain the speaker's attitude toward his predicament. Which phrase best describes his attitude?
   a. bitterness and deep anger
   b. good-humored perplexity
   c. giddy euphoria
   d. hopeless sorrow

   6. ______

(continued)

7. In stanza 3, the speaker says his heart has been snared by many foolish things before now. What is different this time?
   a. He has never before felt so much like a child.
   b. He has never before been so much the slave of imagination.
   c. He has never before realized how shallow his wit is.
   d. He has never before been snared by someone as beautiful as a flower. 7. ______

8. In stanza 3, when the speaker refers to "us who sing" and the "children of fancy," he probably means
   a. older people
   b. youths
   c. poets
   d. lovers of nature 8. ______

9. In stanza 3, what does the speaker say "was always so with us"?
   a. the fact that children sing songs, follow dreams, and enjoy flowers
   b. the tendency to enter into hopeless love affairs, knowing they will never blossom
   c. the fact that time marches on relentlessly, no matter how young one feels
   d. the tendency to be captivated by the wonders of dreams and beautiful things 9. ______

10. Odes often express personal reflections about serious subjects. Which main idea does this ode express about the difference between physical appearance and state of mind?
   a. A person's physical appearance can strongly affect his or her state of mind.
   b. People may grow old physically but still feel emotionally young.
   c. Even youths can have the mental maturity of age, though they never know it.
   d. A person's state of mind is always betrayed by his or her physical appearance. 10. ______

C. Writing About an Ode. What insights does Hafiz reveal about life or love? On a separate sheet of paper, write a paragraph in which you explain one insight in the poem about life or love. Use at least two specific details or quotations from the poem to back up your ideas. You might begin your paragraph with a statement like the following: "Hafiz's ode reveals that love ______________. This is clear because ______________."

(40 points)

UNIT 7: PERSIAN AND ARABIC LITERATURES

UNIT INTRODUCTION TEST/
Persian and Arabic Literatures
(Textbook pages 622–629)

1. b	5. c	8. c
2. b	6. a	9. b
3. c	7. c	10. d
4. a		

ON HER BROTHER

al-Khansa
translated by Willis Barnstone
(Textbook page 631)

REVIEW AND RESPONSE WORKSHEET

Reviewing the Selection

Responses will vary.

1. Anger, sadness, and pride are all present. Students' supporting examples will differ.
2. That he gave his family happiness and will be remembered (lines 9 and 10) may be the good of his life.
3. Students may choose phrases from lines 1 and 2 that tell what he was *not*, phrases about his physical prowess (lines 5 and 6), or others.
4. She says they overtook her brother and shouted like shepherds at daybreak.

Reader's Response

Responses will vary. Other issues are animal rights, the homeless, and environmental concerns other than the rain forests. For the rain forests, listed feelings might be outrage and depression; images could be dense ferns, soaring trees, birds and animals in the branches, bulldozers, etc.

from the KORAN

translated by N. J. Dawood
(Textbook page 635)

VOCABULARY WORKSHEET

Responses will vary.

VOCABULARY TEST

A. 1. c	3. a	5. b
2. d	4. e	
B. 6. b	8. a	10. c
7. c	9. a	

REVIEW AND RESPONSE WORKSHEET

Reviewing the Selection

1. He is asking for guidance to the straight path, the path of those whom Allah has favored.
2. Answers will vary, but might include two of the following: when the sun stops shining; when the stars fall; when the mountains vanish; when pregnant camels are left untended; when wild animals come together; when the seas flame; when people's souls are reunited; and so on.
3. The life to come will be more rewarding than this one.
4. When your task is ended, you should resume your work, and seek your Lord.

Reader's Response

Responses will vary. Students who respond with "clear and vivid" may find abstractions easier to understand through images. Those who choose "confusing and difficult" may prefer directness and find, for example, two uses of a single word (such as *orphan*) confusing.

(continued)

LANGUAGE SKILLS WORKSHEET

Pronoun and Antecedent Agreement

Exercise 1

1. Mohammed/he
2. speeches/them
3. Koran/it
4. everyone/his or her; neighbors/they
5. girl/her

Exercise 2

1. their 2. its 3. his or her 4. their
5. their 6. his or her 7. their 8. its
9. his 10. his or her

Exercise 3

Responses will vary. Possible revisions are:

1. Fearing that Mohammed's words would be lost forever, early Muslims wanted to gather the sayings in one place.
2. Though surrounded by wealthy people, Mohammed was disturbed by the sufferings of the poor, whose plight caused him to withdraw to the mountains to meditate.
3. Mohammed and Gabriel were in a hillside cave when Gabriel began to dictate the words of Allah.
4. Mohammed's numerous visions, some of which contained images of Judgment Day, were the source of his preaching.
5. When the angel Gabriel appeared, Mohammed's wife told Mohammed to accept what was happening.

SELECTION TEST

1. b 2. c 3. b 4. b 5. c

from THE THIRD VOYAGE OF SINDBAD THE SAILOR

translated by N. J. Dawood
(Textbook page 640)

VOCABULARY ACTIVITY WORKSHEET

Responses will vary.

VOCABULARY TEST

1. b
2. c
3. a
4. b
5. c
6. a
7. c
8. b
9. a
10. c

REVIEW AND RESPONSE WORKSHEET

Reviewing the Selection

1. Sindbad sets sail from Basrah with a group of merchants.
2. The apelike dwarves commandeer the ship, sail it to the island, and carry Sindbad and the others to the beach.
3. the bones, the oven, the huge pans, the spits
4. A giantess guides him; they both hurl massive boulders at the sailors escaping on the raft.

Reader's Response

Responses will vary. In groups, students could pool their ideas to write one-paragraph descriptions of each character.

LANGUAGE SKILLS WORKSHEET

Exercise 1

1. O
2. P
3. P
4. O
5. O
6. P
7. O
8. O
9. P
10. P

Exercise 2

Responses will vary. Sentences in the ornate style should include elegant diction, figurative language, lengthy clauses, inversions, and/or circuitous statements. Sentences in the plain style should include direct statements, simpler diction, shorter sentences, fewer modifiers, and/or less figurative language. Sample responses:

(continued)

1. The troll was very ugly, and evil shone in his eyes.
2. As we approached, cautious but curious as deer entering a forest clearing, the magnificent and looming palace appeared deserted.
3. Hesitantly, I suggested that we try to stop the monster from eating us.
4. As softly as if in dream did we perceive the sonorous murmur of Neptune's abode, the restless sea, lapping the shore.
5. As usual, I enjoyed all the sights, sounds, bustle, and scents of the Baghdad market.

Exercise 3

Responses will vary, but strong responses should omit many of the modifiers, metaphors, similes, and allusions used in the original. Strong responses should also contain shorter clauses, replacing elegant diction with everyday terms but retaining concrete details. Sample response:

The men worked stealthily, for they knew they would face death if they were caught. In spite of the afternoon heat and the swarms of insects, they managed to gather enough wood for a raft. At sunset, with the raft not yet finished, we began to lose hope. But finally the raft was done, and it seemed a great ship to us. It was roughly made, but it might save us.

SELECTION TEST

1. a
2. c
3. a
4. d
5. c
6. b
7. a
8. c
9. d
10. b

from THE TRAGEDY OF SOHRÁB AND ROSTÁM

translated by Jerome W. Clinton
(Textbook page 649)

VOCABULARY ACTIVITY WORKSHEET

Responses will vary.

VOCABULARY TEST

A. 1. c 2. d 3. a 4. e 5. b

B. 6. abase 7. prostrate 8. sever 9. tumult 10. perplexed

REVIEW AND RESPONSE WORKSHEET

Reviewing the Selection

1. Sohráb
2. Sohráb has a seal bound on his arm that his mother has given him. It was his father's gift and proves Rostám is his father.
3. Rostám feels shocked and emotionally destroyed; as a result of his son's death, Rostám tells his army not to fight Turan anymore.
4. Sohráb fights for the Turks.

Reader's Response

Responses will vary. Students may focus on interaction among friends and family or on the interactions of characters in books, films, or television programs. A class discussion of negotiation and problem solving could result.

SELECTION TEST

1. c
2. c
3. d
4. b
5. c
6. b
7. a
8. a
9. d
10. b

from the RUBÁIYÁT

Omar Khayyám
translated by Edward FitzGerald
(Textbook page 656)

VOCABULARY ACTIVITY WORKSHEET

Responses will vary.

(continued)

VOCABULARY TEST

A. 1. b　3. a　5. c
2. d　4. e

B. 6. b　8. b　10. c
7. c　9. a

REVIEW AND RESPONSE WORKSHEET

Reviewing the Selection

1. a. Winter-garment　b. Bird
   c. seed　d. Garden
2. Responses will vary. Possible responses are flinging off winter clothing, taking cash and ignoring the rumbling of a distant drum, making a paradise of poetry, wine, and love.
3. Responses will vary. Possible paraphrases are that the speaker knew no more than when he began or merely went around in circles.
4. Responses will vary. Possible responses are the fluttering bird on the wing, the fallen hyacinth, dust, a harvest of water and wind, a closed manuscript, an empty glass turned upside down.

Reader's Response

Responses will vary. You could display responses on a class bulletin board.

UNMARKED BOXES

Rumi
translated by John Moyne and Coleman Barks
(Textbook page 663)

REVIEW AND RESPONSE WORKSHEET

Reviewing the Selection

1. A child giving up milk for wine mixed with honey.
2. Responses will vary. It moves from cell to cell; in rain; in a growing plant (a rose); in a plate of food; and in a saddled horse.
3. dreams or "phantasms"—forms that the self takes while the body sleeps
4. Responses will vary but might include the idea that both the sun and the loaf of bread contain God, and thus are both impossible to possess totally.

Reader's Response

Responses will vary. Students may also want to suggest original images.

ANECDOTES AND SAYINGS OF SAADI

Saadi
translated by Idries Shah
(Textbook page 667)

VOCABULARY ACTIVITY WORKSHEET

Responses will vary.

VOCABULARY TEST

A. 1. b　3. a　5. c
2. e　4. d

B. 6. lout　8. impassive　10. nurture
7. retinue　9. heedless

REVIEW AND RESPONSE WORKSHEET

Reviewing the Selection

1. c　2. a　3. b　4. d

Reader's Response

Responses will vary. Some possible topics for original sayings and anecdotes are vanity, laziness, selfishness, envy, wisdom, generosity, beauty, strength, selflessness, career choices, and loyalty.

SELECTION TEST

1. c　2. b　3. d　4. c　5. a

(continued)

WORD ANALOGIES/Extending Vocabulary

1. b (perplexed : confused :: curious : interested)
Relationship: synonyms
Perplexed and *confused* are synonyms meaning "puzzled." *Curious* and *interested* are also synonyms.
2. c (nimble : body :: alert : mind)
Relationship: characteristic to object
Being *nimble*, "moving about in a quick or light manner," can be a characteristic of one's body. Being *alert* can be a characteristic of one's *mind*. The analogy is strengthened by the fact that the two sets of words refer to ideal physical and mental states.
3. d (abhor : cherish :: hate : love)
Relationship: antonyms
Abhor, "to draw back in hatred or disgust," is an antonym of *cherish*. *Hate* is an antonym of *love*. The analogy is strengthened by the fact that *abhor* and *hate* are synonyms, as are *cherish* and *love*.
4. a (wax : wane :: bloom : wither)
Relationship: antonyms
Wax, "to grow larger gradually," is an antonym of *wane*. *Bloom* is an antonym of *wither*. The analogy is strengthened by the fact that *wax* and *bloom* have similar meanings, as do *wane* and *wither*.
5. c (nurture : protect :: feed : nourish)
Relationship: synonyms
All four words are synonyms sharing the meaning "to take care of."
6. d (chide : scold :: approve : favor)
Relationships: synonyms
Chide and *scold* are synonyms sharing the meaning "to express disapproval." *Approve* and *favor* are synonyms sharing the meaning "to express approval." The analogy is strengthened by the fact that *chide* and *approve* are antonyms, as are *scold* and *favor*.
7. c (lout : clumsy :: oaf : awkward)
Relationship: person to characteristic
Being *clumsy* is characteristic of a *lout*, "an awkard, foolish person." Being *awkward* is characteristic of an *oaf*. The analogy is strengthened by the fact that *lout* and *oaf* are synonyms, as are *clumsy* and *awkward*.
8. a (disconsolate : miserable :: happy : joyous)
Relationship: synonyms
Disconsolate and *miserable* are synonyms meaning "terribly unhappy." *Happy* and *joyous* are also synonyms. The analogy is strengthened by the fact that *disconsolate* and *happy* are antonyms, as are *miserable* and *joyous*.
9. b (tumult : murmur :: outcry : whisper)
Relationship: antonyms (or differ by degree)
Tumult, "noisy commotion and uproar," is an antonym of *murmur*. *Outcry* is an antonym of *whisper*. The analogy is strengthened by the fact that *tumult* and *outcry* are closely related in meaning, as are *murmur* and *whisper*.
10. b (corpulent : stout :: heavy : bulky)
Relationship: synonyms
All four words are synonyms sharing the meaning "large."

UNIT REVIEW TEST/Applying Skills I

A. Reading Comprehension

1. b 2. c 3. b 4. c 5. b

B. Identifying Characters

6. a 7. d 8. a 9. c 10. c

C. Composition

1. Responses will vary. Students may note:
- Al-Khansa's brother, an honored knight-warrior in their nomadic group, died, perhaps in an ambush while returning from a successful raid on a neighboring group. The grieving relative was al-Khansa herself. She expressed her anger

(continued)

and devastation in the elegy "On Her Brother" (and many other elegies written throughout her life), leaving literature of lasting value to memorialize him.

- Sohráb dies when his father, Rostám, who does not recognize him, kills him in one-on-one combat during a war in which the two lead opposing sides. Rostám recognizes Sohráb before Sohráb dies; Sohráb urges him not to blame himself but to end the war so that Sohráb's troops will be spared further harm on his account. Rostám is crazed with sorrow but does call a halt to the fighting. In this way he, like al-Khansa, uses his grief to attain a positive end.

2. Responses will vary. Ideas students could express are that both Khayyám and Saadi feel that the discussion alone of abstractions is useless and that life experience is essential. Khayyám urges readers to live for the moment, savoring the pleasures life has to offer, because life is brief and death is certain. For Saadi, a Sufi, attaining true wisdom is the main goal. Life is a means to eternal afterlife. He urges readers to gain wisdom from the experience of living according to Sufi precepts and from striving to understand their own essence and the essence of life. Without this central understanding, according to Saadi, the knowledge acquired through studying is of no more use to a person than a load of books is to a donkey.

CRITICAL THINKING AND WRITING/
Applying Skills II

B. 1. c
2. a
3. a
4. d
5. c
6. b
7. b
8. c
9. d
10. b

C. Responses will vary. Students' paragraphs should show a grasp of the poet's humorous and resigned attitude toward life in general and his understanding of human weaknesses. Students should also realize that the poet feels that love has great power, and that it can blossom in people of any age. Students may also point out Hafiz's illustration of the fact that people who are old can still be young at heart, just as young people can be (or think they are) quite wise. Look for at least two specific references to the poem.

NOTES